COCOA

COCOA

by

D. H. URQUHART

*Formerly Director of Agriculture
in Ghana*

LONGMANS

LONGMANS, GREEN AND CO LTD
48 GROSVENOR STREET, LONDON W1
RAILWAY CRESCENT, CROYDON, VICTORIA, AUSTRALIA
AUCKLAND, KINGSTON (JAMAICA), LAHORE, NAIROBI
LONGMANS SOUTHERN AFRICA (PTY) LTD
THIBAULT HOUSE, THIBAULT SQUARE, CAPE TOWN
JOHANNESBURG, SALISBURY
LONGMANS OF NIGERIA LTD
W. R. INDUSTRIAL ESTATE, IKEJA
LONGMANS OF GHANA LTD
INDUSTRIAL ESTATE, RING ROAD SOUTH, ACCRA
LONGMANS GREEN (FAR EAST) LTD
443 LOCKHART ROAD, HONG KONG
LONGMANS OF MALAYA LTD
44 JALAN AMPANG, KUALA LUMPUR
ORIENT LONGMANS LTD
CALCUTTA, BOMBAY, MADRAS
DELHI, HYDERABAD, DACCA
LONGMANS CANADA LTD
137 BOND STREET, TORONTO 2

Second Edition © Cadbury Brothers Limited

First published 1955
Second impression 1955
Third impression with new statistics 1956

Second Edition 1961
Second impression 1962

PRINTED IN GREAT BRITAIN BY
WESTERN PRINTING SERVICES LTD BRISTOL

NOTE

This volume is one of a series of books on tropical agriculture which are being published with the active encouragement of the Colonial Advisory Council of Agriculture, Animal Health and Forestry, under the editorship of Mr. D. Rhind, O.B.E., Secretary for Colonial Agricultural Research, formerly Director of Agriculture, Ceylon.

Already published:
Rice, by D. H. Grist.
Tea, by T. Eden.
Bananas, by N. W. Simmonds.
An Introduction to Animal Husbandry in the Tropics, by
G. Williamson and W. J. A. Payne.
Beekeeping in the Tropics, by F. G. Smith.
Termites, their Recognition and Control, by W. Victor Harris
Tropical Inland Fisheries, by C. F. Hickling

PREFACE TO THE FIRST EDITION

I AM indebted to people in various countries for generous help and my thanks are due to them for providing valuable information for this book.

In Britain I am chiefly indebted to the firm of Cadburys for giving me every facility to write the book, and I have been greatly assisted not only by the encouragement of their Board, but by much technical advice and help from my Bournville colleagues. They have read the drafts of appropriate sections and corrected the proofs, and during my absences abroad have watched over the preparation of the material on my behalf. I would list the following to whom I am especially indebted: Mr. John Cadbury, Mr. W. E. Cossons, Mr. Spencer L. Hale, Mr. W. McL. Hood, C.B.E., Dr. G. R. Howat, Mr. F. T. Lockwood, Miss D. M. Stevens, Mr. R. V. Wadsworth, and Mr. G. A. Ross Wood. I have had valuable advice from Mr. D. L. Martin, a director of Unilever, who is responsible for guiding the immense plantation interests of that company. I have had the advantage of consultations with Dr. A. F. Posnette, whose outstanding work in research in cocoa is well known.

The value of the book is greatly enhanced by the inclusion of the chapter on Virus Diseases by Dr. A. F. Posnette, East Malling Research Station, and the chapters on Rehabilitation, Botany, and Soils, respectively by Professor C. Y. Shephard, C.B.E., Professor R. E. D. Baker, and Professor F. Hardy, C.B.E., all of the Imperial College of Tropical Agriculture, Trinidad.

The subject matter of the chapter on Vegetative Propagation of Cocoa by Rooted Cuttings, etc., is based mainly on the work of Dr. Harry Evans in Trinidad, supplemented by some of his unpublished writing and information provided by his successor, Mr. Dennis Murray. Mr. Moll, of the Trinidad Cocoa Board, supplied information on large-scale production of cuttings.

Much of the information included in the chapters on The Cocoa Plantation is derived from discussions with experienced planters in Trinidad, particularly Mr. Carl de Verteuil and Mr. Neal Fahey, who generously placed at my disposal knowledge gained from many years of practical work.

In Ghana, I received help from members of the Department of Agriculture, notably Mr. James D. Broatch, Deputy Director;

Mr. P. S. Hammond, M.B.E., Assistant Director; Mr. John Paine, formerly of the Department, and Mr. Victor Osei, all of whom are authorities on cocoa culture in West Africa.

I am grateful to Sir Harold Tempany, C.M.G., C.B.E., for ready help and guidance.

Finally, I acknowledge the assistance of my wife who helped me in the work throughout.

The author takes responsibility for views expressed in the book.

D.H.U.

Bournville,
August 1954

PREFACE TO THE SECOND EDITION

A GREAT deal of progress has been made in the cocoa industry since the first edition of this book was published in 1955, especially in the means of controlling the more troublesome pests and diseases of cocoa, which a few years ago constituted a serious problem. Successful experimental work in this field has removed the causes of much anxiety. The object of the present edition is to review recent progress and bring the work up to date. The chapter "The Botany of Cocoa" was specially written for this book by the late Professor R. E. D. Baker, of the Imperial College of Tropical Agriculture, Trinidad.

Since the first edition of this book was published, the Gold Coast has become Ghana and is so referred to throughout the second edition.

D.H.U.

Bournville, 1960

ACKNOWLEDGEMENTS

FACILITIES for writing the book were provided by Messrs. Cadbury Brothers Limited. Members of that firm to whom I am indebted are Mr. John Cadbury, Mr. S. L. Hale, Dr. G. R. Howat, Mr. T. Insull, Mr. F. T. Lockwood and Miss D. M. Stevens.

I have had the benefit of discussions with Mr. D. L. Martin, of Unilevers Limited, which firm is now planting cocoa on a large scale. The Director of Agriculture of Ghana, Mr. James D. Broatch, I.S.O., Mr. P. Hammond, M.B.E., Mr. F. A. Leeds and others of the staff of the Department have provided much information. Mr. Victor Osei, of the Department of Agriculture, Ghana, supplied details of peasant cocoa culture. Mr. James Lamb, Director of the West African Cocoa Research Institute, and his staff gave me information on research in West Africa.

Mr. Alan Jones, of the Soils Department of the Regional Research Centre, Trinidad, made useful suggestions for the chapter on Soils in Relation to the Nutrition of Cocoa. I revisited a number of cocoa estates in Trinidad and had useful discussions with experienced planters including Mr. Carl de Verteuil, Mr. Neal Fahey, Mr. Keith Potter, and Mr. E. R. Moll.

Mr. D. Rhind, O.B.E., Secretary for Colonial Agricultural Research, co-operated willingly in the production of this edition.

As with the first edition I have received much help from my wife.

CONTENTS

xiii

b

PLATES

ACKNOWLEDGEMENTS FOR ILLUSTRATIONS

The author gratefully acknowledges permission to reproduce photographs, as follows:

Ghana Information Services, Nos. 54–56, 76, 80, 82–87, 96, 101, 107, 109, 118, 119.

Mr. D. A. Donald, Senior Agricultural Officer, British Solomon Islands, No. 44.

Imperial College of Tropical Agriculture, Nos. 30a, b, c, 31a, b, 40.

Mr. J. Nicol, Entomologist, West African Cocoa Research Institute, Nos. 3 (from the *Journal of Horticultural Science*), 90, 97, 98.

Señor Manuel Palma (per Mr. Tresper Clarke, of Rockwood & Co., New York), No. 58.

Mr. Paul Holliday and H.M.S.O., Nos. 93 and 94.

COLOUR PLATES:

The picture on the dust-jacket is from a photograph by Mr. Paul Cadbury.

Nos. III and IV were drawn by Mrs. C. S. Watts (I.C.T.A.); No. IX is by Bournville Works Studios.

The others are from photographs by the author and Mr. G. A. R. Wood.

All photographs not otherwise acknowledged are by the author and Mr. Wood, and No. 99 is by Mr. P. B. Redmayne; they are reproduced by permission of Cadbury Brothers Ltd.

DIAGRAMS AND CHARTS:

Fig. 1 is adapted from *Le Cacaoyer à Tafo, Gold Coast*, by L. Poncin (Brussels, 1950); Fig. 2 is from a paper by Mr. C. F. Charter (Cocoa Conference Report, 1949); Fig. 3 is based on drawings supplied by New Zealand Reparation Estates; Figs. 4 and 5 are by Mr. J. Nicol and have been reproduced in *Insect Pests in Cacao Trees*; Fig. 6 has previously appeared in the Trinidad Board of Agriculture Bulletin No. 1 by Mr. R. L. Guppy; Fig. 8 is from *Cocoa—A Crop with a Future*, by Mr. Paul Bareau (Cadbury Brothers, Ltd.); Fig. 10 is reprinted from *Nature*.

Information as to previous publications may not be complete, but the above list is believed to be accurate.

Chapter I

INTRODUCTORY

History—Discoveries in Manufacture and Consequent Importance of Amelonado—Manufacture—Cocoa Butter—Cocoa Butter Substitutes—Production and Consumption—Position of Producer and of Manufacturer—Outlook for the Planter

COCOA and chocolate are articles of common diet and a luxury in many countries. They contain both protein and fat and have a highly concentrated food value in relation to their bulk and weight. The processing of the cocoa bean during manufacture is mainly directed towards the production of eating chocolate, drinking cocoas and cocoa butter, and, to a lesser extent, to the manufacture of theobromine. Cocoa butter is also used in the manufacture of cosmetics and pharmaceutical preparations.

HISTORY

The history of cocoa begins in Central America with the Maya Indians, who were the first known people to have realized the valuable qualities of the bean. Even in those days cocoa prices must have been high as the beans were used for the purchase of slaves and other luxuries, apart from being prized as a food. The Spaniards were the first to import cocoa into Europe, and were the pioneers who introduced it as a plantation crop to many countries of the Americas. From the sixteenth century onwards cocoa was planted in most of the tropical regions of Central and South America and on many of the Caribbean Islands. Although the Spaniards took the lead in developing the plantation industry, other people, including Portuguese, Dutch, British and French, and, at a later stage, liberated slaves also played an important part.

The Spanish, the Dutch and the Portuguese brought cocoa to the islands of the Gulf of Guinea in the seventeenth century, and the Dutch and Spanish were responsible for introducing it to South-east Asia in the sixteenth and seventeenth centuries. It was not until the nineteenth century that the Germans took cocoa to the South Pacific Islands of Samoa and New Guinea.

B 1

Although there are some records of cocoa being brought directly from the American continent to the mainland of West Africa, the plantings which led to significant development were made towards the end of the nineteenth century from cocoa established in Spanish and Portuguese islands in the Gulf of Guinea.

Estates owned by enterprising planters were responsible for the early development of cocoa as a commercial crop, but later there was considerable planting by liberated slaves in Bahia (Brazil) and to some extent in Trinidad and elsewhere. During the present century, estate development by big companies has become important.

The history of the cocoa industry in the American continent is one which is marked by periods of high prosperity and deep depression. The depressions were due to periods of low prices or the onset of diseases. At times there was a combination of both. The large-scale production which took place in the State of Bahia was a serious and lasting shock to the industry in other American countries. It was followed soon afterwards by the emergence of the Gold Coast (Ghana) and Nigeria as major cocoa-producing countries. Gradually, during the past thirty-five years, the picture of world cocoa production has changed. The bulk of the crop is no longer grown on large estates but on small cocoa farms or family holdings.

DISCOVERIES IN MANUFACTURING PROCESSES AND THE CONSEQUENT IMPORTANCE OF AMELONADO

Early in the nineteenth century a process was discovered whereby the fat could be extracted from the cocoa bean, and this made possible the manufacture of more palatable and digestible products which became popular for drinking and eating. A later development, initiated by the Swiss and perfected in England, was the manufacture of milk chocolate, the most popular form of eating chocolate to-day, in which cocoa, cocoa butter and sugar are compounded with milk solids.

The Amelonado type of cocoa, which was planted on such a large scale in Bahia and in West Africa, is a cocoa of mild flavour, particularly suitable for the manufacture of milk chocolate, and processing by the larger manufacturers became geared to the use of Amelonado. Certain cocoas from the Americas and some islands of the Caribbean, especially desirable for the manufacture of chocolates of a particular flavour, commanded a premium, and some of them still do, but the premium being paid of recent years for cocoas with special flavour is less than in the past.

MANUFACTURE

The main constituents of the bean are cocoa fibre, cocoa butter and shell, and these are separated in the process of manufacture, although a certain amount of fat still remains in the powder. The fat-free fibre contains about 3 per cent of theobromine which can be converted into caffeine, for which there is a large demand.

In the manufacture of chocolate, the roasted nib (which is the name given to the beans after the shell has been removed) are ground into a mass to which extra cocoa butter is added along with other ingredients, mainly sugar. In making milk chocolate, the form in which some 70 to 80 per cent of chocolate is consumed, a considerable amount of milk solids is also added to the mass. The paste derived from grinding the cocoa nibs is by itself too stiff to mould into chocolate bars or couverture and the addition of cocoa butter is necessary to make it workable. Of recent years it has been found that the addition of lecithin has the effect of increasing the fluidity of the paste and has reduced the amount of cocoa butter required in the manufacture of chocolate.

COCOA BUTTER

Cocoa butter, which constitutes some 56 per cent of good cocoa beans, is a high-grade vegetable fat which, from the manufacturer's point of view, combines a number of valuable virtues. It melts at body temperature, keeps well and does not readily develop free fatty acids; it is readily digestible and agreeable to the palate. In making chocolate products in the past there was normally an excess of cocoa powder over cocoa butter; recent trends in America, however, are towards the use of larger quantities of powder.

COCOA BUTTER SUBSTITUTES

Those seeking a substitute for cocoa butter have found that it is extremely difficult to reproduce the various qualities embodied in the natural product. The melting point, the good keeping qualities and aromatic properties of cocoa butter are not readily reproduced and there will be a limit to the use of cocoa butter substitutes in those countries where it is forbidden to call products "chocolates" if substitutes have been used in their manufacture. The use of substitutes is considered by some to be in the nature of a menace to the cocoa industry.

PRODUCTION AND CONSUMPTION

In times of low prices, the peasant farmer of West Africa, whose initial outlay was small and whose overheads were negligible, was much less affected by the serious falls in price which characterized the cocoa market in the 'twenties and late 'thirties than were the relatively highly capitalized estates. The combination of periods of low prices and the widespread occurrence of the disease of witches' broom caused a severe setback to the cocoa plantation industry during the present century, in what were some of the more important cocoa-producing countries of the Americas—a setback from which they have never fully recovered.

As production in America, apart from Brazil, stagnated or receded, production in West Africa expanded. At the beginning of the century the Americas produced 81 per cent of the world's crop and West Africa 16 per cent; now West Africa produces some 61 per cent and the Americas about 30 per cent of the world's raw cocoa.

Since 1952–3 world annual output has grown from 787,000 tons to 1,000,000 tons and upwards. Of this amount Africa provides some 559,000 tons and Central and South America about half that amount; the balance comes from Asia and Oceania.

The present position is that production has not kept pace with consumption and the demand is greater than the supply. The price of raw beans during the past few years has at times risen to the level where it has been difficult, and sometimes impossible, to manufacture and market chocolate products at a price which would enable them to be sold on favourable terms of competition with other types of confectionery. The future prosperity of the industry lies in increased production; it is only by expanding output that cocoa can be assured of a favourable place in world markets.

POSITION OF THE PRODUCER AND OF THE MANUFACTURER

Some years ago when prices dropped to low levels, the producer was at a disadvantage in that he was not able to foretell possible fluctuations in price. He often withheld his cocoa hoping to dispose of it later at a better price. If he was unlucky he might eventually have to dispose of it below what he considered to be a reasonable return. Since prices have reached higher levels he has much less to worry about, in that even the lowest prices ruling in recent years would normally give him a fair return. When the prices of £30 and £40 per ton, which were common in West Africa before the war, are compared with the prices that have been current in recent years (up to £560 a ton), it is clear that cocoa-growing is now a much more profitable undertaking, even when due allowance is made for increased costs of production.

The position of the manufacturer is, however, much less happy. Apart from a general rise in price levels, the violent fluctuations in world cocoa prices are a matter of serious concern to him. Large sums of money are necessary for the purchase of beans for his current needs, and a considerable amount of capital is tied up in the stocks of cocoa he may hold as a reserve. As the supply of cocoa is seasonal he is virtually forced to buy his main supplies within a certain limited period, and if he is unfortunate in having to buy a large proportion of his needs during the times when particularly high prices are ruling, it greatly reduces his profit margin.

In times of low prices the producer is inclined to suspect the cocoa manufacturer of depressing the price unfairly to suit his own ends. An examination of prices paid for cocoa beans in recent years does not, however, support the view that manufacturers have in any way influenced the market to their own advantage.

Manufacturers in Europe and in the United States have reiterated their view that a profitable price to the grower is essential to the well-being of the industry, and with equal emphasis they have pointed out that an unduly high price will curtail consumption.

THE OUTLOOK FOR THE PLANTER

Cocoa has undergone many vicissitudes during the course of its development as a plantation crop. It has been subject to a number of diseases, and prices have fluctuated in a disconcerting manner. The cocoa planter, after years of anxiety, can now look forward to better rewards for his enterprise. Research, which has hitherto lagged behind the needs of the industry, is now catching up. Economic methods for the control of major pests and diseases have been found; there is a better understanding of the response of cocoa to environment in the matter of soils, shade and temperature and in other directions; there has been notable progress in the evolution of better planting material, and cheaper methods have been found for multiplying improved material for planting in the field. These and the other advances that have been made for the betterment of the plantation side of the cocoa industry help to make cocoa a more profitable and safer proposition than hitherto. Despite these tremendously improved prospects for the planter, there is no likelihood that world markets will be flooded with an excess of raw cocoa and that the prices will fall. Even minimum prices ruling for a number of years past have been profitable to the producer, and although there are indications of increased world output, the increase can readily be absorbed by world markets.

REFERENCES

Joss, D. H. (Cocoa Conference, London, 1955)

Chapter II

THE BOTANY OF COCOA*

History of Cocoa Planting—Natural Habitat—Habit of Growth—Pollination—Cocoa Varieties—Nomenclature of Cocoa—Present-day Classification

HISTORY OF COCOA PLANTING

THE genus *Theobroma* is indigenous to the New World, and wild species occur from Mexico to Peru, with an apparent centre of origin in the upper Amazon basin. The cocoa tree, *Theobroma cacao* L., belongs to the lower storey of the lowland forests where conditions are warm, shady and humid. It has been cultivated since prehistoric times by the Indians of South and Central America, and opinion is divided as to whether it now ever occurs in a truly wild state or only in areas which have at some time or other been interfered with by man. The Spaniards who landed in Mexico early in the sixteenth century found cocoa an established product with every indication that it had been used, and therefore presumably planted, for centuries. The crop, as grown today, is much more complex than that known to the Mexicans, but in spite of its development having taken place relatively recently, its botanical history is by no means clear.

The Spaniards are said to have planted cocoa in Trinidad as early as 1525, but it is not known whence they obtained planting material. There is no good evidence that the tree is native to Trinidad, though a few wild trees can be found in the forests. These are presumably escapes from early cultivation and actually bear sufficient resemblance to Mexican forms to suggest that there may have been an early importation. Cocoa was certainly being shipped in 1634 from what is now Venezuela and the material there is of uncertain origin. There was probably a native cocoa in the forests which may have been used, as well as material from the same source as the Trinidad plantings. The cocoa called "Criollo" (or native) in Venezuela today is rather different from the Mexican type.

Venezuela was the chief producer until about 1830, when it was passed by Ecuador. A native Ecuadorean type, quite distinct from the Venezuelan, was planted in the latter country. Trinidad was at

* By Professor R. E. D. Baker.

7

that time the third largest producer after Venezuela and Ecuador and was producing a type of cocoa quite different from either. All three, however, were producing what are now classed as fine or high-flavour cocoas.

Ghana started planting cocoa about 1879 with yet another distinct type of material, obtained indirectly from Brazil or Surinam, of a different flavour but superior in hardiness and yield. It is misleading to speak of the cocoas of Venezuela, Ecuador and Trinidad as "high quality" and those of West Africa as "inferior quality." Different kinds of cocoa have different flavours and therefore different uses, but much West African cocoa is now better prepared, and therefore could be said to be of better "quality" than the present-day produce of the older cocoa-growing countries.

NATURAL HABITAT

Ecologically, all varieties of cocoa appear to be trees of lowland tropical forests. Their natural habitat includes very wet spots in the lowest storey of small trees in dense rain forest. The limits of cultivation are about 20° N. and 20° S., with the bulk of the crop within 10° of the equator, and within these limits most of the main producing areas are at low elevations.

The origin of the tree as an under-storey species in forest is probably responsible to some extent for the traditional method of growing it under the shade of larger trees, but it is to be noted that in this respect the "natural" environment does not necessarily give the best conditions for high yield. In fact, the heavily shaded trees in forest usually carry little fruit. Cocoa can survive in heavy shade that would kill many species, but it can also survive a considerable degree of exposure, although general experience is that unshaded cocoa may suffer severe set-backs. The lesson to be learnt from the forest habitat and from experience in cultivation seems to be the necessity for protection from wind and the desirability of shade, except in those instances where experience has shown that shade may be safely omitted.

HABIT OF GROWTH

The various kinds of cocoa differ little in general habit. All are small trees, attaining a height of thirty feet or so, and with few exceptions they all have an uncommon and characteristic mode of branching. The seedling plant forms a straight main stem three to five feet high, and then forks into three, four, or five main, almost horizontal, limbs, forming the so-called fan or "jorquette." The

1. A cocoa farm in Ghana

2. A chupon branch of a cocoa tree with leaves in a $\frac{3}{8}$-spiral giving rise to a jorquette of five fan-branches

3. Cocoa flower, showing the s... surrounded by five pigmented sta... nodes

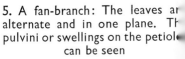

4. Amelonado pod growing o... tree in Bahia. Here it is called th... "Comun" type

5. A fan-branch: The leaves ar... alternate and in one plane. Th... pulvini or swellings on the petiol... can be seen

6. A collection of cocoa pods.
In the background are pods
from I.C.S. clones
The group in the middle shows
the range of size and shape
found on a Trinidad estate
In the foreground are some
Calabacillo and Angoleta pods

7. Rejuvenating old cocoa by raising
a chupon from the base of the tree

8. A chupon arising from a fan cutting. The original fan branches will be removed and the new tree will develop as if it had originated as a seedling

9. A cocoa tree about seven years old grown from a fan-cutting

10. On the banks of the Rio Jequitihonha, Bahia. The height of the trees has not been controlled

terminal bud is used up in the forking, and further increase in height is made by a sucker or "chupon" which arises later, usually just below the jorquette, and grows up vertically between the branches of the latter to repeat, a few feet higher up, the forking of the main trunk and form a second storey. An unpruned tree may add a third, or even a fourth tier of branches, and plantation practice varies, so that on different estates one may see trees kept to one jorquette and trees with two or three. In certain wild *Theobroma* species the terminal bud is not used up in branching, and growth continues from above the jorquette, giving the tree a distinctive and very regular appearance.

TYPES OF BRANCHES

There are thus two types of branches, (*a*) the upright or chupon type, including the first main axis of the seedling, and (*b*) the fan type. Both bear flowers and fruits, but they differ in several other respects. The chupon type of branch bears its leaves in a $\frac{3}{8}$-spiral, and is determinate in its growth, as sooner or later it always gives rise to a terminal fan. The fan branch has its leaves two-ranked and is indeterminate, growing indefinitely and giving rise to laterals of its own type.

As a general rule, chupons give rise to chupons except in the jorquette, and fans to fans. There is, however, a certain variability about this so-called "dimorphism" of branching. It is very rare for a fan to be produced from a chupon below the jorquette, but it is by no means uncommon for chupons to be produced on fans. The exception to this rule is to be found in certain Central American cocoas. These have no chupon branches; the main stem starts from the seed with spirally arranged leaves, but the spiral quickly opens into a two-ranked arrangement with no jorquette, and all subsequent branches are of the fan type. These trees are uncommon in most countries outside Central America, though a few occur in Trinidad.

THE LEAVES

The leaves of the tree, when mature, are dark green in colour and thin but firm in texture. When young they are light green or of various shades of red, and very soft and limp, hanging vertically from their petioles. Stipules are conspicuous on the young leaves. These are normally soon shed, but may persist when certain diseases are present.

The petiole has a well-marked pulvinus or swelling at each end, possibly facilitating the turning of the leaf in response to photo-tropic stimuli. The fan branches make their growth in "flushes," the length of the internodes gradually increasing from start of growth up to a maximum, and decreasing again as the bud returns to a dormant condition. The stipules of the last-formed leaves of a flush, being close together, leave characteristic scars on the twig when growth is resumed, so that the extent of successive flushes can easily be seen on examination of a branch. The leaves usually persist through two flushes and are dropped from the third length back from the terminal bud, so that there are normally leaves of three distinct ages on each branch.

FLOWERS

Theobroma cacao is "cauliflorous," which means that the flowers and fruits are produced on the older leafless parts of the trunk and branches. In some *Theobroma* species, such as *T. bicolor*, the flowers are produced in the leaf axils of the current shoots. In *T. cacao*, although the flowers are produced on the old wood, they arise at cushions which were originally leaf axils. According to Stahel, they occur in the axils of the reduced first leaves of the axillary branch, which then normally develops no further. Occasionally on healthy trees, and more frequently on trees attacked by witches' broom disease (*Marasmius perniciosus*), the axillary branch develops into a small leafy shoot, and in such cases the position of the inflorescence is very clear. Cushions can also arise adventitiously.

The flower is quite regular and hermaphrodite, and has the formula K5 C5 A5 + 5 G($\underline{5}$), or in other words, five sepals, five petals, ten stamens in two groups or whorls, only one of which is fertile, and a superior ovary of five united carpels. The pink or whitish sepals are valvate in arrangement; the petals are very narrow at the base and expanded above into a cup-shaped pouch, beyond which they end in a relatively broad spatulate tip or ligule. The androecium or male part of the flower consists of five long, pointed staminodes, and five fertile stamens, which, being the inner whorl, stand opposite the petals. All ten are joined at the base into a very short tube. The stamens are so bent that their anthers lie concealed in the pouched portion of the corresponding petals, whilst the staminodes stand erect and form a sort of ring fence around the style. The stamens are double, each representing two, fused along their filaments, and each has therefore four pollen sacs. The ovary is simple, having five compartments containing numerous ovules which are arranged around a central axis in the ovary, and the style is partially divided into five stigmatic lobes, which usually more or less adhere together. There is a constriction, at which the flowers absciss, at the base of the pedicel.

POLLINATION

The pollination mechanism of cocoa is still imperfectly under-stood, and presents features of much interest. A conspicuous feature is the enormous wastage of flowers which normally occurs, and examination shows that the vast majority are never pollinated. As a rule, according to several independent estimates, the proportion of pollinated stigmas is about 5 per cent.

There is no record of what the natural pollinating agent in the native haunts of the tree may be, and if the flower is examined criti-cally the conclusion must be formed that the structure is not such as to facilitate pollination by any of the regular means, but rather to hinder it. There is neither scent nor nectar to attract insects and, on the other hand, the pollen is too sticky to be that of a wind-pollinated plant, neither is the position of the anthers suitable for such a habit, but distinctly the reverse. In fact, both the position of the anthers, hidden in the pouched petals, and the ring-fence of staminodes hindering access to the stigmas, are features incapable of being regarded by any stretch of a teleological imagination as facilitating pollination.*

* Since Professor Baker's account of pollination was written, further work has been done and this was summarized in a paper by Dr. A. F. Posnette and Mrs. Helen M. Entwistle which was presented at the London Cocoa Con-ference of 1957.

In Ghana it was found that about 12 per cent of flowers are pollinated during heavy flowering, and over 40 per cent when flowers are scarce. These are higher proportions than occur in Trinidad, where the trees flower more profusely. Pollen is carried comparatively long distances—as much as fifty yards or more —and is deposited in clusters of grains on the stigma or style; most of the pollination takes place before noon. The chief pollinating agent must there-fore "be able to fly or be carried on air currents at least 50 yards, and to carry clusters of over 50 pollen grains; they must occur throughout the wet tropical regions and have easily detached bristles. In addition, the insects must be small enough to enter the petal hood.

"The insects that satisfy these requirements are the Heleid midges—a group that includes the sandflies—whose ability to penetrate mosquito nets is well known to many of us and whose invisibility is implied in the West Indian name 'no-see-'ems'. The presence of Heleid midges (Ceratopogonidae) in cocoa flowers was first reported in 1941 in Trinidad and they have since been reported in Brazil, Costa Rica, Ghana, Java, Nigeria, Puerto Rico, and Venezuela.

"The reason why the midges enter rubber and cocoa flowers is now known. In cocoa flowers, they are particularly attracted to the purple-pigmented tissue that constitutes the staminodes and 'guide-line' in the petal hoods, and they appear to feed on it. Any observer who has watched midges in cocoa flowers will agree with Baker's opinion . . . that 'both the position of the anthers, hidden in the pouched petals, and the ring-fence of staminodes hindering access to the stigmas are features incapable of being regarded . . . as facilitating pollination.' Certainly these features hinder accidental self-pollination, but they adapt the flower conveniently for pollination by small insects feeding on the purple tissue and so presenting their backs in turn to the stigma, style and pollen."

Dr. L. G. Saunders studied the Forcipomyia midges and their role in

Several investigations in recent years (Harland, 1925; Stahel, 1928; Billes, 1941; Posnette, 1944) have shown fairly conclusively that pollination is effected by the agency of insects. A certain amount of self-pollination is effected by small crawling insects, such as flower thrips and aphides. These, however, are evidently not the only agents. Flowers on sections of the trunk protected against crawling insects by sticky bands show a certain number pollinated, presumably by a flying insect. Furthermore, it has been known since 1931 that many clones are self-incompatible (i.e. set no fruit with their own pollen) yet some of these are heavy yielders. Clearly there must be some agent, presumably winged, conveying pollen from tree to tree. Billes found that a Ceratopogonid midge of the genus *Forcipomyia* pollinated cocoa in Trinidad. Two species—*F. quasiingrami* and *Lasiohelea nana*—have since been identified in Trinidad and different species of the same genera have been found in West Africa, but there may be other winged pollinators, and the subject needs still more investigation. Unpollinated flowers are usually shed the day after opening.

THE FRUIT

The fruit, which is botanically a berry, usually contains from twenty to forty seeds, occasionally as many as fifty, each surrounded by a pulp which is developed from the outer integument of the ovule. The outer layers of cells of this integument become prismatic in shape during the growth of the seed, and their contents become highly mucilaginous. At full ripeness they break down and release the mucilage. At least one important function of the fermentation to which the beans are subjected after harvest is the removal of this mucilage by the action of micro-organisms; this facilitates subsequent handling and drying of the beans.

As the ripe pods do not open and scatter the seed, nor drop off the tree, and as the seed will presumably be dead by the time the pod is decayed, natural dissemination can only be carried out by animals. Monkeys, rats and squirrels will open the pods for the sake of the beans from which they suck the surrounding sweet pulp before spitting them out.

pollination of cocoa in Trinidad and Costa Rica. He encountered great difficulty in finding these insects but concluded that "midges present in such scarcity that they can be observed only by exceptional chance can still bring about a satisfactory set of fruit over a period of time. This appears to apply to Costa Rica as well as to Trinidad, and in both countries the midges may be reduced at some seasons to a level too low to ensure adequate pollination."

COCOA VARIETIES

In the brief history of the crop already given, it was recorded that the first exporter of cocoa to the European markets was Venezuela, and for this reason it is hardly surprising that the terminology of the markets is still based on standards applicable to Venezuelan cocoa more than a century ago. This terminology must be understood.

From the earliest plantings in the late sixteenth and early seventeenth centuries up to about 1825, Venezuela grew only one kind of cocoa. It was not a highly uniform variety because the ripe pods from different trees varied in colour (some red and some yellow) and to some extent in size and shape. There was, however, a general and fairly close similarity between them. The pods were relatively long and narrow, pointed, conspicuously ridged and furrowed, and warty. The seeds inside were almost round in cross-section and, when cut across in the fresh state, either white or pale violet in colour. The quality was high; in fact, it has never been surpassed, and the small quantities of this same cocoa now available on the world's markets are still regarded as the highest quality of all cocoas.

About 1825 another kind of cocoa was introduced into Western Venezuela from Trinidad. This was much less uniform and included trees bearing pods that were shorter and relatively broader than those of the old cocoa, less sharply pointed, or in some cases not pointed at all, less conspicuously ridged and furrowed, and often entirely unwarted. Above all, the seeds were somewhat flattened in cross-section and when cut across showed a deep purple colour in the cotyledons. This new cocoa was welcomed because it was hardier than the old kind, grew more strongly, and yielded more, and it was soon extensively planted. To distinguish the two kinds, the older was called "Criollo" (native) and the newer "Forastero" (foreign) or "Trinitario" (the cocoa of Trinidad).

The cocoa from Trinidad, though in the "Fine" category, was distinctly inferior to the more delicate Venezuelan Criollo. So it soon came about that on the European markets "Criollo" became synonymous with "highest quality" and "Forastero" with "lower quality." Cocoa from Trinidad naturally fell into the "Forastero" group in the trade sense, but so did the cocoa from Ecuador, which at that time was becoming increasingly important. The Ecuador cocoa was entirely different, botanically, from that of Trinidad or the "Trinitario" of Venezuela. Furthermore, it was a native of Ecuador and therefore, in the literal Spanish sense (but not in the trade sense), "Criollo" there. The Ecuadoreans, however, happen to use the word "Nacional" rather than "Criollo" to indicate its indigenous status, and so the confusion does not arise. But the original meanings of "Criollo" and "Forastero" were lost from that time on in the cocoa market, and the words have to be completely re-defined today in their application to cocoa varieties.

NOMENCLATURE OF COCOA

The "native" (or long-established) cocoas of Mexico and Central America have white beans and are essentially similar to Venezuelan Criollo, though superficially distinguishable. They scarcely enter the export market, but to the extent that they do are classified as "Criollo" and are also classified agriculturally as Criollos. The original Venezuelan Criollo was introduced to Ceylon, Java, Mada-gascar and Samoa, and the produce of these countries came on the market as "Ceylon Criollo," "Java Criollo," etc., although the terms, taken literally, would be absurd.

It should be noted that the distinction between "Criollo" and "Forastero" is *not* the distinction between "Fine" and "Ordinary." All the cocoas so far mentioned are "Fine" cocoas in the modern sense. The distinction of "Fine" and "Ordinary" is a later develop-ment, rendered necessary by the increasing complexity of the cocoa crop as production spread; and it is that complexity which necessi-tates this lengthy explanation.

Confusion arose when, about the beginning of the twentieth cen-tury, there came on the market from West Africa and Brazil cocoa of another new kind, different from that of any of the Forastero cocoas hitherto known. It was quite naturally grouped for con-venience with the Forastero (or "lower quality") cocoa, and the term now included three separate qualities: (*a*) Trinidad cocoa, and Trinitario of Venezuela, (*b*) Cacao Nacional of Ecuador, (*c*) West African and Brazilian cocoas. As the last group increased in pro-duction it came to dominate the whole market.

We may briefly summarize in a slightly different manner all the cocoas on the market today as follows: (1) Criollos, the finest of the "Fine," but almost negligible in quantity, which will apparently disappear altogether unless special steps are taken to preserve them. (2) Fine Forasteros, including Ecuador cocoa, Trinidad cocoa, and cocoa from Trinidad grown in Venezuela, Ceylon, Indonesia, and a number of other countries of small output. (3) Ordinary Foras-teros, grown in West Africa, Brazil and San Domingo.

PRESENT-DAY CLASSIFICATION

Botanically, we recognize three groups which correspond almost exactly with this market division, only the position of Ecuador cocoa being anomalous. These three groups are:

Criollo Cocoas. We define the Criollos by the characters already given for the old Venezuelan Criollo population, which will include also the native or long-established cocoas of Mexico and Central America, and also of Colombia. They have pods either red or yellow in colour when ripe, usually deeply ten-furrowed, very warty and conspicuously pointed; the pod wall is relatively thin and easy to cut, the seeds are plump, almost round in section, and the fresh cotyledons either white or pale violet in colour. The seed characters are the most important, as the whole group is variable and occasional trees may have smooth or scarcely pointed pods, but as a rule all the characters mentioned occur together. Though their early history is entirely obscure, it seems likely that the Central American group was carried up from South America by human agency and is not truly indigenous.

Amazonian Forasteros. The Amazonian cocoas comprise the ordinary cocoas of Brazil and West Africa and the Cacao Nacional of Ecuador. They are called Amazonian because they are apparently distributed naturally throughout the basin of that river and its tributaries. They probably originated around the headwaters, but the cocoas of that region are as yet little known in cultivation. Variation decreases down the river and the members of the group taken into cultivation in Brazil and carried over to West Africa form a fairly uniform population.

The pods of all Amazonian Forasteros are yellow when ripe, and, in the better-known representatives in cultivation, they are inconspicuously ridged and furrowed, smooth and round-ended or very blunt-pointed. The pod wall is relatively thick and often has a woody layer difficult to cut. The seeds are more or less flattened and the fresh cotyledons are dark violet in colour, sometimes almost black.

As with the Criollos, the seed characters are the most important, and more constant than the pod shape, but they are not invariable. Members of this group, which in some way long ago got over the Andes into Ecuador, evolved into a variety with plumper seeds and paler cotyledons than any other known Amazonian Forastero. That variety is the Cacao Nacional and, on account of those characters it is a "Fine" cocoa on the market, though its botanical affinities are with the "Ordinary" kinds.

Trinitarios. The Trinitario cocoas are botanically a complex group, and to explain them we have to go back to history. It has already been mentioned that the Spaniards are supposed to have planted cocoa in Trinidad in the sixteenth century and that the material planted was possibly from Mexico. It is certain that cocoa was grown in Trinidad in the seventeenth century and that the variety was a Criollo in the modern sense. But in 1727 something happened which in the literature is called a "blast"; and whether it was a hurricane or an epidemic outbreak of disease, it virtually wiped out the cocoa cultivation of Trinidad. Some thirty years later the industry was re-established with planting material of a new and hardier variety of cocoa brought in from Venezuela. Details are lacking, but there can be little doubt that the importation was from Eastern Venezuela, and probably it came from the Orinoco valley. The cocoa concerned was certainly not the Venezuelan Criollo being grown at that time in Western Venezuela. It was hardier but of lower quality. We cannot tell whether it was a fairly uniform Amazonian Forastero or whether it was already a mixture. If uniform, it very soon became mixed by being interplanted with the relics of the old "Trinidad Criollo"; but it seems more likely that it had already become mixed in the Orinoco basin by the overlapping of more than one parental type. However that may be, its characters are those of a hybrid population, and its most outstanding characteristic is its heterogeneity. When some of this cocoa was sent to Western Venezuela about seventy years after its introduction to Trinidad, it was not recognized there as a Venezuelan variety, and, being quite different from the Criollo grown in that district, was distinguished as Forastero or Trinitario.

The group of cocoas now included under the term Trinitario is important for more reasons than its local connection with Trinidad. When reintroduced to Venezuela, the Trinidad cocoa became popular there because it was hardier and more productive than the high-quality but delicate Criollo. Then cross-fertilization took place with the Criollo trees and when seedlings were raised from them they were no longer pure Criollo. By selection the Criollo was gradually supplanted and today very little of it is left in pure stands.

The history of Venezuela was repeated both in Ceylon, which grew Venezuelan Criollo from about 1834 but introduced Trinidad cocoa about 1880, and in Java which appears to have got Criollo cocoa first from Ceylon and then got it mixed with a Trinitario introduction in 1888. The process is continuing today in the Central American countries and in Colombia, which have Criollos but have introduced either Amazonian or Trinidad cocoa and interplanted it with their own. Wherever we find a hybrid mixture of recent origin we may, for convenience, call it a Trinitario population. This means that Trinitarios differ according to their different histories and parentages, but all are highly heterogeneous. It is precisely their heterogeneity which makes them of the most interest and also of the most promise to the plant breeder.

REFERENCES

For a fuller discussion of the different groups of Cocoas and their origins see:

Cheesman, E. "Notes on the nomenclature, classification, and possible relationships of cacao populations." *Tropical Agriculture* (Trinidad, 1944), **21**, 144.

Stahel's finding on the morphology of cocoa flowers:
Stahel, G. *Annales du Jardin Botanique de Buitenzorg* (1918), Vol. 30.

Information on pollinating insects:
Billes, D. J. "Pollination of *Theobroma cacao* in Trinidad, B.W.I." *Tropical Agriculture* (Trinidad, 1941), **18**, 151.

Guanaranam, J. K. "Pollination mechanism of the cocoa flower." *Trop. Agric.* (*Ceylon*) (1954), **110**, 98.

Harland, S. C. "Studies in cacao: I. The method of pollination." *Ann. applied Biology* (1925), **12**, 403.

Posnette, A. F. "Natural pollination in the Gold Coast, I, II." *Trop. Agric.* (Trinidad, 1942), **19**, 1; **19**, 188.

Posnette, A. F. "Pollination of cacao in Trinidad." *Tropical Agriculture* (Trinidad, 1944), **21**, 115.

Posnette, A. F. "The pollination of cacao in the Gold Coast." *J. hort. Sci.* (1950), **25**, 155.

Posnette, A. F., and Entwistle, H. M. "The pollination of cocoa flowers" (Cocoa Conference, 1957, 66).

Saunders, L. G. "The pollination of cacao." *Cacao* (1958), **3**, 15.

Stahel, G. "*Beiträge zur Kenntnis der Blüten-biologie von Kakao* (*Theobroma cacao*, L.)." Reviewed by S. C. Harland in *Trop. Agric.* (1928), **5**, 290.

Van der Knaap, W. P. "Observations on the pollination of cacao flowers." *Rept. 14th Internat. Hort. Congr.* 1955, 1287.

Self-incompatibility in cocoa:
Knight, R., and Rogers, H. H. "Incompatibility in *Theobroma cacao*." *Heredity* (1955), **9**, 67.

Pound, F. J. "Studies in fruitfulness in cacao. II, Evidence for partial sterility." *1st Annl. Rept. on Cacao Research*, 1931. (I.C.T.A., Trinidad, 1932.) (The first reference.)

C

Chapter III

CLIMATE AND ENVIRONMENT

*Possibility of Making the Cocoa Tree Adaptable—Discussions
at the London Cocoa Conference—Rainfall—Temperature—
Humidity—Light and Shade—Wind—Altitude—Importance
of Environment*

THE climate suitable for cocoa is usually to be found in a great
part of the rain forests of large land masses and islands in the tropics,
within about 20 degrees north or south of the equator. Important
factors which make up the environment and provide the conditions
under which cocoa can be grown are rainfall, temperature, humidity,
light and shade.

THE POSSIBILITY OF MAKING THE COCOA TREE ADAPTABLE

Although cocoa originated as an under-storey tree in the shade of
high tropical forests, the view that the reproduction of similar conditions is desirable for the best growth of the crop has undergone
considerable modification.

Most plants which have been developed as economic crops give the
best results in conditions and environments far removed from those
in which they originated. The evolution of cocoa from the status of
a plant of the forest towards that of a highly specialized tree which
can respond to intensive cultivation has lagged behind the evolution
of most other crops. It is reasonable to assume that as cocoa progresses farther on the road towards a greater degree of adaptability,
and becomes responsive to manuring and other practices normally
applied to field crops, and, possibly, to radical modification of
environment, greatly improved results will be obtained from plant
material of high potential yield.

DISCUSSIONS AT THE LONDON COCOA CONFERENCE

At the Cocoa Conference held in London in 1955, papers presented
by Murray, Havord, Adams and McKelvie covered a great deal of
the ground concerned with the influence of climatic factors on the
growth of cocoa. Much of the discussion which follows is based on
the information provided by these papers.

18

Murray outlines his approach to the subject by defining what is implied by ecological and physiological studies in an endeavour to assess their importance. An ecological study deals with the measurement of environmental factors including rainfall, air and soil temperatures, relative humidity, evaporating capacity of the air, soil moisture and solar radiation, and with the correlation of these factors with the growth of the tree. "Certain general relationships are established, but the interpretation of a single environmental effect is handicapped, not only by the fact that it is constantly varying, but also on account of the complex relations which exist between the factors measured and the tree." The physiological study aims at determining responses to controlled experiments, and although complete control of environmental factors is difficult in biological experiments, uncontrolled variations are estimated by statistical methods.

RAINFALL

The minimum rainfall in which cocoa will grow in the absence of irrigation is dependent on the distribution of rainfall and the type of soil on which the crop is grown. Figures of 40 to 45 inches and 45 to 50 inches have been quoted as the annual minimum in the absence of irrigation, but most cocoa is grown in rainfalls above 50 inches. The extent to which cocoa can be grown in the lower rainfall limits is dependent on the distribution of the fall and the capacity of the soil to hold moisture.

Consideration of the total rainfall alone may be misleading. In Ghana, for example, where the dry season in the forest belt may extend from November to March, Adams and McKelvie point out that the growing of cocoa is confined to the areas which have a rainfall of at least 10 inches during these months.

The upper limit is difficult to determine and it might be said that theoretically there is no upper limit. Here again the nature of the soil and distribution of precipitation are important. Where the rainfall is distributed over the greater part of the year on a free-draining soil, cocoa will tolerate a much higher precipitation than in a heavier soil where drainage is liable to be impeded. Cocoa has been grown in rainfalls of up to 200 and 300 inches. High rainfalls, of course, are liable to give rise to various kinds of soil erosion and consequent loss of nutrients, especially through leaching.

Where the rainfall is so distributed that there is at least 3·5 to 4 inches in each month, cropping will be distributed over the greater part of the year, whereas a pronounced dry season is associated with peak cropping within limited periods. The theory has been advanced that the resting period provided by a marked dry season benefits the cocoa tree, but as it has been shown that cocoa grows and yields well in countries with little or no dry season, this view is no longer widely held.

TEMPERATURE

Erneholm, in his study of limitations imposed on cocoa-growing in South America, concludes that cultivation on a commercial scale is limited to those areas where the minimum daily temperature does not fall below 15° C. (59° F.), the absolute minimum below 10° C. (50° F.) and the annual mean temperature is not less than 21° C. (70° F.).

In their studies on the effects of temperature in Ghana, Adams and McKelvie have made a number of important observations and among them are:

That there is a surprisingly large diurnal range of temperature in cocoa plantations. "Shade maxima may reach 35° C. (95° F.) and minima may be as low as 13° C. (55° F.). . . .

"Shade reduces temperature variation inside the cocoa plots by several degrees. Posnette (1943) found that shaded plots have maximum temperatures 1°– 4° F. lower than unshaded plots and minimum temperatures 1°–3° F. higher. Artificial shade was found to depress the maximum temperature but to have no effect on the minimum. This reduction of maximum temperature by shade may be one of the reasons why flushing is more intense in unshaded cocoa.

"Pods grow more quickly from March to June than they do from July to September when, amongst other factors, temperatures are lower. When the mean of the daily maximum temperatures falls below 28·3°–29·4° C. (83°–85° F.), pod growth declines. With a mean daily temperature of 32·2° C. (90° F.) during growth, ten-week-old pods average 9·9 cm. in length, whereas similar pods at a temperature of 26·6° C. (80° F.) average only 8·5 cm. in length. Variations in pod growth from day to day also depend on temperature."

Van Hall states that pods on cocoa trees grown in the lower temperature zones at higher altitudes in Java take longer to reach maturity.

HUMIDITY

Good growing conditions for cocoa are associated with high humidity, and the degree of humidity is influenced by rainfall and temperature. The lower relative humidity of the dry season accelerates the loss from the tree by transpiration. Where the supply of moisture in the soil is good the cocoa tree may not suffer from the increased transpiration, but if the loss of water exceeds the uptake the tree will of course be adversely affected. It follows that when the atmospheric humidity remains high, the tree is better able to tolerate the lack of moisture in the soil in the dry season.

Adams and McKelvie instance cases where cocoa grew perfectly well in exposed unshaded areas in which humidity was as low as 40 per cent at midday. In the Bisa area of Ghana many of the mature cocoa trees died out on hill slopes exposed to the drying effects of the harmattan wind. It has been observed that under these conditions trees growing on relatively alkaline soils throve better than those on acid soils.

LIGHT AND SHADE

The amount of light admitted to a plantation is normally controlled by the use of shade trees, to some extent by windbreaks, and by the development of the canopy in relation to the spacing of the cocoa trees themselves. A steep slope, especially one facing east or west, may be in shadow for a great part of the day and get much less sunshine than relatively level land.

The light intensity is probably the most important factor to be considered. Measurement of light intensity is usually expressed as a percentage of full light. The daily incident light will be affected by cloud, rainstorms, dust and other factors. Photosynthesis proceeds at a greater rate in a plantation without shade than where shade is present, and the response to manures generally increases with the decrease of shading; this applies especially in the case of nitrogen. In experimental work in Trinidad it was found that the relative growth of unmanured plots was best at about 50 per cent light intensity.

The general conclusions arrived at as a result of experimental work in Trinidad are that shade requirements of cocoa are related to the availability of soil nutrients, and that heavy shade reduces early yield, irrespective of mineral nutrition. On the other hand, under little or no shade, early yields are determined by mineral nutrition. On a poor soil too much light may affect the yields adversely, but the highest yields may be expected on a good soil in absence of shade.

WIND

Hurricanes and gales of high velocity may cause considerable mechanical damage to plantation crops such as cocoa, coconuts, coffee and citrus. Devastatingly high winds are of infrequent occurrence in any one area and are, therefore, accepted as a normal risk. Wind of even low velocity blowing persistently will have an unfavourable effect on the climate within the plantation, and if it blows from the sea an accumulation of chlorides on the leaves of the cocoa trees may give rise to leaf scorch.

ALTITUDE

Cocoa is commonly grown at altitudes of up to 2,000 feet and can be grown at much higher altitudes in sheltered conditions, even up to 5,000 feet. The lower temperatures may be the chief limiting factors at the higher altitudes. Again, where the higher altitudes are subject to prolonged periods of mist and overcast skies, the trees are liable to suffer heavy attack from fungus diseases, particularly black pod.

IMPORTANCE OF ENVIRONMENT

There is much yet to be learnt about the effects of environment, and how to adjust conditions of environment to the best advantage. Adams and McKelvie (1955) estimate that under certain conditions in Ghana losses of 900 lb. of cocoa per acre are sustained through ignorance of the effects of environment, and this is ten times the loss due to pod disease and rodent damage. Fennah's work in Trinidad emphasizes the correlation of maladjustment of environment and heavy attacks of insect pests.

The meteorological data are derived from the following sources:

TAFO: *W.A.C.R.I. Annual Report 1952–3.*
ST. AUGUSTINE, Trinidad: I.C.T.A. (from information given to students).
URUÇUCA, Bahia: Figures for 1937 from *Cocoa in Brazil*, by L. J. Schwarz; 1941–50 figures from Experimental Station, Uruçuca.
MALAYA: "Report on suitability for cocoa-growing of the territories of Malaya, Sarawak and British North Borneo," by D. Gillett. (Private Report to Cadbury Brothers Ltd., 1948.)
RABAUL, New Britain: *The Growing of Cacao in Papua and New Guinea* (Appendix 7), by D. H. Urquhart and R. E. P. Dwyer (Cadbury Brothers Ltd., 1951).
MULINU'U, Western Samoa: *Cocoa Growing in Western Samoa* (Appendix 1), by D. H. Urquhart (Technical Paper No. 39, South Pacific Commission).

The graph (Fig. 1) is adapted from *Le Cacaoyer à Tafo* (*Gold Coast*), by L. Poncin (Brussels, 1950).

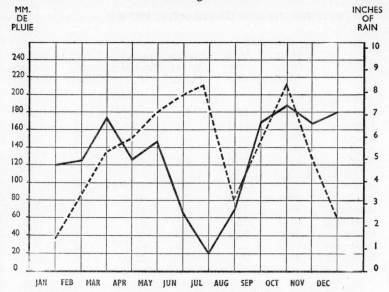

LUKOLELA ———— (Average Annual Total 1548 mm. or 60·9 inches)

TAFO ------ (Average Annual Total 1536 mm. or 60·6 inches)

FIG. 1

AVERAGE MONTHLY RAINFALL (1938–47) AT TAFO, GHANA, AND
LUKOLELA, BELGIAN CONGO

TABLE No. 1

METEOROLOGICAL DATA OF SOME COCOA-GROWING COUNTRIES

1. TAFO, GOLD COAST (15-year period, 1938–52)

Month	Shade Temp. Mean Max. (degrees Fahr.)	Mean Min.	Mean Rel. Humid. 9 a.m. (%)	3 p.m. (%)	Mean Rainfall (inches)	Average No. of Wet Days
January ..	91·4	59·1	85·9	54·1	1·56	3·4
February ..	93·7	61·2	83·7	51·3	3·63	7·3
March ..	93·5	65·8	81·6	54·7	6·09	11·6
April ..	93·7	66·1	80·5	57·9	5·80	11·2
May ..	92·1	66·6	81·7	62·3	7·07	13·4
June ..	89·3	66·1	84·7	67·9	8·33	18·4
July ..	86·8	66·2	86·0	68·9	5·53	13·4
August ..	86·4	65·0	85·9	61·3	2·79	12·8
September..	88·0	66·6	85·1	70·6	6·23	13·9
October ..	89·8	66·3	83·1	69·8	8·65	18·0
November..	90·5	65·0	81·8	65·4	5·08	11·0
December ..	90·6	62·7	84·2	61·4	2·44	5·0
Total for year ..					63·20	139·4

2. ST. AUGUSTINE, TRINIDAD (21-year period, 1929–49)

	Temperature Mean Max. (degrees Fahr.)	Temperature Mean Min. (degrees Fahr.)	Sunshine Dly. Av. (Hrs.)	Humidity Mean Min. (%)	Mean Rainfall (inches)	Average No. of Wet Days
Dry Season:						
January ..	84·0	68·0	7·6	57·0	2·8	16·0
February ..	85·0	67·0	8·2	52·0	1·3	11·0
March ..	86·0	68·0	8·0	51·0	1·3	21·0
April ..	87·0	71·0	8·1	52·0	1·9	10·0
May ..	88·0	72·0	7·8	57·0	5·0	16·0
Wet Season:						
June ..	86·0	72·0	6·7	63·0	8·6	22·0
July ..	86·0	72·0	7·2	63·0	8·6	23·0
August ..	87·0	71·0	6·9	63·0	9·8	23·0
September..	87·0	72·0	6·5	62·0	7·9	19·0
October ..	87·0	72·0	7·0	62·0	6·4	17·0
November..	86·0	71·0	7·0	63·0	7·8	28·0
December ..	85·0	70·0	7·1	62·0	6·4	20·0
			Total for year ..		67·8	226·0

3. URUÇUCA, BAHIA

	1937 Temperature Mean (degrees Fahr.)	Max. Shade (degrees Fahr.)	Min. Shade	Ave. Hum. (%)	1941–50 Rainfall (in.)	No. of Wet Days
January ..	77·5	92·0	64·4	84·6	4·25	17
February ..	77·0	91·6	66·2	87·1	4·52	16
March ..	77·7	94·0	67·5	84·2	8·32	22
April ..	75·2	94·3	64·4	87·9	9·95	22
May ..	73·4	95·4	57·6	85·3	4·37	18
June ..	70·7	93·2	59·4	88·4	10·22	22
July ..	69·4	88·0	58·3	88·0	5·50	21
August ..	70·3	89·2	55·4	85·8	4·61	20
September..	70·3	89·6	53·6	86·0	4·14	18
October ..	74·8	93·2	60·8	85·2	5·87	18
November..	76·8	93·0	61·9	88·6	8·69	20
December ..	77·2	94·3	63·5	85·2	6·80	19
			Total for year ..		77·24	233

4. MALAYA (Rainfall)

					Kuala Lumpur	Kuala Trengganu
No. of years recorded :					58	12
					(*average in inches*)	
January ..	..	..	..	..	6·68	11·77
February	..	..	..	..	6·18	7·51
March ..	..	..	..	..	9·20	10·72
April ..	..	..	..	..	10·73	5·35
May ..	..	..	..	..	8·48	5·21
June ..	..	..	..	..	5·07	5·36
July ..	..	..	..	..	4·13	5·34
August ..	..	..	..	..	6·31	5·61
September	..	..	..	..	7·33	6·31
October ..	..	..	..	..	11·09	16·22
November	..	..	..	..	10·19	31·98
December	..	..	..	..	9·53	23·40
Total for year				..	94·92	134·78

5. RABAUL, NEW BRITAIN (25 years)

	Temperature			Rel. Humidity			Average No. of
	Mean Max.	Mean Min.	Average Monthly	Mean Max.	Mean Min.	Mean Rainfall	Wet Days
	(*degrees Fahr.*)			(%)	(%)	(*inches*)	
January ..	90·7	73·5	82·1	79·0	72·0	14·13	20·8
February	88·9	73·8	81·3	79·0	72·0	10·44	13·1
March ..	88·4	73·4	80·9	83·0	75·0	9·42	19·5
April ..	89·3	74·0	81·6	83·0	72·0	9·80	18·0
May ..	88·9	73·9	81·4	79·0	72·0	5·17	13·3
June ..	88·5	73·8	81·1	79·0	72·0	3·62	12·7
July ..	88·7	72·8	80·7	87·0	72·0	5·59	14·7
August ..	88·8	73·5	81·1	79·0	72·0	4·40	14·8
September	89·8	73·6	81·7	75·0	72·0	3·65	12·5
October ..	90·3	73·6	81·9	75·0	68·0	5·25	12·7
November	90·8	74·1	82·4	76·0	76·0	6·30	15·7
December	90·4	73·4	81·9	75·0	72·0	10·19	18·3
Total for year ..					..	87·96	186·1

6. MULINU'U, WESTERN SAMOA

Month	Temperature Mean Monthly (a)	Mean Max.	Mean Min.	Avge. Sun-shine (hours)	Rel. Humidity (%) (a)	Mean Rainfall (inches)	Avge. no. of Wet Days	Cloudi-ness (8ths)	Wind Speed (mph)
		(degrees Fahr.)							
January ..	79·51	85·1	75·2	178·3	84·7	17·54	23	5·4	5·8
February..	79·50	85·3	75·2	163·0	84·8	14·94	20	5·2	5·9
March ..	79·53	85·6	75·0	199·8	84·8	13·67	21	4·9	5·2
April ..	79·43	85·7	74·8	211·5	84·5	9·77	18	4·6	5·3
May ..	78·98	85·3	74·1	222·0	83·9	6·81	15	4·2	6·0
June ..	78·37	84·5	73·0	224·1	82·3	5·28	12	3·8	7·7
July ..	77·77	83·9	72·5	245·2	81·7	3·52	12	3·6	8·1
August ..	78·25	84·1	72·8	249·7	80·4	3·77	12	3·6	9·4
September	78·57	84·4	73·4	235·5	81·2	5·45	13	4·0	8·6
October ..	79·03	84·8	74·0	229·2	81·5	7·11	15	4·3	8·1
November	79·12	85·1	73·1	203·1	82·8	10·26	19	4·8	6·4
December	79·48	85·1	74·8	181·9	83·5	14·77	21	5·1	6·4
Mean or Total:									
Year ..	78·96	84·9	74·0	2,543·3	83·0	112·89	201	4·5	6·9
Wet Season	79·40	85·2	74·6	726·3	84·0	57·51	83	5·1	6·1
Dry Season	78·24	84·2	72·9	954·5	81·4	18·02	49	3·8	8·5
No. of years	62	61	61	27	29	62	61	56	19

(a) 24-hourly values.

Table No. 2 THE COCOA SEASON

DURATION OF SUNSHINE FOR TYPICAL COCOA ZONES
HOURS OF SUNSHINE PER DAY

	Jan.	Feb.	Mar.	Apr.	May	June	July	Aug.	Sept.	Oct.	Nov.	Dec.	Average
	July	Aug.	Sept.	Oct.	Nov.	Dec.	Jan.	Feb.	Mar.	Apr.	May	June	
(1) Costa Rica (La Lola)	4·2	4·6	4·9	4·8	4·1	3·8	3·4	4·5	5·9	4·0	3·7	3·6	4·3
(2) Trinidad (I.C.T.A.)	7·6	8·2	8·0	8·1	7·8	6·7	7·2	6·9	6·5	7·0	7·0	7·1	7·3
(3) Ghana (W.A.C.R.I.)	4·8	5·7	5·9	6·7	5·5	3·9	2·6	1·6	3·4	4·7	5·5	5·1	4·6
(4) Brazil (Uruçuca)	5·4	6·9	5·7	7·6	5·6	5·5	6·5	7·0	7·6	5·7	3·5	4·9	6·0

MONTHLY RAINFALL FOR TYPICAL COCOA ZONES
Centimetres

	Jan.	Feb.	Mar.	Apr.	May	June	July	Aug.	Sept.	Oct.	Nov.	Dec.	Av.	Total
	July	Aug.	Sept.	Oct.	Nov.	Dec.	Jan.	Feb.	Mar.	Apr.	May	June		
(1) Costa Rica (La Lola)	35	14	14	17	32	24	39	25	13	30	38	53	28	334
(2) Trinidad (I.C.T.A.)	8	4	3	5	13	22	22	25	20	16	19	16	14	172
(3) Ghana (W.A.C.R.I.)	4	9	15	14	18	21	14	7	15	22	13	6	13	158
(4) Brazil (Uruçuca)	14	16	9	12	20	16	13	11	16	23	15	16	15	176

Inches

	Jan.	Feb.	Mar.	Apr.	May	June	July	Aug.	Sept.	Oct.	Nov.	Dec.	Av.	Total
(1) Costa Rica (La Lola)	13·9	5·5	5·6	6·8	12·8	9·5	15·7	10·1	5·3	12·0	15·4	21·2	11·2	133·8
(2) Trinidad (I.C.T.A.)	3·0	1·8	1·3	1·9	5·1	8·9	8·8	9·9	7·9	6·2	7·5	6·3	5·7	68·6
(3) Ghana (W.A.C.R.I.)	1·6	3·6	6·1	5·8	7·1	8·3	5·5	2·8	6·2	8·7	5·1	2·4	5·3	63·2
(4) Brazil (Uruçuca)	5·5	4·6	3·6	4·7	8·2	6·3	5·2	4·6	6·4	9·0	6·0	6·3	5·9	70·4
	July	Aug.	Sept.	Oct.	Nov.	Dec.	Jan.	Feb.	Mar.	Apr.	May	June		

PERCENTAGE MINIMUM RELATIVE HUMIDITY FOR TYPICAL COCOA ZONES AT 2 OR 3 P.M.

	Jan.	Feb.	Mar.	Apr.	May	June	July	Aug.	Sept.	Oct.	Nov.	Dec.	Av.	Dry	Humid
(1) Costa Rica (La Lola)	64	62	60	61	63	61	65	65	59	61	62	62	62	—	62
(2) Trinidad (I.C.T.A.)	57	52	51	52	57	63	63	63	62	62	62	59	59	52	63
(3) Ghana (W.A.C.R.I.)	54	51	55	58	62	68	69	61	71	70	65	62	62	54	66
(4) Brazil (Uruçuca)	76	72	72	70	77	70	74	74	68	76	77	77	72	68	75
	July	Aug.	Sept.	Oct.	Nov.	Dec.	Jan.	Feb.	Mar.	Apr.	May	June			

Supplied by Dr. P. de T. Alvin.

Centigrade (°C.)

		Jan.	Feb.	Mar.	Apr.	May	June	July	Aug.	Sept.	Oct.	Nov.	Dec.	Av.
(1) Costa Rica (La Lola) (6)	Mean	23·8	24·0	24·5	25·2	26·1	26·1	25·6	25·9	26·2	25·6	25·1	25·0	25·2
	Max.	28·0	28·4	29·3	29·9	30·4	30·6	29·6	30·2	31·2	29·9	29·1	28·4	29·5
	Min.	19·5	19·5	20·0	20·5	21·8	21·6	21·5	21·5	21·2	21·2	21·0	21·5	20·8
	Dif.	8·5	8·9	9·3	9·3	8·6	9·0	8·1	8·8	10·0	8·7	8·1	6·9	8·8
(2) Trinidad (I.C.T.A.) (20)	Mean	24·4	24·4	25·0	26·1	26·7	26·1	26·1	26·1	26·3	26·3	25·7	25·2	25·7
	Max.	28·9	29·4	30·0	30·5	31·0	30·0	30·0	30·5	30·5	30·5	30·0	29·4	30·0
	Min.	20·0	19·4	20·0	21·7	22·3	22·3	22·3	21·7	22·3	22·3	21·7	21·1	21·1
	Dif.	8·9	10·0	10·0	8·9	8·8	7·7	7·7	8·8	8·2	8·2	8·3	8·3	8·9
(3) Ghana (W.A.C.R.I.) (6)	Mean	25·6	26·6	26·8	27·1	26·4	25·4	24·5	24·1	25·1	25·6	26·1	26·0	25·7
	Max.	31·2	32·4	32·2	32·4	31·2	29·2	27·7	27·4	28·6	29·8	31·1	31·2	30·3
	Min.	20·1	20·8	21·4	21·7	21·6	21·5	21·3	20·7	21·6	21·4	21·2	20·7	21·1
	Dif.	11·1	11·6	10·8	10·7	9·6	7·7	6·4	6·7	7·0	8·4	9·9	10·5	9·2
(4) Brazil (Uruçuca) (6)	Mean	21·5	21·2	22·4	23·4	24·8	25·5	25·6	25·7	25·4	24·2	23·7	22·7	23·8
	Max.	26·5	26·2	27·5	28·4	28·8	30·3	31·4	31·4	30·6	29·5	28·7	27·0	28·9
	Min.	16·5	16·3	17·2	18·4	20·0	20·4	19·8	19·9	20·1	18·9	18·6	18·3	18·6
	Dif.	10·0	9·9	10·3	10·0	8·8	9·9	11·6	11·5	10·5	10·6	10·1	8·7	10·3
		July	Aug.	Sept.	Oct.	Nov.	Dec.	Jan.	Feb.	Mar.	Apr.	May	June	

Meteorological Data

Fahrenheit (°F)

		Jan.	Feb.	Mar.	Apr.	May	June	July	Aug.	Sept.	Oct.	Nov.	Dec.	Av.
(1) Costa Rica (La Lola) (6)	Mean	74·8	75·2	76·3	77·3	79·0	79·0	78·0	78·5	79·1	78·0	77·2	77·0	77·4
	Max.	82·5	83·3	84·7	85·7	86·8	87·2	85·5	86·4	88·1	85·9	84·5	83·3	85·3
	Min.	67·2	67·2	67·9	69·0	71·3	70·8	70·6	70·6	70·2	70·2	69·9	70·6	69·5
	Dif.	15·3	16·1	16·8	16·7	15·5	16·4	14·9	15·8	17·9	15·7	14·6	12·7	15·8
(2) Trinidad (I.C.T.A.) (20)	Mean	76	76	77	79	80	79	79	79	79·5	79·5	78·5	77·5	78·3
	Max.	84	85	86	87	88	86	86	87	87	87	86	85	86
	Min.	68	67	68	71	72	72	72	71	72	72	71	70	70
	Dif.	16	18	18	16	16	14	14	16	15	15	15	15	16
(3) Ghana (W.A.C.R.I.)	Mean	77·9	79·9	80·3	80·8	79·5	77·7	76·1	75·4	77·1	78·1	79·0	78·8	78·3
	Max.	87·9	90·3	90·0	89·9	88·2	84·6	81·9	81·4	83·4	85·7	87·9	88·2	86·6
	Min.	68·0	69·5	70·5	70·7	70·9	70·8	70·3	69·4	70·8	70·6	70·0	69·4	70·1
	Dif.	19·9	20·8	19·5	19·2	17·3	13·8	11·6	12·0	12·6	15·1	17·9	18·8	16·5
(4) Brazil (Uruçuca) (6)	Mean	70·7	70·3	72·2	74·2	76·9	77·8	78·1	78·2	77·7	75·7	74·6	72·8	74·9
	Max.	79·6	79·3	81·5	83·3	83·9	86·7	88·7	88·7	87·2	85·3	83·7	80·6	84·0
	Min.	61·8	61·4	63·0	65·2	68·1	68·9	67·6	67·7	68·2	66·1	65·6	65·1	65·7
	Dif.	17·8	17·9	18·5	18·1	15·8	17·8	21·1	21·0	19·0	19·2	18·1	15·5	18·3
		July	Aug.	Sept.	Oct.	Nov.	Dec.	Jan.	Feb.	Mar.	Apr.	May	June	

REFERENCES

Adams, S. N., and McKelvie, A. D. "Environmental requirements of cocoa in the Gold Coast" (Cocoa Conference, London, 1955).

Erneholm, I. *Cacao Production of South America.* Gothenburg, 1948.

Fennah, R. G. "The epidemiology of cacao thrips on cacao in Trinidad." A report on Cacao Research, *I.C.T.A.*, 1954, 7.

Fennah, R. G., and Murray, D. B. "The cocoa tree in relation to its environment" (Cocoa Conference, 1957, 222).

Murray, D. B. "Climatic requirements of cocoa with particular reference to shade" (Cocoa Conference, London, 1955).

Thorold, C. A. "Observations on *Theobroma cacao* in Fernando Po." *J. Ecol.* (1955), **43**, 219.

Chapter IV

SOILS IN RELATION TO NUTRITION OF COCOA

*Soil-aggregate and Crumb-structure—Clays—Sandy Soils—
Alluvial Soils—Acidity, Alkalinity and Chemical Factors
—Soil Depth—Forest Soils—Effects of Certain Trees on
Character of Soil—Treatment of Forest in West Africa
—Stage at which Cocoa can be Planted—Effects of Re-
moving Forest and of Burning—Previous Land Use—Soil
Fertility—Ghana's Forest Soils—Two Main Groups—Base
Status of Ghana's Soils—Divalent Bases for Optimum Cocoa
Production—Sickle-leaf of Cocoa and Magnesium Deficiency
—Magnesium in Plants and Soils—Cultivation*

Cocoa, in common with most other plants, requires a soil which can be easily penetrated by its roots, is retentive of moisture during the dry season and permits the circulation of air and moisture. In other words, its physical qualities must be suitable for the development of a root system and for the provision of "root-room" for its growth. It follows, of course, that the necessary nutrients such as nitrogen, potassium, phosphorus, calcium and magnesium must be present in an available form. If the physical condition of the soil is right, the roots will utilize the available nutrients. A great proportion of the cocoa of the world is grown on structured clay-loams, loams and sandy loams.

Many of the soils where cocoa grows well in West Africa are derived from igneous rocks such as granites, granodiorites and gneisses containing feldspars, black mica and hornblende. In the course of weathering they set free potassium, magnesium and calcium. In Trinidad, the most fertile soils are formed from marine sediments containing carbonate of lime and glauconite and are rich in potassium and phosphorus. In the isolated example in this island where the soil is derived from igneous basalt rock, the content is high in calcium and magnesium, but that of potash is low. Many, although not all, volcanic soils are particularly well supplied with nutrients. Most of the cocoa lands of the Pacific are of volcanic origin.

32

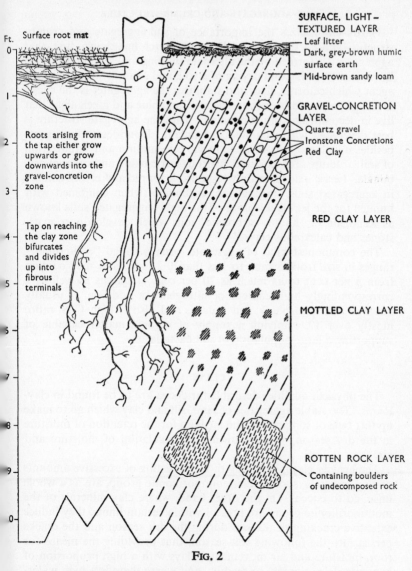

SURFACE, LIGHT–
TEXTURED LAYER
— Leaf litter
— Dark, grey-brown humic
surface earth
— Mid-brown sandy loam

GRAVEL-CONCRETION
LAYER
— Quartz gravel
— Ironstone Concretions
— Red Clay

RED CLAY LAYER

MOTTLED CLAY LAYER

ROTTEN ROCK LAYER
— Containing boulders
of undecomposed rock

Ft.

Surface root mat

Roots arising from
the tap either grow
upwards or grow
downwards into the
gravel-concretion
zone

Tap on reaching
the clay zone
bifurcates
and divides
up into
fibrous
terminals

Fig. 2

DIAGRAMMATIC PROFILE OF THE RED WELL-DRAINED SOIL OF THE
UPLANDS OF GHANA SHOWING HOW THE TYPICAL COCOA ROOT
SYSTEM EXPLOITS THE VARIOUS LAYERS

D

SOIL-AGGREGATE AND CRUMB-STRUCTURE

Hardy emphasizes the importance of soil-aggregate and crumb-structure and goes on to say "Recent research has shown, first, that aggregates are formed by the alternate swelling and shrinking caused by repeated wetting and drying of a soil, and secondly, that the chief agent which cements, fixes and stabilizes the aggregates is the sticky mucilage produced by certain bacteria, and blue and green algae that live in decomposing organic matter. Thus the aggregate structure is best developed where humus is abundant. Doubtless other agents besides mucilage are concerned in the cementation and stabilization of soil structure; for example, hydrous ferric oxide and calcium carbonate. Ferric oxide is mainly responsible for red and brown colours in aggregated soils, and calcium carbonate (when combined with humus) for the jet black colour of the highly aggregated soils known as Rendzina or 'humus-carbonate' soils which develop over marlstones and calcareous clays."

The commonest kind of aggregate, usually called "soil-crumb," ranges in size from 5 mm. to less than 0·2 mm., and may contain from 5 per cent to as much as 20 per cent of humus as well as a correspondingly high content of nitrogen. In addition, it usually has available phosphate and potash, and also a high C/N ratio, mostly over 12, implying a supply of organic matter capable of supporting a large population of soil bacteria.

CLAYS

The physical qualities desirable for cocoa are to be found in clay-loams. The stable aggregates of sand, silt and clay which go to make up this type of soil provide the medium for the retention of moisture in the dry season, while allowing the circulation of moisture and air.

The heavier clays, including those consisting of excessive amounts of clay minerals, such as the montmorillonite group, are as a whole unsuited to cocoa. On the other hand, where clay minerals of the montmorillonite group are present within certain limits, they induce extensive cracking of the soil during the dry season and the cracks persist into the following wet season, thus providing the means for root, moisture and air movement. Clays with a high proportion of kaolinite do not crack so readily, and where there is a high water-table the process of cracking in the heavier clays may be insufficient to allow of root development. Soils consisting of considerable proportions of hydrous oxides of iron and aluminium are non-plastic, do not crack and do not retain moisture.

SANDY SOILS

Of the lighter soils, sandy loams, where the sand is aggregated with clay and silt, are to be preferred. Sandy soils with sand particles of about 0·5 mm. diameter may be satisfactory in conjunction with a good distribution of rainfall or a high water-table. Coarse-grained sands have little capacity for retaining moisture, while fine-grained sands and soils consisting of mixtures of coarse-grained sand and silt are usually unsuitable, as they are liable to become compacted and impede root penetration. Sandy soils as a whole constitute a certain risk where there is the possibility of a prolonged dry season, and this risk is of course greater where the land is on a hillside or steep slope and is therefore more readily drained. It cannot be expected that lighter sandy soils will be as fertile as clay-loams and loams, and the matter of applying fertilizers at an early stage would have to be considered.

ALLUVIAL SOILS

Alluvial soils, many of which are deep loams, especially those deposited on the banks of slow-flowing rivers, can be fertile, and some have the advantage of an annual deposit which enriches the surface layer and keeps it in a state of high fertility. The fact that a plantation may be flooded for several weeks by slow-moving water does not adversely affect the trees.

ACIDITY, ALKALINITY AND CHEMICAL FACTORS

Relatively acid soils of pH 4·5 or below are usually low in nutrients. The better soils in West Africa have a reaction of pH 5·5 and upwards, the most fertile being of the order of pH 6·5 to 7. Cocoa is grown on soils of up to pH 8·5, but alkaline soils are sometimes associated with an excess of calcium carbonate, which may give rise to chlorosis in the leaf of the cocoa tree. Havord, speaking of lime-induced chlorosis, says "It has been shown recently in Trinidad that, even where young seedlings were planted in the greenhouse in soil containing a high percentage of lime, it has been possible to cure it simply by the application of organic matter, either as a surface layer or mixed in with the soil, even if the organic matter itself contains 30 per cent of lime. As a matter of general observation it is apparent that in the 'chocolate' soil of Trinidad the lime-induced chlorosis or 'iron deficiency' is only serious where there is, in addition to lime, a shortage of organic matter."

The Imperial College of Tropical Agriculture, Trinidad, gives the following provisional limits of adequacy of chemical factors for cocoa soils based on Professor Hardy's findings:

		In the top 6″ of soil		
	Total N %	Organic Matter %	Avail. P₂O₅ p.p.m.	Exch. K₂O p.p.m.
Sands and Loams	0·15	2·5	30	100
Silts and Clays	0·20	3·5	50	170

SOIL DEPTH

The lateral root system of the cocoa tree radiates outwards for ten or twenty feet, and on the main roots there are fine fibrous rootlets that grow upwards and explore the surface layer for nutrients and moisture. The tap-root with its fine terminals, in its turn, explores the lower layers of the sub-soil for a depth of from five to ten feet. While the cocoa tree may thrive for a time on a thin surface layer of humus, its eventual survival and profitable growth will depend on the continual replenishment of humus. Where the tap-root can reach decomposing rock of the kind which yields the desired nutrients, the profitable growth of the tree will be ensured for long periods. The importance of soil depth is to some degree related to the supply of nutrients in the surface layers. There are extreme cases where cocoa has been grown quite successfully on a rich surface layer of less than two feet overlying heavy clay, in conditions of adequate and well-distributed rainfall. On the other hand it is common to see cocoa dying off where the tap-root has met with rock, hardpan, or an impermeable layer of clay. It is rarely and only under special conditions that cocoa can be grown on a shallow soil.

FOREST SOILS

The height of tropical forests in different parts of the world varies enormously—from a high proportion of tall trees of 150 feet or over to a mixture of trees with storeys at various lower levels, and finally with the undergrowth. Cocoa is mainly planted on land which has at some stage been in forest, and some is planted in partly thinned forest. The effect of the forest on the soil and the changes which take place at various stages after the forest has been removed are of the greatest importance in the culture of cocoa.

The forest growth extracts nutrients from the soil and rocks, and deposits them on the ground in the form of leaves and fallen branches and thus enriches the surface layer with organic matter essential for the growth of cocoa. While the forest is present, this process goes on continuously. When the forest is removed, exposure causes the rapid decomposition of organic matter, and its dissipation is accelerated by various forms of erosion. Even where the removal of the forest is immediately succeeded by the planting of cocoa, there may be a serious loss of the humus accumulated when the land was under forest, and the store of organic matter may become progressively less, unless there is provision of adequate ground cover and shade trees. The main root system of the cocoa plant operates chiefly in the surface layer, particularly where there is a poor sub-soil. In these conditions the cocoa plant makes little or no addition to the nutrients in the upper horizon. It therefore follows that it is vital to take steps to preserve the organic matter in near-marginal or marginal soils.

EFFECTS OF CERTAIN TREES ON THE CHARACTER OF THE SOIL

Charter, in emphasizing the importance of vegetation in soil genesis, instances the differences to be found in a forest of mixed hardwood and pine forests in America. "The soil under the pine trees was different from the soil under the broad-leaved trees. Under each pine tree a podsol had developed, which is extremely acid and is characterized by an almost white, sandy top soil overlying a brown, iron-stained sub-soil. Under the broad-leaved trees you had brown soils towards the surface and they were not nearly so acid." He goes on to say that in West Africa there are several trees which can affect the soil character, and these include *Chlorophora excelsa* and *Afzelia africana*, which collect vast quantities of calcium carbonate. *Sarcocephalus* spp. also collect various substances. It follows that under a mixed forest stand the soil pattern may be very varied.

TREATMENT OF THE FOREST IN WEST AFRICA

The peasant farmer in West Africa employs several methods of treating the forest before planting cocoa. If his chief purpose is to plant cocoa, any food crops he plants being subsidiary to that objective, he may thin out the forest leaving a number of large trees *in situ*, and plant his cocoa, with coco-yams and plantains as ground shade. If his first objective is to raise a food crop and later establish cocoa, he usually cuts out all the trees with the exception of a few of the bigger ones which may be beyond his capacity to remove.

STAGE AT WHICH COCOA CAN BE PLANTED

It is common experience that it is always easier to establish cocoa through the thinned forest or immediately after the removal of the forest. Where the land has been farmed for food crops subsequent to the removal of the cocoa, the process of re-establishing it is rendered even more difficult. Charter has shown how the type of flora which grows at a certain stage of recovery of the land after the forest has been removed may be a guide as to when cocoa may be planted. Grass is normally followed by shrubs, then secondary bush and finally the forest trees assert themselves. The plants that grow in full sunlight have light yellowish-green leaves, but the shade-enduring plants, such as *Rhinoria*, have relatively dark-green leaves, and it is when these shade-enduring plants appear that the land is ready for planting cocoa. The indication is that cocoa is incapable of competing with the light-loving plants, apart from the fact that the environment is unsuitable.

EFFECTS OF REMOVING THE FOREST AND OF BURNING

There is still a great deal to be learned about the various ways in which the soil is affected by the removal of the forest and the measures which can be adopted to restore the land to the condition where it is again suitable for growing cocoa. Hardy quotes a case where the clear-felling of forest led to a reduction of the moisture content (in a loose sandy soil) in the top six inches by two-thirds in the dry season. The organic content of the soil down to twenty-four inches diminished considerably and there was rapid loss of crumb structure.

Where the felling of the forest is accompanied by burning, plant-ash temporarily raises the mineral content of the soil and greatly reduces its acidity. It may lower the nitrogen content and may also have a deleterious effect on the beneficial micro-organisms and fungi which inhabit the soil, these being gradually replaced by harmful bacteria.

Regarding the effect on the base status of the soil, Charter says "Destruction of the forest means loss of organic matter and consequent loss of bases and other plant nutrients combined with it. Not only is there this absolute loss in nutrients but it would appear probable that there would be changes in the proportions in which the nutrients, particularly bases, are present."

He emphasizes that where forest has been converted to farmland, the divalent bases, calcium and magnesium, tend to be depleted and potassium to increase in amount. Under subsistence farming calcium and magnesium decrease proportionately to the increase in potassium. Excess potassium can make it difficult for the plant to absorb magnesium, of which cocoa has considerable need. Grasses generally show a preponderance of the monovalent bases, potassium and sodium, over divalent bases. Where grass grows, the potassium content will build up and calcium and magnesium will be found in decreasing amounts.

While something is known of the unfavourable effects of the removal of the forest and the subsequent progressive deterioration that occurs in the soil, much less is known about the measures that might be taken to restore such soils to a good level of fertility. It is accepted that most soils could be restored to the desired level if they were left sufficiently long to revert to high forest, but this means of "fallowing" would normally be uneconomic and it is urgent that other ways of resuscitating worn-out land be found.

PREVIOUS LAND USE

Adams and McKelvie (1955), in their discussion of Ghana soils, say "The suitability of a soil for cocoa depends on the soil type and the soil phase. The soil type is conditioned by geology and topography, and soil phase often by the previous history of land use on the site."

They go on to assert that previous land use is of particular importance in cocoa establishment. "At present, there are large areas of the Eastern Province where the soil type is ideal for cocoa, but is quite unsuitable as the land is either food-farmed or under poor secondary bush. It is possible to establish cocoa on such soils (Benstead, 1951), and on certain favoured patches the growth may be good, but in general the growth is poor in comparison with that obtained on a virgin soil. Cocoa-growing under these secondary conditions has not yet been shown to respond to mineral fertilizers, and research is in progress to solve this problem."

SOIL FERTILITY

Two important problems confront the scientists and growers of cocoa in general, namely, the maintenance of fertility in the soil when the forest has been removed, and the rehabilitation of degraded soils to the condition where they may again be profitably used for growing cocoa. Ample supplies of raw cocoa in the future will depend in a great measure on the solution of these problems.

It is tempting to speculate in advance how they will be solved. It is possible that the maintenance of fertility could be greatly helped by incorporating into the plantation trees especially beneficial to cocoa. These could take the form of shade trees or even frequent windbreaks, which, apart from providing the necessary shade, would help to keep up the supply of humus and sustain the circulation of nutrients. This, together with the application of mineral manures and the prevention of erosion, may prove to be the answer. The use of shade trees is, of course, a practice of long standing, but the best trees to use and the density at which they should be planted, particularly in conjunction with a system of manuring, are things yet to be learned.

The rehabilitation of degraded soil is an issue of much greater complexity. It is possible that the establishment of certain trees which have a special virtue in the restoration of the soil to a condition suitable for cocoa, together with the use of mineral manures, may shorten the time in which the land may be brought back to profitable use. In Western Samoa it is common to plant *Erythrina lithosperma* ("Dadap") cuttings in the land before planting cocoa, and the Dadap is allowed to grow until smothered out by the cocoa canopy. It is claimed that this practice is beneficial to the land.

Whatever the answers to these intricate problems may be, it is certain that they will vary under different conditions of soil and climate, and that they offer unlimited scope for research.

GHANA'S FOREST SOILS

In a paper entitled "The Nutrient Status of Gold Coast Forest Soils" read at the Cocoa Conference in London in 1955, the late C. F. Charter presented valuable facts about the soils of that country and information which is of significance in relation to cocoa soils in general. In view of the importance of Ghana's cocoa production, some of the salient points of his paper are enumerated below.

TWO MAIN GROUPS

There are two main groups: the ochrosols and the oxysols. "The ochrosols consist of red to yellowish-brown kaolinitic earths with characteristic reaction profiles: the surface horizons vary from moderately acid to mildly alkaline, and lower horizons become increasingly acid. The surface 2 to 3 inches are frequently slightly calcareous.

"These soils are developed over a variety of parent materials, including the weathering products of granodiorites, biotic schists, phyllites, epidiorites, etc., both accumulated in place (residual soils) and transported as terrestrial deposits (peneplane drift soils). Under forest, ochrosols occur under rainfalls varying from 40–50 inches to 70–80 inches. It is on this great soil group that the vast majority of cocoa is produced.

THE OXYSOLS

"The oxysols typically consist of pale orange-coloured kaolinitic earths, though red examples also occur. This great soil group also displays a characteristic reaction profile: the surface horizon is highly to very highly acid and the lower horizons are only slightly less acid. Oxysols are developed in parent materials similar to ochrosols but typically under rainfalls exceeding 70–80 inches and, outside the Gold Coast, up to 200 inches or more; where they occur under lower rainfalls they have been derived from the weathering products of highly siliceous rocks, i.e. quartzites, or from those pyritiferous sediments which set free sulphuric acid during decomposition. The soils of this great soil group produce little cocoa. Fortunately they are not extensive in the Gold Coast but elsewhere in the very humid forest regions of the tropics they are extremely widespread.

"The distinguishing characteristic of oxysols, apart from colour, is the fact that they are inhabited by distinctive indicator plants such as *Lycopodium* spp., *Gleichenia* spp., abundance of *Melastomaceae* and blue-fruited *Rubiaceae*."

THE OCHROSOLS

Ochrosols are abundantly supplied with the divalent bases, calcium and magnesium; dilute-acid-soluble phosphorus is present in greater amounts than in the oxysols.

"It is considered that modal oxysols have surface reaction of *p*H 4–5 and modal ochrosols surface reactions between 5 and 6. Such inter-grades are abundant in the Gold Coast forest zone and observation suggests that they are far less productive for cocoa than the ochrosols proper.

"Ochrosols with reactions above *p*H 7 inter-grade with calcimorphic soils, derived from basic or calcareous rocks, which are abundantly supplied with divalent bases and approach neutrality throughout the profile. Calcimorphic soils are excellent producers of cocoa but are very inextensive in the Gold Coast and only locally of importance elsewhere.

THE BASE STATUS OF GHANA'S SOILS

". . . as one passes from the slightly calcareous ochrosols, through the non-calcareous ochrosols and inter-grade soils to the oxysols, the divalent bases, calcium and magnesium, diminish in amount and there is a tendency for magnesium to be lost to a greater extent than calcium. On the other hand the proportions of potassium diminish far less, or hardly at all."

It is assumed that cocoa was planted on a wide range of soils in Ghana but that it has survived to a greater extent on soils approaching neutrality or slight alkalinity than on those which were more acid or highly acid. Charter considers that the 6 per cent or so of the cocoa planted on soils between pH 4·5 and 5 is giving a poor yield; that the 20 per cent growing on soils of pH 5·5 to 6 gives a significantly better yield, but that the 35 per cent on soils with a reaction of pH 6·5 to 7 gives an outstandingly good yield.

DIVALENT BASES, PARTICULARLY MAGNESIUM, NEEDED FOR OPTIMUM COCOA PRODUCTION

"The evidence to hand suggests that the divalent bases, calcium and magnesium, and particularly the latter, play a highly significant role in the nutrition of cocoa, and for soils to produce cocoa satisfactorily these bases must be present in adequate amounts.

"It is also evident from observation that the best cocoa soils in the Gold Coast are those developed from rocks rich in ferromagnesian minerals such as hornblende (the hornblende granodiorite of W.A.C.R.I. and the epidiorites of the upper Tano basin) and biotite and magnesium mica (the biotite schists of the Ayensu basin and the biotite granodiorite of the Upper Densu basin)."

SICKLE-LEAF OF COCOA AND MAGNESIUM DEFICIENCY

The foliar distortion of the leaf known as "sickle-leaf" has been observed in Ghana and is a common occurrence on certain estates in Ceylon. In Ghana it has been attributed to excess of potash arising from the accumulation of cocoa pods discarded around the trees, the pods being rich in potassium. "However," says Charter, "this evidence of nutritional disorder occurs apart from such contamination. Sickle-leaf has been proved to be brought about by zinc deficiency and the condition can be remedied by spraying with zinc solutions. Such a deficiency, however, may be an induced one. Thus Camp, discussing magnesium deficiency on the sandy citrus soils of Florida, states that this can affect the health of the roots and can result in an inadequate uptake of zinc and copper from soils with a satisfactory supply of these elements; zinc deficiency symptoms, however, disappear after applications of magnesium. In this connection it is of considerable interest to note that sickle-leaf, under the name of magnesium deficiency, has been cured in Ceylon by the application of dolomitic, i.e., magnesium limestone, it having been observed that cocoa did not exhibit sickle-leaf on soils developed over limestone."

Potassium and magnesium exhibit an "antagonism," excess of the former depressing the uptake of the latter. Magnesium is increasingly lost as the soils become increasingly acid, but the potassium content remains the same. "A similar trend occurs when forest is replaced by bush. It is probable, therefore, that unfavourable ratios of magnesium to potassium may occur under both conditions."

MAGNESIUM IN PLANTS AND SOILS

The vital importance of this mineral to the cocoa plant is especially emphasized by Charter. He states: "Magnesium is an essential component of chlorophyll, the green colouring matter of plants essential in the synthesis of carbohydrates and hence in the production of fats." It is concerned in fat production and is always characteristically high in oil seeds, including cocoa. "It is concerned in the transport of phosphorus into and within the plant, magnesium materials often being mixed with phosphorus fertilizers with this end in view. It is most abundant until the fruiting stage, in the growing points of plants and must therefore play an important role in early growth and establishment."

CULTIVATION

The cultivation of cocoa has not been generally practised except in Ceylon and Grenada. The extent to which cocoa in general would benefit from a greater or lesser degree of cultivation has yet to be discovered. Experiments in this connection now being carried out at the Imperial College, Trinidad, may help to throw some light on the means by which cultivation would improve output. The root system of the cocoa tree, being mainly close to the surface, is liable to be damaged in the course of cultivation. The trees at normal spacing, with their branches radiating from the trunk at low level, would make mechanical cultivation difficult. Furthermore, as the roots feed mainly on the humic matter of the surface layer, any implement which brings the subsoil to the surface and tends to bury the surface soil is not likely to improve conditions for the plant. Nevertheless, there is no doubt that the physical condition of some soils on which cocoa is grown would be improved with cultivation, if this could be achieved without undue damage to the root system. Certain clay soils could be improved with periodic cultivation in the dry season, but whether cultivation should be confined to "conditioning" by implements which do not bring the subsoil to the surface before the cocoa is planted, or whether inter-row subsoiling

TABLE No. 3

ANALYTICAL DATA FOR NINE-INCH SURFACE SAMPLES OF OCHROSOL-OXYSOL INTERGRADES UNDER FIVE VEGETATION TYPES

Vegetation	No. of Samples	Organic Matter %	C/N	pH	Cation Exchange Capacity m.e.% Soil	Exchangeable Cations m.e.% Soil			Ratios			
						Ca	Mg	K	Ca/Mg	Mg/K	Ca/K	Ca+Mg/K
Forest	14	3·05	10·22	5·28	11·15	4·18	1·42	0·25	2·94	5·68	16·72	22·40
Cocoa	7	2·40	10·55	5·34	7·59	4·68	0·88	0·29	5·32	3·03	16·14	19·17
Thicket	4	2·69	10·59	5·25	9·17	4·01	0·78	0·21	5·14	3·71	19·09	22·81
Forb Regrowth	6	2·68	10·74	5·37	9·84	3·57	0·96	0·24	3·72	4·00	14·88	18·88
Farmland	5	2·76	10·99	5·33	9·68	3·69	0·96	0·30	3·84	3·20	13·30	15·50

Forest: Includes recent secondary forest as well as primary forest.

Thicket: Closed formation of shrubs 20–30 ft. high that occupies abandoned farmland after a few years.

Forb Regrowth: The growth of suffrutescent herbs and grasses that takes over abandoned farmland in the first couple of years.

Farmland: Subsistence farming following the cutting and burning of bush; no tillage of the soil is involved.

Source: "The Nutrient Status of Gold Coast Forest Soils," by C. F. Charter, Cocoa Conference, London, 1955, 40.

Table No. 4

ANALYTICAL DATA FOR NINE-INCH SURFACE SAMPLES OF OCHROSOLS UNDER FIVE VEGETATION TYPES

Vegetation	No. of Samples	Organic Matter %	C/N	pH	Cation Exchange Capacity m.e.% Soil	Exchangeable Cations m.e.% Soil			Ratios			
						Ca	Mg	K	Ca/Mg	Mg/K	Ca/K	Ca+Mg/K
Forest	23	3·59	9·74	6·27	14·01	9·49	2·40	0·36	3·95	6·67	26·36	33·03
Cocoa	53	3·22	10·07	6·73	14·38	10·52	2·21	0·41	4·76	5·39	25·66	31·05
Thicket	14	2·56	9·61	6·37	10·14	7·08	1·45	0·30	4·88	4·83	23·60	28·43
Forb Regrowth	21	2·78	9·47	6·63	11·15	8·73	1·72	0·34	5·08	5·06	25·68	30·74
Farmland	16	2·37	10·63	6·25	10·53	6·58	1·73	0·39	3·80	4·44	16·87	21·31

Forest: Includes recent secondary forest as well as primary forest.

Thicket: Closed formation of suffrutescent shrubs 20–30 ft. high that occupies abandoned farmland after a few years.

Forb Regrowth: The growth of suffrutescent herbs and grasses that takes over abandoned farmland in the first couple of years.

Farmland: Subsistence farming following the cutting and burning of bush; no tillage of the soil is involved.

Source: "The Nutrient Status of Gold Coast Forest Soils," by C. F. Charter, Cocoa Conference, London, 1955, 40.

could be continued after the plantation has been established, remains to be proved. The benefits of judicious cultivation might more than offset the damage caused to the roots.

In those rather rare cases where cocoa is planted on a rich, deep alluvial soil, it is possible to apply mechanization to most operations of clearing the forest, including bulldozing the tree stems and stumps into wind-rows, and still have good soil on the surface in which to plant the cocoa. In this case nutrients are available for the cocoa for a considerable depth, so the matter of turning up the subsoil is of less consequence.

In its issue of February 1958, the agricultural periodical *World Crops* had some interesting observations to make on cultivation. Tea estates in Assam were deep-hoed to a depth of 9 inches each year, and the aim was to light-hoe each month and to trench between the rows of tea every three years to a depth of 18 inches. Experiments in tea cultivation demonstrated that the less the soil was disturbed the bigger the crop, and that what was of greatest importance was the control of weeds which had an adverse effect on the tea bushes. Eventually cultivation was cut down to shallow hoeing in the spring, and the tea bushes were pruned to give the maximum spread for the purpose of shading the ground and thus helping to control weed growth. These elementary discoveries in tea culture greatly reduced the cultivation costs. Apart from reducing costs and increasing the crop, the drastic reduction in cultivation of the tea estates reduced the tendency to soil erosion.

It is reasonable to conclude that what holds good for tea in regard to cultivation applies also to cocoa, and unless there is ample evidence to show that cocoa fields benefit from a degree of cultivation in certain soils, there would seem to be no advantage in embarking on a programme which might in fact reduce the cropping capacity.

REFERENCES

Adams, S. N., and McKelvie, A. D. "Environment requirements of cocoa in the Gold Coast" (Cocoa Conference, London, 1955).

Charter, C. F. "The characteristics of the principal cocoa soils" (Cocoa Conference, London, 1949). "The nutrient status of Gold Coast forest soils" (Cocoa Conference, London, 1955).

Havord, G. "Soil conditions for cocoa and their amendment for maximum Yield" (Cocoa Conference, London, 1955).

Homès, Professor M. V. "The mineral nutrition of cocoa" (Cocoa Conference, London, 1957).

Reports on Cocoa Research by the Imperial College of Tropical Agriculture.

Chapter V

THE MANURING OF COCOA

Difficulty of Arriving at a Manuring Formula—Addition of Organic Matter—Mineral Manures—Work on Manuring at the Imperial College of Tropical Agriculture—Some Manuring Practices—Recent Work on Manuring

DIFFICULTY OF ARRIVING AT A MANURING FORMULA

VARIOUS experiments and trials have been carried out in manuring cocoa, especially at the Imperial College, Trinidad, but there is as yet no formula to guide the planter in this connection. The experiments now in train at this College go a long way towards solving those problems of manuring which up to the present have been so obscure. It would appear that the matter of applying manures to cocoa to good advantage is much more complicated than it is with most other tropical crops. Some of the difficulties have been due to the genetic heterogeneity of the cocoa material used in earlier trials, heterogeneity of the soil, and damage to the trees by insect pests which upset the experiments. Nevertheless, it is certain that the output of cocoa could be greatly increased if the means of manuring the trees to advantage were understood. The following notes are not intended so much to give specific guidance on the manuring of cocoa as to review the subject.

ADDITION OF ORGANIC MATTER

It may be assumed that manures will give the best results where the physical condition of the soil is right, drainage adequate and the required trace elements present. As a good supply of organic matter in the surface layer is a basic requirement, the possibility of adding organic matter to the soil should be the first consideration. Mulches of grass, sawdust or sugar cane waste, and bagasse, where readily available, can be applied. On decomposing, these should improve the physical condition of the soil and add to the nutrient supply. Pen manure has been much used in Grenada, Ceylon and Trinidad in the past. It has been applied by digging it into the ground, placing it in trenches between the trees, and, sometimes as in Grenada, by tethering cattle in the plantation. Pen manure operates much like a

47

mulch in that it is probably of more use in improving the structure of the surface soil than as a supplier of nutrients. It may also contain trace elements. Compost is sometimes used in the same way as pen manure. It must be admitted that the application of organic manures in the above forms is only possible in a few places in a few countries. The cost of labour is so high that unless such materials are readily available it would be impracticable to use them.

A word of caution is necessary in the matter of applying quantities of unrotted material to the soil. In the process of rotting, such material may absorb the available nitrogen as well as minor elements and compete with the cocoa for soil oxygen. It would probably be unwise to apply a very large amount of undecomposed organic matter to the soil at one time, and it may be desirable to apply a certain amount of mineral manure containing nitrogen as well so that there is enough to meet the needs both of the cocoa tree and of the decomposing vegetable matter.

A cheaper method of adding organic matter to the soil before planting (until the canopy of the cocoa trees has developed to the stage where it completely shades the ground) is by growing leguminous trees or shrubs such as *Erythrina lithosperma, Gliricidia, Crotalaria, Tephrosia* or similar plants, and cutting them back in order to supply material for mulch.

MINERAL MANURES

Charter, in stressing the need for experimental work on the manuring of cocoa, says: "Besides five or more trace elements needed in minute proportions, there are six primary elements obtained from the soil in relatively large quantities that are essential to plant growth: these are nitrogen, phosphorus, potassium, calcium, magnesium and sulphur." He emphasized the desirability of not overlooking sulphur in manuring trials, and underlined the importance of calcium, magnesium and potassium, especially magnesium, in the nutrition of cocoa.

WORK ON MANURING AT THE IMPERIAL COLLEGE OF TROPICAL AGRICULTURE

The following is derived from unpublished notes on work done by the staff of the Soils Department, Imperial College.

The Imperial College of Tropical Agriculture, Trinidad, has carried out a number of manuring experiments and more have recently been started. The experiments are taking place on River Estate, where the

I. HEALTHY COCOA TREE IN BEARING: The pods are of Amelonado type.

II. TYPES OF COCOA PODS: (*Left to right*) Two yellow Angoleta, red Amelonado, orange Calabacillo, and two Criollo types.

III. VEGETATIVE PROPAGATION: A stem-cutting prepared for the rooting bin. The upper surface of the stem has begun to turn brown.

IV.   VEGETATIVE PROPAGATION: Underside of cutting shown in Plate III.   This is a
light shade of green with no browning on the stem.

V. TEMPORARY SHADE FOR YOUNG COCOA: Young clonal trees growing under the temporary shade of bananas.

VI. YOUNG COCOA PLANTATION: Clonal trees growing under Immortelle shade.
(River Estate, Trinidad.)

VII. EFFECT OF SHADE: These two-and-a-half-year-old trees form part of an experiment in shading and fertilizing in Trinidad. The small tree has grown without shade. Those in the background were shaded until two years old, when the shade was removed.

VIII. DRYING COCOA: A drying shed with movable roof, typical of plantation equipment in Trinidad. The shed on the right holds the sweat-boxes.

1

5

2

6

3

7

4

IX. SECTIONS OF COCOA BEANS
AFTER PREPARATION FOR THE MARKET

(1) Unfermented or slaty bean; compare
with (5) a fully-fermented bean of good
chocolate-brown colour. (2), (3) (4)
Underfermented or purple beans. The
bright colour and cheesy cut of these beans
indicate that they are little better than
unfermented beans. (6) and (7) These
purple beans are also insufficiently fermented, although they have been better
prepared than those on the left.

A sample of well-fermented cocoa should not contain
any beans of the type on the left, and should consist
of a high proportion—preferably 100 per cent—of
fully-fermented beans like No. 5.

X. COCOA GROWING UNDER FOREST SHADE IN THE GOLD COAST: The cocoa trees are in the centre and background of the photograph.

soil is mainly alluvial fine sandy loam and drainage varies from good to impeded.

The findings are that nitrogen is most needed in the absence of shade, and this particularly applies to young cocoa before overhead shade has been established. The need for nitrogen may diminish as the tree develops its canopy. Phosphorus balances nitrogen uptake and stimulates bacterial multiplication, and it is possible that bacteria have an important function in root development. Potassium is necessary in shade; it "conditions" the plant against diseases, and a deficiency of this mineral would appear to be an important factor in cherelle wilt.

No reliable evidence has yet been deduced from experimental work in Trinidad as to the amounts or proportions of mineral manures required for cocoa at different ages, but it is presumed that these would necessarily vary with the soil. The trace elements listed are iron, magnesium, manganese, zinc, copper, molybdenum and boron; some others may be desirable.

As a guide to the amount of mineral nutrients removed by a cocoa crop, the following example is given. A crop of 500 lb. of dry cocoa per acre removes:

Nitrogen   12 lb. N   = Sulphate of Ammonia (approx.) 60 lb.
Phosphorus 6 lb. P_2O_5 = Superphosphate 30 lb.
Potassium $9\frac{1}{2}$ lb. K_2O = Muriate of Potash (KCl) 20 lb.

Manurial Experiments at the Imperial College of Tropical Agriculture. It was found that certain manures gave a significant and favourable response and that the poorer clones gave a relatively greater response than the better clones.

Field 20: Shade, Spacing and Fertilizer Experiment. In a field of eleven acres, clone ICS 1 only was used and the experiment was designed to compare the effects of (1) shade versus no shade; (2) wide versus close spacing; (3) fertilizers versus no fertilizers. The spacings used were 12 by 12 ft. and 8 by 8 ft. The fertilizers applied were ammonium sulphate (N), superphosphate (P), and potassium chloride (K), and the combinations were O, N, P, K, NP, NK, PK, NPK; eight treatments in all. The quantities used were arbitrary, and varied according to the age of the tree.

The experiment was begun in 1949 and fertilizers were first applied in October 1949. The results noted in 1952–3 were that significant increases in yield were obtained from (*a*) close planting, (*b*) nitrogen-fertilized plots, and (*c*) phosphate-fertilized plots. The shade treatment had no effect owing to the uniform provision of temporary shade. The mean yield of the whole experiment was 264 lb. dry

E

cocoa per acre, and the best yielding plots, receiving NP treatment, gave nearly 600 lb. per acre. Fertilizer responses were accompanied by a smaller weight of beans per pod but more pods per tree. The increase from the closely spaced trees over the more widely spaced was due entirely to the greater number of trees per acre, not to increased yields per tree.

In 1953–4 and 1954–5 the close-spaced plots gave a significantly higher yield than the wide-spaced plots, but the latter yielded far more per tree. Nitrogen fertilizers significantly increased yields, but the increment was far greater in unshaded and wide-spaced plots. Phosphate fertilizer gave a small but non-significant increase in 1953–4, and a still smaller increase in 1954–5. There was a tendency for potassium fertilizer to reduce yields in the absence of nitrogen and shade, but to maintain or slightly increase yields in the presence of these factors. The mean yields were: 1953–4, 408 lb. dry cocoa per acre; 1954–5, 1,028 lb. per acre. The best treatments yielded over 500 lb. per acre in 1953–4, and over 1,400 lb. per acre in 1954–5.

Field 6: Leguminous and Non-Leguminous Shade Experiment. This is a field of three acres where four clones were tested, ICS 1, 8, 16 and 98. The leguminous shade trees were Immortelle and *Peltophorum ferruginum*, and the non-leguminous shade trees were pink poui (*Tabebuia pentaphylla*; Bignoniaceae) and *Theobroma bicolor* (Sterculiaceae). The spacing of the cocoa trees was 12 by 12 ft., and the shade trees 24 by 24 ft., to be thinned later to 34 by 34 ft. Phosphate and potash were applied throughout, but a nitrogen fertilizer treatment versus no nitrogen was superimposed. Planting was begun in August 1950, and fertilizers were first applied in June 1951, and repeated in May each year.

It is noted that in the earlier experiments with fertilizers on shaded (Immortelle) and unshaded cocoa on River Estate, response to nitrogenous fertilizers, such as ammonium sulphate, was obtained only with unshaded cocoa, and that the yields of shaded cocoa were depressed by nitrogenous fertilizers.

By 1954–5 it was found that the best yields were obtained under Immortelle and *Peltophorum*, being better than under non-leguminous trees. Nitrogen fertilizer increased the yield under *Peltophorum* and pink poui, but not under Immortelle or *Theobroma bicolor*. The mean yield was 549 lb., but ICS 1 gave 1,058 lb. dry cocoa per acre.

Field 23A: Mulching Experiment. In this experiment, which incorporates 32 mulch-treatment combinations, the first application was in the dry season of 1951. The amount of grass-mulch applied annually was about 25 tons per acre, and of bagasse, 19 tons per acre. A mixture of equal amounts of grass and pen manure was applied in trenches at the rate of 36 tons per acre, but this will only be applied every four years.

By 1954–5, cut bush mulch gave the best yields and trench mulching was better than the controls, but bagasse mulch showed no increase. The mean yield was 963 lb. of dry cocoa per acre, bush mulched plots gave 1,246 lb. per acre, and the controls 749.

In a *Tillage and Manurial Experiment*, begun in September 1950, Field 22B, with three tillage and four manurial treatments, the results of 1953–4–5 were that yields showed a large variation between duplicate plots, but with ICS 1, non-cultivated plots were better than those cultivated. There was a variable response to fertilizers, but mulches gave a large increase in the absence of cultivation.

All the experiments described and others initiated more recently are still at an early stage, and the most interesting and useful results are yet to come. No information is available from Trinidad regarding the response of cocoa to magnesium.

SOME MANURING PRACTICES

It had been standard practice when planting cocoa in Trinidad in the past to dig a hole 16 in. by 16 in. and 8 in. deep, the soil from the hole being thoroughly mixed with the contents of a 16 lb. basket of pen manure. The plant is then set in the hole with a ball of earth attached. The mixture of soil and manure is packed round it and the surplus material piled around the stem.

As there is less pen manure now than formerly, the Cocoa Board recommends the application of mineral manures to seedlings and to young cocoa and suggests alternate doses of $\frac{1}{2}$ lb. NPK, followed by $\frac{1}{4}$ lb. of sulphate of ammonia per plant every eight weeks. Some estates apply to the young seedlings of three to four months NPK 10.10.10 at the rate of 4 ounces per plant, alternated with similar applications of sulphate of ammonia. This may be stepped up to 1–1$\frac{1}{2}$ lb. as the plants get older. Certain estates believe in quite heavy dressings of mineral manure for mature cocoa. For instance, an application of 1$\frac{1}{2}$ lb. of superphosphate per tree in May, $\frac{7}{8}$ lb. NPK 10.10.10 in July followed by 1 lb. of similar NPK in August.

Ceylon has practised manuring for many years and some estates applied 400 lb. of NPK annually for two years, followed in the third year by 360 lb. of the same dressing, together with 12 tons of farmyard manure. Another rate was 130 lb. of mineral manure annually for two years, followed by five tons of farmyard manure in the third year. Grenada has used pen manure ever since cocoa was

grown there. At one time it imported pen manure from Venezuela. Where sickle-leaf was prevalent in Ceylon, the condition has been improved by the addition of dolomitic, e.g. magnesian lime. Similarly, in Eastern Malaya, where the soil is acid, and on analysis showed a lack of phosphates, the addition of magnesium lime and Christmas Island rock phosphate brought about a remarkable improvement.

On the estates of the Huileries du Congo Belge there have been interesting results in the manuring of cocoa. The application of equal parts of sulphate of potash, magnesium sulphate and superphosphate, with the addition of one per cent trace element mixture of copper, manganese, boron, zinc and molybdenum, gave a marked increase in yield under the conditions obtaining at Yaligimba, where the manurial trial was carried out.

RECENT WORK ON MANURING

In a paper presented at the Cocoa Conference in London in 1957, Professor M. V. Homès discussed the results of manurial trials undertaken at I.N.E.A.C. in the Belgian Congo. Large concrete tanks containing washed sand were used for a series of experiments, and each plant received a complete nutrient mixture containing nitrogen, sulphur, phosphorus, potassium, calcium and magnesium, as well as some other minor elements. Superimposed on this basic dressing different batches of plants received additional quantities of the first three elements (N, S and P) in combination with additional amounts of each of the second group of three elements (K, Ca and Mg).

Nine combinations were thus possible, which could be distinguished according to the dominant elements within each of the two groups, namely: nitrogen-potassium, nitrogen-calcium, nitrogen-magnesium, sulphur-potassium, sulphur-calcium, sulphur-magnesium, phosphorus-potassium, phosphorus-calcium, and phosphorus-magnesium. To these nine treatments, a control was added in order to ascertain the natural fertility of this poor sand, a fertility which, while very low, was clearly not absolutely non-existent.

Since the experiments have so far been in operation for only one year, the results apply to the first stage of development of the plant. The manured plants, with one exception, made much better growth than the control; in certain cases the growth was ten times greater. The following table gives the dry weight of the aerial part of the plant expressed in grammes:

Con-trol	Treatment								
	NK	*NCa*	*NMg*	*SK*	*SCa*	*SMg*	*PK*	*PCa*	*PMg*
11·5	51·5	89·3	107·7	40·5	62·0	97·5	7·0	73·9	80·4

This table makes it clear that one of the treatments (PK) gives a lower yield than the control, and this emphasizes the fact that an unbalanced fertilizer can be extremely harmful. Although this fertilizer included all the elements necessary for life, the example demonstrates that the relative proportions of the elements in a fertilizer formula are of the greatest importance.

The table, moreover, includes a sufficient number of combinations to permit a simple empirical comparison, which shows that the treatment NMg is markedly superior to the others. Again, taking into account the fact that this formula contains all the other elements and not only the two predominant ones, we may conclude that the cocoa tree responds favourably to a fertilizer formula in which nitrogen is the dominant anion and magnesium the dominant cation.

After some further discussion Homès goes on to say: "However, we may note from the data given that the dominance of potassium in relation to the other cations is always unfavourable in the case of the cocoa tree. Whatever the dominant anion, i.e., whatever the anion formula, the treatments which contain additional K are always inferior in their effect to the corresponding treatments in which increased amounts of the other cations are applied. It appears also that this unfavourable effect of an excess potassium can be particularly serious when it is associated with an excess of phosphorus.

"These two facts already afford some guidance to the cultivator in search of a fertilizer. Moreover, if one groups the treatments according to their anion dominance, one sees that nitrogen dominance is markedly favourable to the development of the plant.

"Once again, a knowledge of soil types which might guide the cultivator on the nitrogen available to the plant would be a valuable indication as regards the choice of soil in the first place and the modification of the fertilizer programme in the second. Furthermore, it can be said that, in general, the foliar symptoms, which are currently used to ascertain the general state of health of the plant, are in perfect agreement with the weight records. In fact, the most marked pathological symptoms appear in the treatment PK and the healthiest leaves in the treatment NMg.

"There is also another way in which the data from this study can be applied in practice."

In relation to potassium, magnesium and phosphates he states: "Thus the potassium content of the plant in relation to the magnesium content is influenced by the relative dominance of nitrogen or of phosphorus in the mineral fertilizer. One can conclude for example that when the ratio of potassium to magnesium in the plant exceeds three, while the ratio K/Ca is close to unity, it is necessary to apply an increased proportion of nitrogen. This last information, given only as an example, forms the basis of a comprehensive study of the relationship between fertilizer and mineral composition which is being undertaken at present.

"Let us now see how this knowledge may be applied in practice. In the first place, depending on whether cocoa is cultivated in forest clearings or on previously cultivated soil, it is clear that the quantities of humus and nitrogen will be different. The proportion of nitrogen applied can naturally be reduced in soils containing an adequate amount of humus and of soil organisms which liberate nitrogen. Moreover, in many Congo soils phosphates rapidly become unavailable and can only be used by the plants at a very slow and steady rate. For these soils, which include those in which cocoa is likely to be cultivated, it is necessary to increase the phosphate in the anion group up to proportions which can easily reach 50 per cent. With regard to cations, the soils always contain magnesium, but in the absence of analysis it is best to assume this magnesium is not adequate to ensure optimum development and it is wise to include some in the fertilizer mixture. Finally, the very great importance of potassium, and especially its toxic effects when present in excess, invites caution and suggests that one should not use potash fertilizers except where analysis of the soil shows it to be particularly low in this element."

Based on the following formula quoted earlier in his paper:

Anion composition (equivalents as percentages of their total)
NO_3 : 37; $\frac{1}{2}SO_4$: 29; $\frac{1}{3}PO_4$: 34
Cation composition (equivalents as percentages of their total)
K^+ : 21; $\frac{1}{2}Ca^{++}$: 35; $\frac{1}{2}Mg^{++}$: 44

he says: "If the formula of basic requirements, such as that given above, is used as a basis and the analysis of the soil is taken into account, it is possible to conclude that in all cases nitrogen and phosphorus should be added. These two elements may, for example, be added in the form of agricultural ammonium nitrate and bicalcium phosphate. If the phosphorus is applied in triple super form, which appears to be effective in many Congo soils, sulphur must be added at the same time. The agricultural ammonium nitrate also supplies calcium. Magnesium should then be added and the most suitable form seems to be magnesium sulphate (Kieserite), which gives little trouble. Depending on the results of chemical analysis of the soil, one must then decide whether or not to add potassium. To summarize, with the aid of three, or possibly four, simple fertilizer compounds, mixed in the correct proportions to provide the balance considered most suitable to meet the basic requirements of the trees as modified by conditions, a complete fertilizer will be obtained that will assure satisfactory growth. A dose of the order of 500 kg/hectare will probably be adequate for a first application."

Professor Homès is discussing manurial requirements in relation to soils with which he is concerned in the Belgian Congo, but much of his discussion has a bearing on the use of mineral manures in general. The further outcome of work on the application of mineral manures to cocoa in the Belgian Congo will undoubtedly be of great value.

Soil analyses have further shown in Malaya that Jerangau soils are very low in exchangeable calcium. Leaf injections of calcium have recently given noticeable responses.

Both at Jerangau and in Perak leaf-tip and marginal scorch have been traced to applications of muriate of potash, especially in the absence of added phosphates. For this reason it has been decided recently to use only sulphate of potash in fertilizer mixtures for cocoa.

At W.A.C.R.I., it was found that the application of sulphate of ammonia significantly reduced the uptake of phosphate. There were interesting results in an experiment carried out by A. D. McKelvie to test the effect of organic and inorganic mulches in relation to shade and fertilizer treatment. Three types of shade treatment were used: (i) no shade; (ii) artificial shade of cut palm fronds; (iii) sparse, living top-shade of tree cassava and *Gliricidia*. The experiment was carried out for nine months. Artificial shade was found to be better than no shade or natural shade, and organic mulch with or without nitrogen was superior to the other soil treatments. Without shade, all soil treatments were ineffective. Under artificial shade, organic mulch, nitrogen, and the two together were effective; under living shade only organic mulch without added nitrogen gave satisfactory results.

A shade and manurial trial to test the effect of major nutrients on cocoa has given some striking results. At the present early stage of the experiment the responses to the removal of shade and the application of a complete major nutrient fertilizer have been significant. The following table supplied by R. K. Cunningham, who is conducting the experiment, gives the yields to 1959:

TABLE NO. 5

YIELDS EXPRESSED IN LB. OF DRY COCOA PER ACRE

Treatment	Pre-treatment			Post-treatment*		
	1954–55	1955–56	1956–57	Unadjusted 1957–58	Adjusted 1957–58	1958–
Shade, no fertilizer	30	44	205	615	586	95
No shade, no fertilizer	19	29	170	1,079	1,100	2,34
Shade, fertilizer	24	32	211	869	849	1,21
No shade, fertilizer	20	18	173	1,574	1,602	3,09

* Fertilizer mixture applied October 1956; shade removed March 1957.

Shade, provided mainly by *Gliricidia*, gives approximately 35 per cent shade. There are 3,600 ten-year-old Amelonado experimental trees planted in straight lines at 8 ft. by 8 ft.

Experimental Design: 2^2 – Shade – Fertilizer
Replication: 3
Guard Rows: 8 ft. guard rows and two 88 ft. guard strips
Spacing: 8 ft. by 8 ft.
Cocoa: Amelonado planted in May 1947

Area of Experimental Plots: = 19,200 sq. ft.
                      Sub-plots   = 6,400 sq. ft.
Nos. of Experimental Trees per plot: 300 (per sub-plot = 100)

TABLE NO. 6

SCHEME OF FERTILIZER APPLICATIONS

Date	Application	Fertilizers used in mixture	Rates in lb./acre			
			N	P_2O_5	K_2O	MgO
October 1956	1	Ammonium phosphate (11% N, 46% P_2O_5) Single superphosphate (18% P_2O_5) Sulphate of potash (48% K_2O) Magnesium sulphate (16·2% MgO)	13·4	90·7	90·4	45·8
April 1957	2	Urea (46% N) Triple superphosphate (47% P_2O_5)	50	30	—	—
September 1957	3	Urea	50	—	—	—

TABLE No. 7

SOIL ANALYSIS FOR EXPERIMENT IN GHANA

Treatment	Profile	C %	N %	C/N	pH	Available P in p.p.m.*	Exchangeable bases in m.e./100 gm.			Mineralization of N† in p.p.m.		
							Ca	Mg	K	Change in NH_4-N	Change in NO_3-N	Change in total mineral N
Shade, no fertilizer	0–2 in.	4·37	0·341	12·8	7·48	24·1	9·01	2·90	0·54	−9·0	+94·2	+85·2
	2–6 in.	1·78	0·171	10·4	7·44	15·3	5·40	0·94	0·26	−5·6	+67·0	+61·4
Shade, fertilizer	0–2 in.	4·04	0·335	12·0	7·49	25·5	7·48	2·57	0·52	−12·0	+106·5	+94·5
	2–6 in.	1·83	0·183	10·0	7·46	17·6	5·14	0·87	0·27	−6·6	+67·0	+60·4
No shade, no fertilizer	0–2 in.	3·85	0·359	10·7	7·28	27·3	9·28	2·16	0·51	−9·4	+91·5	+82·1
	2–6 in.	1·57	0·160	9·8	7·39	16·0	5·20	1·01	0·23	−5·2	+61·2	+56·0
No shade, fertilizer	0–2 in.	3·56	0·297	11·9	7·22	22·5	6·74	2·29	0·42	−8·8	+93·4	+84·6
	2–6 in.	1·50	0·151	9·9	7·19	13·6	3·21	0·81	0·21	−5·0	+63·5	+58·5

* Estimated by Truog's method.
† Air-dried soil incubated for 14 days at 25° C. and 50 per cent of its moisture-holding capacity.

REMOVAL OF SHADE

In March–April 1957 the shade was removed from the non-shaded plots by poisoning all the shade trees with a proprietary mixture of 2,4-D and 2,4,5-T. The dead trees have been allowed to stand and they have been falling during the dry season with little damage to the cocoa.

The soil is derived from hornblende granodiorite and is a typical Ochrosol. It is a well-drained sandy loam with little structure. It would be classified as one of the better soils of Ghana. Table 7 gives the soil analysis.

It is too early yet to draw far-reaching conclusions from this experiment. The *Gliricidia* shade in the first case was quite heavy and obviously had the effect of preventing the cocoa trees yielding normally. This is an interesting and important experiment; it has shown that the application of mineral manures can increase the yield under certain conditions of environment on this type of soil. It demonstrates that Amelonado cocoa can give a yield per acre as high as any type of cocoa. Further results from this experiment will be followed with great interest.

REFERENCES

Bartolomé, R. "Effect of fertilizer application on the incidence of cherelle wilt of cocoa in Costa Rica." *Cocoa* (1951), **2**, 6.

Charter, C. F. "The need for manuring cocoa in the Gold Coast in order to maintain and augment the level of production." Cocoa Conf. 1953, 145.

Charter, C. F. "The nutrient status of Gold Coast soils with special reference to the manuring of cocoa." Cocoa Conf. 1955, 40.

Crowther, P. C., and Raymond, W. D. "The analysis of soil and foliage material in connection with sickle leaf disease of cocoa in Ceylon." *Col. Pl. & An. Prods.* (1954), **4**, 257.

Cunningham, R. K., and Lamb, J. "A cocoa shade and manurial experiment at the West African Cocoa Research Institute, Ghana. I. First year." *J. hort. Sci.* (1959), **34**, 14.

Cunningham, R. K. "A review of the use of shade and fertilizer in the culture of cocoa." *West Afr. Cocoa Res. Inst. Tech. Bull.* No. 6, 1959.

Evans, H. "Some problems in the physiology of cocoa." *J. Agric. Soc. Trin. Tob.* (1951), **51**, 277.

Greenwood, M., and Djokoto, R. K. "Symptoms of mineral deficiency in cocoa." *J. hort. Sci.* (1952), **27**, 223.

Greenwood, M., and Hayfron, R. J. "Iron and zinc deficiencies in cocoa in the Gold Coast." *Emp. J. exp. Agric.* (1951), **19**, 73.

Havord, G. "Soil conditions for cocoa and their amendment for maximum yield." (Cocoa Conf. 1955, 35.)

Himme, M. van, and Petit, J. "First results of an experiment on artificial shade for cocoa trees at Yangambi," (Cocoa Conf., 1957, 227).

Homès, M. V. "The mineral nutrition of cocoa." (Cocoa Conf. 1957, 257.)

Homès, M. V. "L'Alimentation minérale du cacaoyer." *I.N.E.A.C Ser. Sci.* No. 58, 1953.

Murray, D. B. "Shade and fertilizer experiments with cacao." *Rept. on Cocoa Res. Trin.* 1952, 11; 1953, 30; 1954, 32.

Chapter VI

THE COCOA PLANTATION (1)

ESTABLISHMENT AND MAINTENANCE

I. PRELIMINARY PREPARATION

Overall Considerations—Choice of Site—Soil Assessment—Communications, Water Supply, etc.—Preliminary Operations—Subsequent Operations

OVERALL CONSIDERATIONS

THIS chapter describes in their sequence the operations entailed in laying-out a plantation and in its subsequent care. Some of the points are discussed at greater length in other chapters.

No description of plantation practice could cover all the various methods employed in the tropical countries where cocoa is grown. Variations are sometimes dictated by climate and soil, by the type of labour available, and by traditions and fashions evolved in each country.

While actual practice varies, the basic principles which make for the profitable growing of cocoa are similar. The planter who would make a success of the work in one part of the world would be most likely to make a success of it in another.

CHOICE OF SITE

The choice of site for a plantation will be dictated by certain basic considerations.

Although in the past, sound judgment based on experience guided the more successful planters in their selection of suitable land for cocoa, many plantations of cocoa and other tropical crops have been sited on unsuitable soils. The assumption that soils which carry dense forest must necessarily be productive if the forest is replaced by a plantation has led to much disappointment. It may also be misleading to judge the quality of the soil by its cover in the absence of an intimate knowledge of the type of flora that indicates fertility.

The African peasant built up the greatest cocoa-growing industry

60

in the world without the aid of scientific knowledge, as we understand the term. He achieved success by growing cocoa widely; where it grew well, he grew more of it. In course of time wisdom born of experience prompted him to test the suitability of the soil for cocoa by planting a few trees in advance of any general planting, and he thus acquired a considerable degree of judgment.

This method of trial and error was sufficient for a peasant community at a certain stage in its progress, but for the prospective planter at the present time it is not a practical way of choosing land for cocoa.

SOIL ASSESSMENT

Where such services are available, the assistance of the Department of Agriculture or Research Institute, with staff trained in the study of soils, or the advice of experienced local planters, should be sought. In the absence of these, large companies contemplating development in unsurveyed territory would normally import the necessary skill for their own guidance. In assessing the suitability of a new area, the condition of growth of certain forest plants or farming crops, such as bananas, plantains, and tannias (coco-yams), the luxuriant growth of which is accepted as indicating good conditions for cocoa, would be noted. Similarly, the presence of certain trees which are known to thrive on poor soils or which are indicative of waterlogged or other conditions unsuitable for cocoa would be observed. In the absence of professional skill or guidance on the spot, anyone with a working knowledge of soils can gain a great deal of information by the use of a soil auger. An ordinary carpenter's auger, about 1 inch in diameter, can be converted for the purpose by having the stem lengthened to about 3 to 4 feet. It can probe the ground and bring up enough of the soil to give an indication of its constituents, the depths of its various layers of heavy or light soils, its general texture and its capacity for drainage or retention of moisture. Soils in the tropics are liable to vary widely within a small area, and a simple survey with a soil auger, used up and down the site, will often provide more useful information than any other form of investigation. A preliminary assessment of the acidity and the presence or absence of potash, etc., can be made by the use of soil examination kits. Such assessment should be supplemented by a report on soil samples by an appropriate authority.

Soils which will sustain the growth of the cocoa tree must contain enough clay to enable them to retain sufficient moisture to assure the growth of the plant through dry periods, but it must not be so heavy as to impede drainage or the circulation of moisture and air.

The extent to which organic matter or humus is present in the surface layer may decide at the outset whether cocoa can or cannot be established. Organic matter helps to keep a clay soil friable and makes a sandy soil more retentive of moisture. In addition to improving the physical character of the soil, organic matter is the medium from which the feeding roots will draw most of the plant's nourishment. The care with which the accumulated organic matter is conserved when opening up land for planting, and the skill with which it is maintained and augmented throughout the life of the plantation will greatly influence the productivity of the trees.

COMMUNICATIONS, WATER SUPPLY, ETC.

Accessibility by road or water is important as means of communication have an important bearing on costs.

Water supplies must be studied from the point of view of the needs of the labourers and also of the nurseries.

The number of labourers and the amount of accommodation required for them, and also the size and equipment of the buildings necessary to carry on plantation operations, will be calculated in relation to the size of the venture planned.

Where circumstances permit, it is cheaper in the long run to erect the more expensive permanent buildings at an early stage, rather than to put up temporary buildings which are later to be replaced by permanent structures. If temporary buildings are made they should be such that they will last ten years at least without requiring major repairs. The chief accommodation required will be housing for labour, overseers, and owner or manager, and houses for fermenting and storage.

A number of roads will be required in the early stages, but a more complete road system will be developed gradually. A cambered road with offsets leading to deep holes to take the run-off is much better than one with deep ditches on both sides. Nowadays, even the smaller tractors can be fitted with light bulldozers or road graders, which reduce the costs of earth-moving, road-making and maintenance.

There will be expenditure on basic equipment in the form of axes, saws, machetes, shovels, crowbars, and files. The number of lorries and tractors required will depend on the size of the venture and the availability of local transport and machinery for hire.

PRELIMINARY OPERATIONS

The preliminary operations involved in making a cocoa plantation will vary to some extent from country to country, and with the condition of the land to be planted, depending on whether it is in high forest or secondary bush or has been recently planted with another crop.

High and secondary forest will have to be selectively thinned or cleared. Where the land is already cleared, provision for ground cover and shade must be made at an early stage.

Nurseries will be required, whether the method of planting is by seedlings first grown in the nursery and then planted in the field, or by direct planting of seed. In the latter case nursery plants will be required to replace those which have weakened or died during the first two years.

Nurseries to provide permanent shade trees and, perhaps, temporary shade trees will also be required.

SUBSEQUENT OPERATIONS

Subsequent operations, such as the removal of chupons or suckers, pruning or shaping of trees, and weeding, will be necessary in most countries. Control of temporary and permanent shade trees will depend on how much shade is desired. Cultivation to a greater or lesser extent, especially in the early years, is common in many countries, but manuring is less common. Drainage may require attention.

The need for measures of disease or pest control at various stages differs from country to country; in some they may be necessary at all stages, and in others the need may be negligible.

II. PREPARATION OF THE LAND

Complete Felling and Burning—Selective Thinning—Partial Clearing—Sale of Timber—Sequence of Operations—Use of Chemicals in Removing Forest—Mechanization in Felling— Planting in Old Plantation Land or Land without Forest— Prevention of Erosion—Drainage

COMPLETE FELLING AND BURNING

Where the land is in forest, operations usually begin by clearing the undergrowth at the end of the wet season, or early enough in the dry season to permit of burning the forest growth (if burning is to be done) before the rains begin again.

The time when preparation of forest land for planting should start will depend on the length of the dry season. Where this is of short duration it may be necessary to begin before the end of the wet season; on the other hand, where there is a long dry season, it may be possible to do all the preparation and clearing in dry weather. Initial operations would be the clearing of the undergrowth and smaller trees, followed by the felling of the larger trees. If the aim is to burn all the standing timber, a good deal of cutting of the larger trunks and branches will be necessary. Brushwood and logs would be stacked against the larger trunks and tree stumps in order that these may be effectively burned. This is especially necessary for hardwood.

The extent to which the land should be stumped and how much effort should be made to remove the roots of forest trees from the ground is a matter on which the planter will be guided by local experience. Unless there is considerable depth of surface soil, the process of digging up stumps and roots might expose the sub-soil unduly to the disadvantage of the cocoa crop.

SELECTIVE THINNING

Overhead shade can be provided by leaving a sufficient number of deep-rooted forest trees which can create a canopy for shading the cocoa, and which are not incompatible with its growth. It is better to thin out the forest and leave a sufficient number of the original forest trees as shade, rather than to cut them all out. This method allows all the usual operations of brushing, lining and holing to be carried out. It has been practised in the Congo with great success. It is also

11. Clearing jungle in Malaya for cocoa planting. A building for nursery use is in course of erection

12. Potential land being cleared for planting in Papua and New Guinea

13. In Papua and New Guinea it is usual practice to burn the stems and brushwood after felling the forest

14. Clearing secondary forest Ghana for cocoa planting. This type forest is dominated by the Umbre tree (*Musanga smithii*)

15. Seedlings growing in baskets showing type of basket used and spiral arrangement of leaves on chupon

practised in West Africa to a greater or lesser extent, but not with the same degree of skill.

PARTIAL CLEARING

When clearing the lines of trunks and brushwood, some saving in labour can be achieved by merely making a partial clearance in the first year. If, for instance, the planting distance between rows is to be nine feet, rows can be cleared and planted in the first year at eighteen feet. The tree trunks and brushwood are piled in the intervening space where they will settle down and rot. Incidentally, they provide shelter for the first rows of young cocoa. A year later, the inter-rows are cleared and planted. This method of establishing cocoa is commonly used on the Lukolela cocoa estates in the Congo and is considered to be economical of labour. The result is that the odd-numbered rows are a year younger than the even-numbered rows (or *vice versa*), but this is of no consequence.

It has been a common practice in some South American countries to establish young cocoa in three- to four-foot wide rides or rentices in the forest, the remaining trees being killed off by ring-barking or by the use of arboricides. Under this arrangement, the proper adjustment of shade in the early stages of the plantation's growth is difficult. There may be too much shade at first and too little later.

SALE OF TIMBER

Clearing may be done by the use of daily labour and some or all of the operations may be given out on contract. Where there is timber of commercial value, it may be possible to sell it to offset part of the clearing costs. Where the site is near a settled community, the less valuable timbers may find a sale as firewood or for charcoal-making.

SEQUENCE OF OPERATIONS

In establishing a cocoa plantation it is possible with advantage to vary the sequence of certain operations. In high forest much time is gained by lining, holing, and planting temporary shade before the major felling takes place.

Clearing of the underbrush is usually done early in the dry season. The timing of the operations should be arranged so that conditions are suitable for planting cocoa early in the wet season and for its being well established before the dry season sets in.

F

USE OF CHEMICALS IN REMOVING FOREST

Chemical compounds have been widely used in Malaya and elsewhere for killing off the forest prior to planting rubber and other crops. Sodium arsenite has been commonly employed for this purpose. A more recently introduced arboricide is a synthetic hormone known as Trioxone, one of the 2,4,5-T hormones, which is now much used in West Africa. It is not toxic. There is no fear of its efficiency being affected by rain and it can be used at any time of the year because fuel oil is one of the diluents.

An effective strength in which this arboricide may generally be used is a 5 per cent concentration—that is, one part of Trioxone to nineteen parts of diluent.

The usual procedure is to dilute Trioxone with a mixture of sump oil and kerosene and apply with a spraying machine in a band 12 in. to 15 in. wide around the bole of the tree. A brush can of course be used instead of a spraying machine where only a few trees are to be treated. The best results are to be obtained by applying the mixture when the bark is dry. Where trees have buttresses, it is more economical to treat the bark above the buttress.

Another way in which this chemical can be used is to cut a ring of bark off the tree, leaving a frill on the lower edge, in the same way as is done in ring-barking and apply the arboricide above the frill. This ensures a quicker kill but the advantage is offset by the extra cost in labour.

Most trees treated with Trioxone die within twelve months, but a few are particularly difficult to kill. For instance, *Triplochiton scleroxylon*, known in Ghana as "Wawa," requires a 15 per cent instead of a 5 per cent concentration of Trioxone.

It is obvious, of course, that it is desirable to use certain sprayers for arboricides and others for other types of spraying such as insecticidal work. Where a sprayer is to be used for other work after being used with an arboricide, it will naturally have to be well cleaned before use. When sump oil with kerosene is used as a diluent it is advisable to apply the arboricide as a high-pressure spray. For example, when the Mysto 155 sprayer, fitted with O25 blue nozzle, is being used it requires a pressure of 30 lb.

MECHANIZATION IN FELLING

Where the plantation is to be laid out on a large scale, and the forest is to be completely felled as distinct from being selectively thinned, felling by means of drawing through the forest a heavy chain attached to two tractors will speed up the operation. Where reasonably efficient labour is available, however, the cost of this type of felling would need to be carefully compared with that of felling in the usual way.

For trees up to eighteen inches in diameter, tractor-powered winches are usually better than those which are hand-powered, especially when the ground is soft.

Large-scale clearing by mechanized means would normally be restricted to deep soils with a fertile sub-soil. The extensive use of machinery for pulling down and removing trees and stumps on a shallow soil, where the sub-soil is unsuitable, would create un-favourable conditions for cocoa.

PLANTING IN OLD PLANTATION LAND OR IN LAND WITHOUT FOREST

Where cocoa is to be established on land previously planted with cocoa or another crop, and shade trees are already in existence, most of the operations in establishing the new plantation can be done before replacing the old shade trees. These are carefully felled later and replaced with new trees. The necessity for establishing ground cover and lateral shade at an early stage is as important here as where planting is done in forest country.

If the land to be planted has few trees and little cover, then the first consideration is to plant ground cover, lateral shade and permanent shade. If time and circumstances permit, the first to be planted should probably be the permanent shade as it usually grows more slowly than the others.

SOIL EROSION AND ITS PREVENTION

Soil erosion in its various forms is one of the chief causes of soil degradation in the tropics. Where the annual rainfall is high and there are frequent heavy precipitations, severe erosion may occur unless steps are taken to prevent it. Water coursing down steep or even gentle slopes carries away the surface layer, exposes the roots of the cocoa tree and denudes the surface soil of nutrients. It has the general effect of destroying the crumb structure and lowering the carbon-nitrogen ratio. On level land the main effect of large quantities of water percolating through the soil is leaching, whereby the nutrients are carried down to lower levels beyond the reach of the roots of the tree. Calcium, magnesium and potassium may be carried away, leaving behind a relatively acid surface- and sub-soil.

Complete felling and burning of the forest exposes the land to erosion, and prevention of erosion is best secured by leaving a number of the trees *in situ*, or by planting ground cover and temporary or permanent shade to protect the ground from the drying effects of the sun and from wind and rain. Ground cover, in the form of bananas, tannias or other plants commonly used for this purpose, will prevent erosion, if planted in time. The remedy in a mature plantation on a slope is contour drainage and the erection of earth or other barriers to check the flow of water.

If the plantation is on a long slope liable to erosion, the cocoa trees should be planted on the contour, and tree trunks and brushwood piled in rows along the contour between cocoa trees to form a barrier and slow down the rush of water. On very steep slopes it may be necessary to do a certain amount of terracing and planting with soil-holding shrubs and grasses.

Erosion will be reduced by keeping the ground covered in the early stages with shrubs and shade trees and, later, with cocoa and shade trees, filling in the spaces left by fallen trees by extra planting, and by the provision of efficient drainage.

DRAINAGE

Where draining is required, the sooner it is done after the land is sufficiently cleared the better. Cocoa may be unaffected by being flooded for several weeks at a time by overflowing rivers, but is usually adversely affected by stagnant water.

The necessity for draining will be determined by a study of local conditions. The number of drains, and their depth and width, will depend on the lie of the land, the type of soil, and the distribution of rainfall. The drains should naturally be made along the contour, with sufficient fall to ensure that the water drains away gradually. The distance between drains should be adjusted to fit in with the spacing of the rows of cocoa trees.

On all sloping land, drains and roads should as far as possible follow the contour. When making outlets for the drains, erosion can be minimized by widening the outlet into a "fish-tail" shape. If the grass at the outlet is not cutlassed too closely, it will also help to retard erosion.

III. NURSERIES

The Site, Shading and Shelter—Planting Seed—Baskets—
Cocoa in Seed Beds—Supply and Treatment of Nursery Plants
—Nursery for Shade Trees—Nursery for Rooted Cuttings
—Nursery Work and Planting in Malaya

A nursery may be necessary because seed is not available at the time of planting, and because it may be cheaper to grow young plants in a nursery than to supervise them in the field. Where labour is short a large number of plants can be supervised more carefully in the small area of a nursery. During dry spells they are more convenient for watering and they provide a supply of quick-growing plants from which only the better-grown and more vigorous are selected.

THE SITE, SHADING AND SHELTER

The site chosen for the nursery should have a good, deep, free-draining surface soil, within easy reach of an ample supply of water free from objectionable minerals. A gentle slope will make drainage easier. The nursery should be as near the fields as is practicable.

Shading can be arranged by means of bamboo uprights and cross-pieces over which palm fronds are laid, or a more permanent structure can be made with timber scantling and wooden slats. The aim should be eventually to allow about 50 per cent sunlight to penetrate to the young plants for a great part of their time in the nursery. Palm fronds used as overhead covering have the advantage that as they wither with age they become more pervious to light, thus providing automatically the conditions for hardening the young plants in preparation for planting out.

A sheltered site in the forest will not need lateral shade, but where the forest is not available, lateral shade can be provided by planting stakes of some quick-growing tree, such as *Gliricidia*, which grows quickly from long cuttings pushed into the ground. The lateral shade will, of course, be planted several months before the cocoa is planted in the nursery, and it will require cutting back, so that maximum shade is provided in the dry season.

Where a more permanent nursery is required, a structure made with timbers which have been treated to resist termite attack may be erected. A series of lean-to roofs made with wooden slats so as to admit the right amount of light will be satisfactory and will prevent most of the rain and dew from falling on the cocoa plants.

There is often a tendency to confine nurseries, especially the larger ones, within too small a space. As most of the transport nowadays is by lorry, sufficient room should be left between different units of the nursery to allow easy passage.

PLANTING SEED

The seed to be planted is usually rubbed with sand or wood-ash to remove the mucilage, but this is not necessary. It is better to plant seeds hilum or scar-end downwards, although they can be planted on their sides. Any other way of planting results in a distorted plant. Good seed should give not less than eighty per cent germination.

BASKETS

Seedlings in baskets have the great advantage that when they are being planted out, their roots are not disturbed and they develop in a good soil. The basketed plants are easily handled and transported, and are less liable to damage than where baskets are not used.

The lightest and most durable baskets are made from split cane. Bamboo pots can be used but they may restrict root development and must be removed before planting in the field.

The size of the cane basket is a matter on which opinions vary. Large baskets require more soil or compost to fill them and are heavy to carry. The size will depend to some extent on the size of plant aimed at for planting. Where cocoa is difficult to establish, a larger basket is to be preferred. The Dutch in Java favoured a basket 18 in. to 24 in. deep by about 7 in. wide. The Ghana Department of Agriculture recommends baskets which are 8 in. deep, 7 in. wide at the top and 5 in. wide at the bottom. The base of the basket should not be completely woven but should be left as open as possible, with only a few strands across it to retain the soil. This gives the tap-root complete freedom to develop. Cheap baskets can be made by a simple weaving of palm fronds, but will not last long or stand much handling, and are liable to disintegrate before they reach the planting site.

When baskets are required in large numbers a contract is usually given to village communities. If baskets have to be made by labour on daily pay they may prove to be an expensive item.

The baskets are filled with good surface soil and some sub-soil, reinforced with compost, leaf mould, or farmyard or artificial manure, unless the original soil is rich. Surface soil alone may be unduly alkaline. They should be renewed from time to time if they have deteriorated, or if the tap-root of the seedling outgrows the original basket. When renewal is necessary, the plant along with its soil is transferred to the new basket and fresh soil packed around it.

Where bamboo pots are being used, a layer of coir or fibre at the bottom of the pot will help to retain the soil and moisture. A covering of fibre over the top of the basket will slow down evaporation from the soil and reduce the amount of watering required.

COCOA IN SEED BEDS

Where the cocoa seed is to be planted in beds these must be prepared with care. The best available soil should be well worked and mixed with pen manure or decayed vegetable matter and put in a bed slightly raised from the ground. The beds should be divided by paths and made narrow enough to permit attention to the plants from the paths. When the beds have been slightly consolidated, the seeds are pressed into the soil and spaced sufficiently far apart to allow of being removed by a trowel when ready for transplanting.

Where the seedlings are being grown from hybrid or Trinitario type cocoa, it will be found that some seedlings grow with much greater vigour than others. Where this occurs it is worth while removing the vigorous growers to another bed by themselves. This will avoid competition between the vigorous and the less vigorous and make better and more even growth throughout the nursery.

SUPPLY AND TREATMENT OF NURSERY PLANTS

Whichever method of raising plants in the nursery is adopted, it is necessary to have a constant supply of healthy, vigorous seedlings to replace casualties in the field during the first 24 to 30 months.

Watering in the dry season can be delayed as long as is consistent with the good growth of the young plants, as once begun it will have to be continued.

A high percentage of losses in the field is due to the fact that the plants have not been sufficiently hardened in the nursery before planting out. These losses can be greatly reduced by subjecting the nursery plants to a process of hardening by gradually reducing the shade over the beds until the seedlings are growing in the minimum of shade. Damage to the tap-root during transference of the plants from the nursery can also account for unduly high losses in the field.

NURSERY FOR SHADE TREES

Where shade trees are to be planted as seedlings and not as seed at stake a nursery will be required. The seed of certain forest trees is difficult to germinate. The local Forest Department has usually a good deal of experience in germinating seed of forest trees and their advice should be sought in case of difficulty.

NURSERY FOR ROOTED CUTTINGS

Where the size of the plantation or estate justifies it, it is better to raise a supply of rooted cuttings on the spot than to buy them or obtain a free supply from a central nursery. A careful selection of material for planting is thus possible. Recent experience in Trinidad shows that where the large central nurseries send supplies to plantations, it is impossible to provide clonal plants which are all up to the standard desired by the discerning planter.

NURSERY WORK AND PLANTING IN MALAYA

The Department of Agriculture in Malaya has issued a small publication setting out, among other things, its recommendations as regards nursery work and field planting. Baskets 9 in. deep, 7 to 9 in. wide at the top, and 6 to 7 in. wide at the bottom are suggested. Baskets are treated with preservative in the form of copper naphthenate-kerosene mixture, but it is noted that if the copper content is too strong the baskets might take too long to disintegrate in the ground and thereby obstruct root growth.

"Cuprinol" and "Cuprotect," two proprietary solutions of which the copper content is specified, should be reduced to about 1·2 per cent by dilution with kerosene. Baskets are dipped in the mixture for two minutes, allowed to drain and kept dry for a week before use.

The Department has used tubes made from wood veneer and treated with copper naphthenate-kerosene mixture containing 3 per cent copper. Veneer is manufactured locally and is bought in sheets of 9 in. by 15 in., with the grain of the wood running parallel to the 9-in. edge. The sheets are formed into tubes by wrapping them round a metal cylinder of $4\frac{1}{2}$ in. diameter, and retained in shape by two galvanized wire rings (22 gauge wire being used). Coir or other fibre is placed in the bottom of the tubes which are then filled with potting mixture, as they cannot be stored empty.

The potting mixture recommended and the one which has given the best results at Serdang is:

$$\left.\begin{array}{l}\text{7 parts loam, }p\text{H 5·5–6}\\\text{3 parts dried cattle manure}\\\text{2 parts sharp sand}\end{array}\right\}\begin{array}{l}\text{plus 1 oz. of double}\\\text{superphosphate}\\\text{per basket}\end{array}$$

Serdang loam required a pH correction and this was achieved by adding 6 lb. of finely ground limestone per cubic yard.

In Eastern Malaya, at Jerangau, where there is a better-textured top-soil, only ½ oz. each of double superphosphate and ground limestone per basket were necessary.

IV. PREPARATION FOR PLANTING

Spacing—Lining—Holing

SPACING

CLOSE *v.* WIDE

Spacing, like shading, has given rise to a good deal of controversy.

Professor Hardy holds the view that the main factor affecting spacing is the root-room in the soil, and that the feeding roots of the cocoa tree will explore the top layer of a soil which has a good crumb structure. As the depth of a good crumb structure varies considerably, so also does the root-room. Where the crumb structure is shallow, planting distances will be greater than where it is deep. In other words, a good soil permits of closer spacing than does a poor soil. This view is shared by Carl de Verteuil of Trinidad.

On the other hand, De Blank, of Huileries du Congo Belge, who has wide experience of tree plantation crops in the tropics, considers that where soils provide less good growing conditions, closer spacing is indicated. His theory of productivity is based on the estimated potential production per unit of surface area, which can be determined by multiplying the average individual production by the number of plants on a given area. The optimum density is a function of three factors:

(*a*) The variety to be planted.

(*b*) The potential production of individual trees.

(*c*) The soil and climatic conditions under which the crop is to be grown.

OPTIMUM SPACING

Fashions and practice in spacing have varied from country to country and within countries. Optimum spacing of cocoa is that which gives the greatest yield per unit of land over a given period.

Experience so far seems to show that close spacing gives a greater yield in the early years, but where a close and a wider spacing have been compared over a number of years, the yield per acre per annum eventually becomes approximately the same. Close spacing in the early years, with thinning-out as the trees develop, has been advocated as the best means of getting maximum yields over a long period.

Planting by the triangular or quincuncial method results in more trees per acre being planted than when they are planted on the square. For instance, at 15 ft. spacing there will be 13 per cent more trees per acre when planted on the triangle than when planted on the square. If the trees are planted at close spacing with the intention of thinning out later, adjustment of spacing by thinning is more easily done when planting is on the triangle.

CLOSE SPACING

Close spacing has the advantages that the canopy of the cocoa trees soon meets and shades the ground, thereby suppressing weeds, and that if one tree dies the canopy of the adjacent trees soon closes up and covers the intervening space. In West Africa the quick closing of the canopy discourages capsid attack. There is also less tendency for the plant to develop chupons or suckers.

A spacing of 10 ft. by 10 ft. will control weed growth when there is fairly rapid development of the trees. Some consider that there should be a distance of twelve feet between cocoa rows to allow of easy access to the plantation. Whereas in the early years of bearing, close spacing makes for higher returns and less expense in weeding, the outlay in plants is greater if selected material is being bought or produced at high cost. This is a point to be borne in mind when close planting is done with the intention of thinning later to provide wider spacing.

THINNING

Where cocoa is planted at close spacing and is to be thinned after seven or eight years, it may be planted 9 ft. by 9 ft. by the triangular or quincuncial method. The first thinning could be done to give a space of just over twelve feet between rows. There is a natural tendency to postpone thinning when a good yield is being obtained from the plantation. If it is unduly delayed, the general shape of the trees is affected and several years may elapse before a desirable form is attained. The time when thinning should take place must be a matter for the good judgment of the planter. When it comes to thinning the plants in the rows, a certain amount of selection may be done. Two good vigorous plants may be left growing close together and weaker plants on either side removed, provided that the gaps left are not too wide.

PRACTICE IN DIFFERENT COUNTRIES

In the past Trinidad favoured 12 ft. by 12 ft.; Ceylon, New Guinea and Samoa spaced at 15 ft. by 15 ft. and sometimes 16 feet apart; the Belgian Congo for some years used a spacing of 4 metres by 4 metres, but more recently 3 metres by 3 metres (about 10 ft. by 10 ft.) has been adopted. In experiments in Nigeria where spacings of 8 ft. by 8 ft., 12 ft. by 12 ft., and 15 ft. by 15 ft. were tested on different soils, the best yields were obtained in the early years at close spacing on good soils. The West African peasant farmer, when planting cocoa seed through his food farm, plants closely ($3\frac{1}{2}$ ft. to 4 ft. apart), but, more recently, spacing of 5 ft. by 5 ft. is being adopted. Such cocoa farms are thinned out by the deliberate action of the farmer and some trees are killed off by pests and diseases, but the final stand is usually very close-spaced when compared with the standards in other countries.

Attention must be given to the matter of filling the land to capacity, while making provision for the labourers to walk between the lines with dusting and spraying equipment.

SPACING OF SHADE TREES

The shade trees will normally be planted in line with the cocoa trees, and the spacing will depend on the size which it is expected they will eventually attain and on the nature of their canopy. *Erythrina* in Trinidad were sometimes planted at 24 ft. by 24 ft. and later thinned out to 48 ft. by 48 ft., or at 15 ft. by 15 ft. and thinned to 30 ft. by 30 ft. The latter spacings were intended to allow the trees to grow to full stature. Where control of the growth of the shade tree by topping and cutting back the branches is envisaged a closer final spacing would be adopted. Bananas and plantains are usually planted at 12 ft. by 12 ft. in the rows of cocoa.

LINING

Lining is necessary in order to place the trees in such a way that the maximum use is made of the available space, and so that the lines of trees are eventually placed as nearly equidistant as is practicable. It is usual to work from a base line which may be across the field or along one side and the lines will generally be orientated in a north and south direction.

Lining before General Felling

If before general felling in forest country it is desired to plant lateral shade and/or permanent shade, or even cocoa itself, lining can be done immediately the underbrush has been cleared.

Lining on the Contour

On hilly land it is most desirable to line on the contour. This will enable soil conservation measures to be applied more easily, and if the distance between the contour rows is twelve feet or more, other operations will be made easier.

HOLING

Holing is designed to provide suitable conditions in which the plant may develop a root-system and establish itself.

In an easily worked fertile soil there is less need for a large hole than in a stiffer soil. Where the soil is heavy the fork is better for digging than the spade, as the latter tends to make the sides of the hole impervious to water. It is more important that the hole should be wide than that it should be deep, because the feeding roots spread outwards, and the tap-root will in any case penetrate a long way below the bottom of the hole. A diameter of two feet or more with a depth of twelve to eighteen inches is a convenient size. Where rocks or large boulders are present, it is well to probe the bottom of the hole for a foot or more with a sharpened iron to ensure that there is none underneath. A similar precaution should be taken where there is the possibility of hardpan or an impervious clay layer.

Where the plants are grown in baskets, the necessity for a large hole is not so great as when they are being transferred from nursery beds. If the seed is to be planted in the field, a good-sized hole should be made and great care taken to fill it with a soil mixture in which the plant can grow.

Treatment of the Soil

It is convenient when holing to keep the surface- and sub-soils separate. The holes should be filled with a friable mixture of a good deal of surface soil and some sub-soil. Surface soil alone may be too alkaline. For the same reason a concentration of wood ash is to be avoided. When it is desired to reinforce the mixture, well-rotted compost or manure is added. If the soil is piled up in a mound over the hole it settles down to ground level. On the other hand, a saucer effect around the plant, due to insufficient soil in the hole to begin with or to the soil having been scraped away in the course of weeding, may give rise to waterlogging.

The soil around the hole should be well hoed before the plants are inserted, as the feeding roots develop most quickly when the soil has been opened up by cultivation. Where forest trees of secondary bush have been left for shade, it is worth while pressing a spade 12 in. into the ground in a circular ring about 3 ft. from the point where the cocoa is planted, in order to sever any roots that may be growing towards the hole.

EXPERIENCE IN GHANA

Although much of what has been described here may be considered as orthodox practice and represents that adopted by successful planters in the West Indies and the Americas, experience in Ghana does not completely support this. Here it has been found that, when seed is planted "at stake," i.e. directly in the plantation, the less the soil is disturbed after cleaning and brushing the better. Deep cultivation tends to retard rather than accelerate the progress of the plant.

There is some doubt here whether there is any advantage in making holes before planting seed at stake, and good results have been obtained without holing. The best results follow the opening of holes immediately before planting, and not when they have been made some time in advance and left to "weather," which is recommended as good practice in other countries. When cocoa seedlings have been planted out in baskets they have grown better when a hole is made of just sufficient size to receive the basket and the soil surface is not otherwise disturbed.

REFERENCES

Bench-terracing:
   World Crops (March and June 1951).

Spacing:
   Freeman, W. G. "Results of cacao research at River Estate, Trinidad."
      Trop. Agric. (1929), **6**, 127.
   Hardy, F. "Soil and soil-types suitable for the hybridization of cacao
      and the improvement of cacao soils by manuring" (Cocoa Research
      Conference, London, 1945).
   Hardy, F. "Some soil relations of the root-system of cacao." *Trop.
      Agric.* (1944), **21**, 184.
   Russell, T. A. "The spacing of Nigerian cocoa." *Emp. J. exp. Agric.*
      (1953), **21**, 145.
   West, J. "The development of cacao selection in Nigeria" (Cocoa
      Research Conference, London, 1945).

Department of Agriculture, Federation of Malaya. Agricultural Leaflet
   No. 31, *Cacao*.
Greenwood, M., and Posnette, A. F. "The growth flushes of cacao."
   J. hort. Sci. (1950), **25**, No. 3.
Henderson, F. C. "Cacao as a crop for the owner-manager in Papua and
   New Guinea." *The Papua and New Guinea Agricultural Journal*,
   October 1954.
Jolly, A. L. *Cocoa Farm Management*, Turrialba (1957), **7**, 88.
Pickles, A. "Methods employed in West Africa for the destruction of
   redundant forest trees." *Emp. For. Rev.* (1958), **37**, 421.
Radwanski, S. A. "Cocoa soils of the Western Ashanti, Ghana."
   (Cocoa Conf. 1957, 310.)

Chapter VII

THE COCOA PLANTATION (2)

PLANTING MATERIAL

Selection and Plant Breeding in Ghana—Results of Cocoa Breeding at I.C.T.A.—Assessment of Imperial College Cocoa Selections—Out-turn of Dry Cocoa from Upper Amazon and Amelonado—Multiplication of Planting Material—Sources from which Cocoa Planting Material may be secured

IT will be necessary at an early stage to find a source of planting material. Cocoa seed can be transported practically any distance by air. Rooted cuttings can be produced cheaply in large quantities with the use of polythene sheet. Where planting is to be done on an extensive scale, hybrid seed would normally be used in the main planting programme.

Included in the plantation requirements will be seed for temporary and permanent shade. If the plantation is isolated, provision may have to be made for seed and planting material for food crops to meet the needs of labour.

A cocoa tree should have the qualities of being high-yielding and early-bearing and have the capacity to thrive in the environment in which it is to be grown. A degree of resistance to prevalent pests and diseases would be an added virtue. The type of bean borne is the ultimate criterion which will decide whether a tree is superior or otherwise. Large beans of even size, with high fat content and a low proportion of shell which, after fermentation, are capable of being transformed into chocolate with a good flavour, are desired by manufacturers. It is the aim of the plant breeder to combine all these and other desirable qualities in the trees which he evolves by selection and breeding.

It is obvious that the plant breeder who sets out to raise a cocoa tree with the maximum number of desirable qualities must be able to draw on a variety of types possessing, individually, one or more of the required characteristics.

The botanical section of the Imperial College of Tropical Agriculture in Trinidad, under the direction of Professor Cheesman, set out,

79

some thirty years ago, to survey and collect plant material from the very mixed population of cocoa in Trinidad. The present range of Imperial College selections are mainly derived from the cocoa collected on this occasion. They have since been supplemented by Dr. Pound's collections in South America (the most important of these being Upper Amazon) and introductions from other sources.

The great variation in Trinidad cocoa has been demonstrated by the fact that one pod from a good tree contained the same weight of cocoa as five pods from an inferior tree. In the large producing countries of West Africa, populated almost exclusively with Amelonado type of Forastero which shows little genetic variation, it was necessary to introduce varieties from elsewhere. The only cocoa of merit available in Ghana, which was not pure Amelonado, was a hybrid derived from an early introduction of Trinitario, and which had interbred with Amelonado. It now breeds true to type, and for convenience is designated as a "local hybrid." In 1944 a number of introductions from the material available in Trinidad were made to Ghana. These included Upper Amazon, Criollos, and seventeen of the Trinitario complex. A number of further introductions were made subsequently.

SELECTION AND PLANT BREEDING IN GHANA

Posnette initiated selection and plant breeding in Ghana during 1939–41 by making selections from yield-recorded trees. Rogers and Knight subsequently worked for several years at the West African Cocoa Research Institute and laid the foundations of what is hoped will provide West Africa with large supplies of improved planting material.

The most interesting material was found among the crosses between Upper Amazons. Some of them were vigorous growers, came into bearing early and bore fruit for nine months of the year, in addition to giving a high yield. Criollo introductions did not do well and were predisposed to capsid attack. Of the seventeen introductions of the Trinitario complex, T9 was particularly promising.

The breeding programme was planned to proceed in stages. First, the mother plants were selected, and this was followed by testing the self-pollinated or cross-pollinated progeny. Finally the progeny was selected at the appropriate stage for issue to farmers as plants raised from cuttings or seed.

Incompatibility occurs in cocoa, a characteristic which is of great advantage to the plant breeder. Some trees will not set fruit with their own pollen and are classified as "self-incompatible"

. A heavy-bearing cocoa tree on a
plantation in Brazil

17. High-yielding Amelonado tree on
S.P.R.O.A. Plantations, Gangoa, Ivory
Coast

. Seven-year-old tree on one of the
iileries du Congo Belge Estates.
e chupon growth has been controlled at the first jorquette

19. One of the first cocoa trees to be planted in the state of Bahia. The original tree
was planted 200 years ago and the stems
seen in the picture have developed from
chupons arising from the original trunk

20. A tree grown from
rooted cutting on an est:
in Trinidad. This tree is
the clone I.C.S. 95

21. A seedling nursery at a Department of Agriculture Station in Ghana.
Shade is provided by tree cassava

22. Young Amazon cocoa tree in eastern Malaya

3. Field of young Amazon cocoa in eastern Malaya

24. Amelonado cocoa in eastern Malaya

25. Nursery trees under *Gliricidia* shade, Trinidad

or "self-sterile." Trees which will set fruit with their own pollen are known as "self-compatible." Pollen from self-incompatible trees may be effective on those which are self-compatible.

Upper Amazon proved to be the best of the introduced material, and, furthermore, it was self-incompatible, which simplified the process of obtaining crosses without recourse to hand-pollination.

The most vigorous Upper Amazon types were the progeny result-ing from crossing individual trees within the Upper Amazon group. It is thought that the robust growth of Upper Amazon may be partly due to the fact that it is never self-pollinated and therefore acquires hybrid vigour.

From work done at the West African Cocoa Research Institute at Tafo, there is evidence of considerable hybrid vigour resulting from appropriate crosses, and of loss of vigour with self-pollinated cocoa. Similar evidence of hybrid vigour has been noted in Trinidad, where some of the Imperial College selections gave greatly increased yields when crossed with Upper Amazon. It has been the aim in production of new varieties at Tafo to utilize hybrid vigour wherever possible, both by crossing different types within the Upper Amazon group and crossing Upper Amazon with other introductions and local Amelon-ado.

The various selections both in West Africa and Trinidad have been given distinguishing letters and numbers. In West Africa, Upper Amazon came into bearing at four years old, and some of the best bearing types gave yields of 1,400 lb. at nine years old. Some of the hybrids recently developed in W.A.C.R.I. are particularly prom-ising. WAE 5, a cross between Amelonado and Upper Amazon, gave a yield equivalent to 850 lb. of dry cocoa per acre in the fifth year. A still higher yield was obtained from certain Upper Amazons themselves, WE 2 and WE 3. One plot of WEB 2, a cross between an Upper Amazon and a local hybrid, gave a yield equivalent to 360 lb. per acre when the plants were between two and three years old.

Table No. 8 overleaf indicates the promising performance of intro-ductions and hybrids in West Africa.

In comparing the performance of clones in the 1st and 2nd Clonal Trials it should be noted that they are at different spacings. Clone SC 4 gave the highest yield, but it was in a single plot on the edge of the trial and therefore in an advantageous position.

RESULTS OF COCOA BREEDING AT I.C.T.A.

In a paper read by Dr. B. G. D. Bartley at the London Cocoa Con-ference in 1957, he discusses the results of cocoa-breeding in

G

TABLE No. 8

PERFORMANCES IN 1956–7

	Years from Planting	Number of trees per acre	Net Weight per pod gm.	Mean dry bean weight gm.	Estimated cocoa per acre lb.
Introductions					
T76	12	222	107[1]	1·05	1,280
T30	12	222	93	1·11	1,185
T12	12	222	92	1·14	1,090
T60	12	222	131	·99	995
Local Hybrids					
(a) Clones					
1st Clonal Trial					
ACU 85	10	435	108	1·32	1,015
A46	10	435	146	1·51	1,000
2nd Clonal Trial					
R 15	8·5	680	132	1·50	1,240
SC 4	8·5	680	128	1·38	1,802[2]
(b) Progenies					
TF 1	15	400	124	1·32	900
E 1	15	400	124	1·27	815
U 6	15	400	115	1·24	755
New Hybrids					
8th Progeny Trial					
WAE 5	5	680	120	1·12	850
WBE 3	5	680	129	1·24	530
For comparison					
Amazon WE 4	5	680	97	1·09	570[3]
Amelonado WA 2	5	680	95	1·00	108
9th Progeny Trial					
WEB 2	3	435	104	1·12	107[4]

[1] T76 and T60 wet weights from 1950–3 data.
[2] A single plot in a good position.
[3] The best plot gave 700 lb. per acre.
[4] The best plot gave 360 lb. per acre.

Trinidad. In Table No. 9 the yields over a three-year period ending in 1956–7 are shown. The trees to which this table refers are only six years old and it is too early yet to draw reliable conclusions as to the future relative performance of individual crosses. The results to date, however, indicate that the yielding capacity of some of these crosses will be very high. He says:

"During the three years the yields of the seedlings have increased consistently, and it is possible that the maximum yields have not yet been obtained. At the present time the crosses with ICS 6 as a parent have given the highest overall yields. The crosses with ICS 60 seem to be less consistent in their behaviour as their yields tend to fluctuate more over the three seasons. With respect to the SCA parents, the SCA 12 crosses generally have given higher yields than SCA 6 crosses.

TABLE NO. 9

SUMMARY OF YIELDS PER ACRE AND PER TREE
(*in Pounds Dry Cocoa*)

Trinitario-Scavina Hybrids at River Estate for the years 1954 to 1957, inclusive.

Cross	1954–5		1955–6		1956–7		1954–7 Total	
	Yield per acre	*Yield per tree*	*Yield per acre*	*Yield per tree*	*Yield per acre*	*Yield per tree*	*Yield per acre*	*Yield per tree*
ICS 1 × SCA 6	853	0·96	1,283	1·44	1,706	1·92	3,842	4·32
ICS 1 × SCA 12	797	0·90	1,432	1·61	1,931	2·17	4,160	4·68
ICS 6 × SCA 6	1,034	1·16	1,461	1·64	2,323	2·61	4,818	5·41
ICS 6 × SCA 12	909	1·02	1,410	1·59	2,455	2·76	4,774	5·37
ICS 60 × SCA 6	684	0·80	1,086	1·25	1,354	1·52	3,124	3·57
ICS 60 × SCA 12	834	0·94	1,504	1·69	1,930	2·17	4,268	4·80

"The differences in yield between SCA 6 and SCA 12 may be due partly to the difference in pod sizes, the pod sizes of the SCA 12 crosses being consistently larger than the other crosses.

"In general, the pod sizes of the hybrid progeny are intermediate with those of the parents. SCA 6 and SCA 12 require about 14·5 pods and 13 pods, respectively, to make one pound of dry cocoa. The ICS clones used as parents in the experiment carry pods which average 6 to 7 to the pound of dry cocoa. The mean dry weights of beans sampled in the wet season (Table 9) show that bean sizes exceed the one gramme dry weight per bean suggested as a lower limit of size. They may at times be slightly smaller owing to the effects of extreme dry weather and increased cropping as the trees become older. In general, there are no marked differences in pod and bean sizes among the six crosses. There is a tendency for the ICS 6 crosses to produce slightly larger beans than the ICS 1 crosses; ICS 6 beans are larger than ICS 1 beans."

Most of the above trials are planted at closer spacing than would be normal in commercial practice, and close-spaced cocoa gives higher yields in the earlier years than that which is wider-spaced. Nevertheless, the results of these trials show that the yields to be expected from some of these clones are far higher than anything that could be expected from cocoa-planting material in the past.

ASSESSMENT OF IMPERIAL COLLEGE COCOA SELECTIONS

The following is a recent assessment of some of the ICS clones:

ICS 1: Is considered a very good clone although it is less hardy under certain conditions than some of the selections. It is adversely affected by exposure to wind, lack of shade and poor drainage, and is susceptible to thrips, but not unduly so to witches' broom. It is self-compatible. At twelve years old it has given yields of up to 1,600 lb. per acre on plantations in Trinidad.

ICS 39, 40, 60 and 61: Are all vigorous, having large beans and yield well.

ICS 46 and 47: Vigorous growers with good beans, Self-compatible.

ICS 89: This is a slow grower and late in coming to bearing, but promises to be high yielding.

ICS 95: This is probably the best clone for general use ever produced in Trinidad. It has done well in a wide range of environmental conditions. It has some resistance to thrips, but is reported to be susceptible to attack of *Steirastoma breve*, the cocoa beetle. It is self-compatible.

The above refers to Trinitario types. Those given below refer to Amazon varieties and are all cross-compatible. They are vigorous growers and crop early.

IMC 57: Appears to be a high yielder but has not been distributed in Trinidad.

IMC 67: This clone is suited to a wide range of conditions, yields early and promises to be a good cropper. It has some resistance to thrips but has suffered from aphis attack at the rooted cutting stage.

P7 and P 18: Very high yielders.

P 46, 121 and 150: Are all rated as very high yielders.

OUT-TURN OF DRY COCOA FROM UPPER AMAZON AND AMELONADO

Upper Amazon types have a tendency to bear small beans, but it is considered that this fault may be remedied in the course of further breeding. During experimental work on fermentation and drying, it has been found that some of the Upper Amazons and crosses with Upper Amazons gave a lower out-turn of dry cocoa than West African Amelonado. For instance in a comparison of Upper Amazon with Amelonado, it was found that the former gave an out-turn of 38 tons of dry beans per 100 tons of wet beans as compared with 44 tons from Amelonado. This is a difference of 13·5 per cent—a point which is receiving the attention of the plant breeders.

MULTIPLICATION OF PLANTING MATERIAL FROM SELECTED SEED

The fact that certain types of cocoa are self-incompatible makes it possible to lay out seed gardens where the seed produced will be of the desired cross. When it is found that a cross between two distinct trees gives good results, and the mother tree is self-incompatible, such trees can be planted in a seed garden as rooted cuttings, together with the necessary number of trees which are to supply the pollen. In this way quantities of hybrid seed can be produced for large-scale planting. This system of multiplication has been adopted in West Africa for the supply of seed to small farmers, and great quantities of this improved planting material have already been distributed. Although the production of rooted cuttings has been greatly simplified in recent years, it will always be slower and more expensive than mass production from seed.

SOURCES FROM WHICH COCOA PLANTING MATERIAL MAY BE SECURED

In most countries where new planting or extension of planting is contemplated there are sources from which supplies of planting material can be secured. In West Africa there are now large quantities of improved material being multiplied and distributed by the Departments of Agriculture of Ghana and of the Western Region and other parts of Nigeria. The Imperial College and the Cocoa Board in Trinidad, and the Inter-American Cacao Centre at Turrialba in Costa Rica are the main sources of supply in Central America. The Department of Agriculture in Ceylon has some good selections and has introduced selections from Trinidad. The Lowlands Agricultural Station, of the Department of Agriculture, Stock and Fisheries of Papua and New Guinea, in Keravat, New Britain, has produced some very high yielding material and multiplies it on a large scale. Most countries interested in cocoa have now introduced some of the more promising selections from Trinidad and West Africa. Modern techniques for the multiplication of vegetative material or seed of superior quality are such that it should be possible to provide the needs of any country in a short time.

When it is desired to introduce vegetative material from another country, it is safer to import it as budwood than in the form of rooted cuttings.

It is obvious that where new planting is contemplated, the material which is expected to give the best returns should be planted. If some of the selections mentioned above have been introduced to a country where they have not previously been tried, it would probably be wise to test out a range of the available selections on a pilot scale before deciding which selections would be used for general planting. The response of different selections cannot be foretold with accuracy under the environmental conditions of a new country.

It is considered safe to introduce seed from a country where normal phyto-sanitary precautions are observed. Some countries prefer not to have cocoa seed introduced in the pod. The seed can be conveniently placed in tin containers with charcoal watered to contain 25 per cent moisture. Provided seed is not chilled in transit, it can travel for long distances by air in this way, and have a high percentage of viability on arrival. Vegetative materials sent eastwards from Trinidad in the form of rooted cuttings have usually been sent through Kew for quarantine. Similar facilities are available in Brussels.

In Papua and New Guinea where seed has to be transported from island to island, special attention has been given to finding a simple method of treating the seed so that it can be transported in a viable condition. Research has been conducted on this problem at the Agricultural Research Station at Keravat under the direction of L. A. Bridgland, agronomist. It was found that the seed was best transported in the pod, the pod having the basal end cut off and then the ends dipped in paraffin wax at 90–110° C. (an in-and-out dip), but leaving an undipped band, $\frac{1}{4}$ to $\frac{1}{2}$ in. wide around the middle of the pod. There was a great variation from tree to tree in the response of pods to treatment for storage, and ripe pods stored better than under-ripe ones. Pods treated in the above manner can be stored from one to three months, depending on the tree from which the pod has been taken. *Phytophthora* has not proved troublesome with pods in storage; *Botryodiplodia* sometimes gave trouble in the first four weeks and then tended to disappear; species of

Colletotrichum and *Fusarium* were the most common cause of pod decay.

Dr. Alvim has recommended the following treatment for cocoa seed which is to be transported over long distances:

1. Add lime to coagulate (dry) pulp of fresh seeds.
2. Peel off tegument of seeds.
3. Wash, keeping the seeds in the water for a short period.
4. Dip in 1 per cent Phygon-XL solution for 1–2 minutes.*
5. Dry in the shade for about 2 hours.
6. Keep in polythene bags in quantities not more than 1–2 kg. per bag.

Cocoa treated in this way has resulted in 100 per cent germination after 3 weeks and 60 per cent germination after 7 weeks. The seed can be packed in a cardboard box for sending by air-freight.

---

* Phygon-XL is an organic fungicide. It is possible that the seed dressing known as "Fernasan" would serve the purpose where Phygon-XL is not available.

REFERENCES

Bartley, B. G. D. "Trinitario-Scavina hybrids. New prospects for cacao improvement." (Cocoa Conf. 1957, 36.)

Dodds, K. S., and Cope, F. W. "Field experiments with clonal cacao. *J. hort. Sci.* (1951), **26**, 249.

Glendinning, D. R. "The performance of introductions and hybrids in W.A.C.R.I. trials." (Cocoa Conf. 1957, 41.)

Knight, R., and Rogers, H. H. "Recent introductions to West Africa of *Theobroma cacao* and related species." *Emp. J. exp. Agric.* (1955), **23**, 113.

Posnette, A. F. "Progeny trials with cacao in the Gold Coast." *Emp. J. exp. Agric.* (1951), **19**, 242.

Russell, T. A. "The vigour of some cocoa hybrids." *Trop. Agric.* (Trinidad) (1952), **29**, 1.

Chapter VIII

THE COCOA PLANTATION (3)

VEGETATIVE PROPAGATION

Rooted Cuttings—The Nursery—Collecting Cuttings—Preparing the Cuttings—Storage of Potted Plants—W.A.C.R.I. Method of Raising Rooted Cuttings—Propagation in Plastic Bags—Other Methods of Propagation

MANY of the cocoa trees which are high-yielding and early-bearing and have other desirable qualities are of mixed parentage so that plants raised from the seed of such trees will differ genetically from the parent tree. Plants propagated vegetatively by cuttings, budding or grafting will have the same genetic constitution as the tree from which the material for propagation has been derived, and may be expected to grow and yield as well as the parent tree. The means most commonly employed for the propagation of cocoa are rooted cuttings and budding.

ROOTED CUTTINGS

Vegetative propagation by means of rooted cuttings consists of taking cuttings from the branches of the tree and treating them in such a way that they form roots. The method was applied to cocoa in Trinidad, the pioneer work having been done by Pyke, Cheesman and Spencer, and later improvements in technique by Harry Evans. Posnette used this method extensively in plant-breeding at the West African Cocoa Research Institute. Archibald and McKelvie, also working at W.A.C.R.I., have made important modifications which have simplified the process. Moll has done much work in organizing and raising the efficiency of commercial production. The pioneer work in Trinidad was based on stem cuttings with several leaves. Stahel in Surinam evolved the idea of the single-leaf cutting. This type is useful in experimental work, but for large-scale production it is less efficient than the stem cutting, and it takes three to four months to reach the stage when it can be planted in the field.

26. The equipment used in preparing stem-cuttings: a bucket for collecting cuttings, a bottle of hormone solution, and a dish to hold the cuttings after preparation

27. Stem- and single-leaf cuttings trimmed and prepared for the rooting-bin

28. Prefabricated structure for cocoa-propagating nurseries, Jamaica

29. Open-bed propagation of rooted cuttings in Hope, Jamaica. The shed extends for 336 feet into the background. The uprights are 8 feet apart; the beds 32 feet by 8 feet; there are 13 beds, each holding 2,000 cuttings, a total of 26,000 rooted cuttings

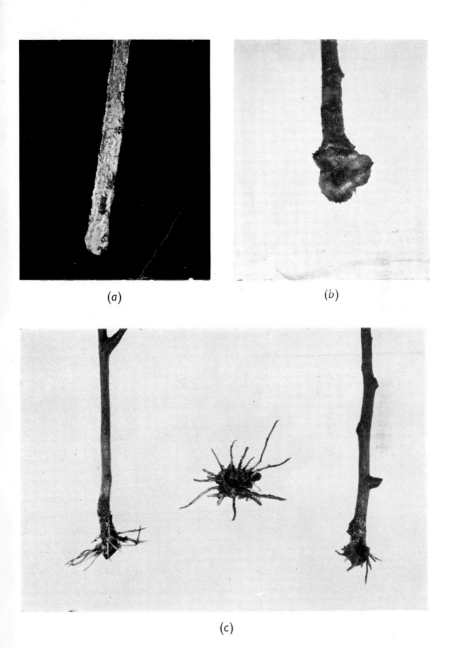

(a)

(b)

(c)

30. Effect of moisture conditions on rooting
(a) Over-watering and inadequate aeration: callus rods developing
(b) Under-watering and excessive aeration: a basal callus pad has developed
(c) Optimum conditions: these cuttings have started to root well; the middle photograph is an end-on view of the base of a cutting

(a)

(b)

31. Effect on leaves of abnormal conditions during rooting
   (a) Excessive loss of moisture due to failure to maintain a high humidity cau
      patchiness which can be seen above; these patches are yellow.
   (b) Inadequate light intensity leads to carbo-hydrate starvation which is shown
      yellowing areas

32. Rooted cuttings being produced
   under polythene sheet

33. Two beds of rooted cuttings cove
   with polythene sheet. The sheet is wei
   ed down at the edges to keep it in p

IMPROVED METHODS FOR RAISING ROOTED CUTTINGS

In the previous edition of this book raising rooted cuttings in bins was referred to as the standard method, one set of bins being used for rooting and another for hardening. As the result of experimental work at W.A.C.R.I., the use of bins has been discarded in favour of rooting and hardening the cuttings under polythene sheet. The method in which polythene is employed is described in a paper by McKelvie which is reproduced later in this chapter.

THE PROCESS OF PRODUCING ROOTED CUTTINGS

Briefly, the process of producing rooted cuttings entails the use of a nursery of selected plants from which a supply of cuttings can be collected. The cuttings, after being treated with a root-inducing hormone, are placed in baskets which have been filled with suitable material, such as rotted sawdust, coconut fibre dust or other rooting medium. While they are in the baskets, they are kept in favourable conditions of temperature and humidity and given the desired degree of light. The baskets are covered with polythene sheet and watered; in due course roots develop and the plants are "hardened" by the gradual raising of the polythene sheet. The process of hardening and developing is continued until the plants are ready to be planted in the field. Although the production of rooted cuttings requires close attention to detail, they can be raised by an intelligent planter after a study of the literature.

THE NURSERY

It is desirable to have the nursery of trees which supply the cuttings conveniently near the propagators. Vigorous, healthy trees, free from mineral deficiencies, provide the best cuttings, and so a well-drained loamy soil, rich in organic matter, is indicated. Where the soil is below the quality required, it has to be enriched by the supply of compost and pen or mineral manures. A soil tending towards acidity (pH value 5·0 to 6·0) is recommended.

Good shading arrangements are necessary to enable the nursery plants to produce a supply of soft branches in a suitable condition for rooting; over-exposure to sunlight may cause poor rooting results. As a general guide, 25 per cent to 50 per cent full sunlight falling on the nursery trees will be satisfactory.

The trees used for shading the nursery plants are usually those which grow quickly from cuttings, such as *Gliricidia maculata*, *Erythrina poeppigiana*, and certain species of *Inga*, but this by no means exhausts the list of trees which may be used. Apart from quick growth, the main essential in a shade tree is foliage which allows of filtered light reaching the nursery plants. Plantains and bananas have also been used to provide shade, but are liable to be blown down and cause damage.

Emphasis has sometimes been laid on the advantage of using leguminous shade trees, but non-leguminous trees can be used equally well.

Shade trees have to be cut back from time to time and controlled to give a suitable degree of shade and light. Where there is a marked dry season, they have to be cut well back before the end of the wet season, so that they may develop thick foliage and provide a greater amount of shade during the dry season.

Although the removal of cuttings automatically prunes the tree, it is necessary from time to time to prune the tree back severely in order to induce a flush of new growth. This is done at the end of the dry season, the trees having been manured beforehand.

When the trees are subjected to repeated removal of cuttings over a period they will require frequent applications of NPK fertilizers. An application of $1-1\frac{1}{2}$ lb. of fertilizer per tree per annum, supplemented with some pen manure, should meet requirements.

COLLECTING CUTTINGS

Cuttings are taken from recently matured flushes when the leaves are fully green. They should have at least three leaves, and the stems should be green but hard, or semi-hard. They are often referred to as "semi-hardwood cuttings." The upper surface of the stem will usually have turned a shade of brown at this stage, but the under surface will still be green (see colour plates III and IV). Greening of the leaves may be delayed when the soil is deficient in certain nutrients, and it is then better to wait until the leaves are green, even if the other conditions of the cutting indicate that it is ready for removal from the parent tree.

If it is desired, for the sake of economy in material, to use single-leaf cuttings, these should be cut at an earlier stage of development when the stem is still green on the upper surface. If two buds are left on the semi-hard stem from which the single-leaf cutting has been removed they will sprout quickly and give further cuttings. This point is mentioned because buds farther down on the hard stem are dormant and will not develop so quickly.

Those parts of the nursery tree which have been attacked by insect pests or fungi, or trees which show signs of serious mineral deficiency, are to be avoided, as such material may give trouble in the propagator.

Cuttings are removed from the tree by a cut just above a node, and may vary in length from five to twelve inches and bear three to seven leaves. Where there are well-defined wet and dry seasons, flushes will grow longer in the wet season, particularly at the beginning, and not so long in the dry season. Where it is desired to get the maximum number of cuttings from the nursery, it may be advisable to use the longer flushes for single-leaf cuttings during the wet season and the shorter flushes of the dry season for stem-cuttings. As the former take longer to develop than the latter, plants of similar size will be available for planting in the following wet season.

Normal practice in Trinidad is to take the cuttings by 8.30 to 9.30 a.m., and only on wet and humid days can they be taken throughout the day. They are placed immediately in a bucket of water to keep them in a moist condition and in due course they are placed in the propagating-bins.

PREPARING THE CUTTINGS

(a) *Stem-cuttings.* The lower leaves are removed by a clean cut close to the stem, leaving three to six leaves, according to the length of the cutting. The longer leaves are cut with scissors to half or a third, depending on the original size. Leaves up to six inches long are left untouched. The purpose of trimming is to prevent mutual shading, and to accommodate a greater number of cuttings in a given space.

After the leaves have been trimmed, a small piece of the base of the stem is cut off to provide a fresh surface, and the base of the stem is immediately dipped in a root-inducing hormone. The hormone mixture which has had greatest success is α-naphthalene-acetic acid and β-indole-butyric acid, used as a concentrated dip. This mixture is made up by dissolving 0·4 grams of each acid in 60 ccs. of 95 per cent alcohol and adding 40 ccs. of water.

(b) *Single-leaf cuttings.* Single-leaf cuttings are not taken, as such, from the tree, but cuttings of a similar size to stem-cuttings are taken and later divided into single-leaf cuttings.

In preparing the single-leaf cutting for the propagator, the terminal bud is removed and the shoot is divided by cutting the stem about $\frac{1}{4}$-inch above each node. The leaves are cut back as for stem-cuttings, but not trimmed back quite so heavily as with stem-cuttings.

The hormone described above for stem-cuttings is diluted with

50 per cent alcohol to reduce it to half-strength for single-leaf cuttings.

In the case of both types of cuttings, where infection with fungi is suspected, subsequent trouble in the propagator may be avoided by dipping only the leaves in Bordeaux mixture before dipping the base of the stem in the hormone mixture.

STORAGE OF POTTED PLANTS

The potted plants will have to grow for several months (five months in the case of stem-cuttings and seven months for single-leaf cuttings) before they are ready for planting in the fields. During this time they should be stored in a greenhouse where the floor is made of concrete and the roof consists of alternating panels of glass and galvanized iron or aluminium sheeting which allow 50 per cent of the incident light to fall on to the young plants. The sides of this greenhouse are left open, but protected from wind by climbing plants or coconut leaves. This type of storage of young plants has the advantage of preventing rain from beating on them. Rain falling directly on the leaves can be particularly harmful to young flushes and also washes soil from the baskets. A film of water may cause the young leaves to stick together, effectively sealing the stomata and causing asphyxiation and death of the young leaves. Attack by *Phytophthora* is also common in young plants which are frequently exposed to beating rain. The danger from such attack may be reduced by spraying the young plants with a suitable fungicide, such as Bordeaux mixture. It is, of course, possible to store the plants under a slatted shade which allows 40 per cent to 50 per cent of the total incident light to penetrate. In this case the slats should be fairly narrow (1 inch – 1½ inches) to avoid too heavy a drip on the plants.

Difficulties may occur in a greenhouse if the plants are watered carelessly. Watering with a hose will have the same effect as beating rain, so a watering-can or a lawn sprinkler should be employed. The most common fault is over-watering, which converts the potting-mixture into a water-sodden unaerated mass.

The growth of the plants during storage is dependent on the suitability of the potting-mixture. A good loam with *p*H value of 5 to 5·5, with adequate amounts of the main nutrient elements present and free from toxic concentrations of minerals, will generally prove suitable without the addition of extra organic matter, provided the structure has not been destroyed by over-watering. If, however, a soil of the above description is not available, and the soil used is neutral to alkaline, it is advisable to incorporate some well-rotted compost.

Alkaline soils or soils containing free calcium carbonate are liable to give rise to iron chlorosis in the potted plants, a condition which is extremely difficult to correct. For this reason sea sand containing shells or coral should not be used.

The application of small doses of sulphate of ammonia, 2 grams per basket every 3 to 4 weeks, or spraying with 1 per cent urea, will encourage the growth of the plants.

THE METHOD OF RAISING ROOTED CUTTINGS AT W.A.C.R.I.

In the following paper read by Mr. A. D. McKelvie, at the London Cocoa Conference of 1957, he describes the method developed at W.A.C.R.I. and adopted as the standard practice in West Africa. It is efficient and simple and is probably the cheapest method of raising vegetative material so far evolved.

"Two-leaf semi-hardwood cuttings with about one inch of stem are taken from fan branches brought in from the field early in the morning. The leaves are normally trimmed to about two-thirds of their original length and the stem is given a quick dip in a growth-promoting substance (0·5 per cent β-indole-butyric acid in 50 per cent alcohol). A basket, 6 in. in diameter and 7 in. high made from palm midribs, is filled with potting soil around a central core of rooting medium (50 : 50 sand and composted palm fibre) and the cuttings inserted in the core. Fifty to 100 baskets are placed together on the ground, and after a liberal watering they are covered tightly with a sheet of polythene weighted down at the edges. Light intensity over the cuttings is reduced to about 15 per cent daylight with slatted bamboo. The polythene as used at present is 3/1000 in. thick but we are experimenting with thicker material. The sheet is re-removed early in the morning every third day and the cuttings lightly watered. It has been found that about one pint of water every three days is adequate for 50 cuttings: more leads to water-logging and poor rooting. After four weeks the cuttings have rooted and hardening can begin. It should not be delayed or roots grow too far out of the baskets and are liable to die back during hardening. This is done by stages: during the first week the cuttings are uncovered from 6.30 a.m. to 10 a.m., and during the second and third weeks until 11 a.m. and 12 noon respectively. The hardened cuttings are then stored under shade until required for planting in the field.

"Apart from its ease the new method is more effective than the use of concrete bins. With the latter, for example, about 75 per cent of clone R15 cuttings root successfully, while nearly 100 per cent take root under polythene. Even with a poor-rooting selection such as T17, over 70 per cent successful rooting can be obtained, compared with only 30 per cent in bins. Buds sprout more rapidly under polythene than in bins, and this early advantage persists until the plants are ready to go into the field.

"No detailed costing has been done but it is estimated that a cutting produced in concrete bins costs two shillings and sixpence compared with about ninepence under polythene. There are considerable savings in both materials and labour. The construction of expensive bins is avoided, very little rooting medium (which is laborious to prepare and difficult to obtain in large amounts) is required, and repotting after rooting is unnecessary. Furthermore, less watering is required than with conventional methods, which may be an important advantage where water supply is difficult. The polythene sheet is relatively cheap and can be used for about 18 months continuously.

"This method of propagation is used in preference to techniques such as budding, for a number of reasons. In contrast to the extreme simplicity of the polythene sheet method, budding calls for considerable manual skill, and it would, in any case, be unwise to apply the method on a large scale until we know more about stock-scion relationships in cocoa. Compared with cuttings in concrete bins or open spray-beds, cuttings under polythene show a remarkable tolerance. Successful results can be achieved with light intensities between 12 and 25 per cent daylight, and provided the soil is not waterlogged, the amount of water which must be added is not critical.

"The polythene sheet method of rooting cocoa cuttings can be recommended for either large- or small-scale propagation. At W.A.C.R.I. this method is used to root large numbers of cuttings for the production of 'clonal' seed by the Departments of Agriculture of Ghana and Nigeria, but it is equally suitable for use by the peasant cocoa farmer."

PROPAGATION OF COCOA IN PLASTIC BAGS

An economic method of propagation has been operated by R. Nichols, Regional Research Centre, Imperial College of Tropical Agriculture, Trinidad, and an account of this, first published in Nature *for February 22nd, 1958, is given below.*

The basic physiological requirements for the vegetative propagation of cocoa (*Theobroma cacao*) have been broadly worked out by

Evans (1951). They may be summarized as follows: In an atmosphere near 100 per cent relative humidity, semi-hardwood cuttings will produce roots in the order of 70–90 per cent rooting efficiency if they are given adequate aeration at the base of the cutting. Light intensity must be reduced to 15 to 20 per cent of the incident sunlight.

A comparison of the costs of commercial propagation in Trinidad has been made by Murray and Bridge. McKelvie has also shown that cocoa may be propagated at greatly reduced cost, on a commercial scale, using sawdust-cored baskets containing cocao cuttings, covered by polythene sheets. This method adequately dispenses with the expensive installation of commercial propagating bins, and considerably reduces water consumption and labour costs. Another method, making use of the properties of polyethylene, which restricts water-vapour diffusion but permits some gaseous diffusion, is being developed here. Cuttings are rooted entirely in plastic bags, transported to the field in the same fashion, and afterwards established there.

The base of a semi-hardwood cocoa cutting bearing 4–6 trimmed leaves is dipped in hormone solution. It is next placed in wet, leached sawdust laid in coconut fibre. The fibre is then folded around the base of the cutting and held in place with an elastic band. The final size of the sawdust and fibre "ball" is about that of a half-clenched fist. The cutting is inserted into a plastic bag (150 gauge, 20 in. by 11 in.), water (150 ml.) is added and the neck closed with string. The bag is suspended under a shade of domestic cloth, and no further attention is required until root formation takes place. The roots emerge through the fibre and can be seen through the plastic. The light-intensity, calculated by means of an actinograph, is approximately seven per cent of the incident sunlight, but is not critical over wide limits providing the light is diffused.

The cutting is transported to the field in the bag and planted under heavy shade with the roots still enclosed in the fibre. The surplus water from the plastic bag is tipped over the plant and the bag is then inverted over the cutting, with the mouth lying loosely upon the soil surface. Two banana leaves, which provide local shade, are arranged in the form of an inverted "V" over the cutting, with the petioles firmly pressed into the soil. Natural drying-out of the banana leaves permits progressively more light to fall on the cutting. After four or five days, the bag is removed and used again for further propagation. The purpose of the inverted bag is to reduce transpiration and replace the conventional hardening procedure. The probable reason why success is achieved by this method is that the roots of the cutting are intimately interwoven with the wet fibre and sawdust, which retains moisture for a considerable time during the critical period when the roots are becoming established in the soil.

The percentage of cuttings rooting in the bag is of the order of 80–90, depending upon the clone, and establishment in the field about 60–70 per cent. Plants of the more vigorous clones are ready for planting 22 days from setting.

The advantages of the method are many. The plastic bag costs 2½d. and may be used a number of times without deterioration. Labour charges and installation are negligible when compared with conventional methods. Plants are introduced into the field more quickly and are very easily transported by hanging the bags from wires in a vehicle. Furthermore, drying-out, which is frequently observed with plants in baskets transported over long distances, does not occur. The combined weight of a plant and basket is between 3½ and 4 lb., as compared with 1 lb. for a plant in a plastic bag. One man may carry up to 20 plants in bags without difficulty, whereas he is restricted to two basketed plants owing to the weight and shape. This means that inaccessible bush areas may be more readily planted with clonal cocoa. Skilled labour is not required at any stage in the process, and normal care is all that is needed at planting.

OTHER METHODS OF PROPAGATION

A Method of Budding Cocoa

A method of shield-budding cocoa has been evolved by Mr. G. F. Topper, cocoa agronomist. The method calls for the use of 1¼–1½ in. long buds taken from mature terminal growths. These are budded on to four-month-old seedlings. The wood is removed from the bud before placing it on the stock. When it is in place, the bud is completely covered by wrapping CT-4 clear budding tape (½ in. by 0·004) round the stem of the stock at the point where the budding has been made.* This wrapping conserves moisture and makes for an early union with the stock and the rapid growth of the young scion. Three weeks after the operation the plastic tape is removed and the stock is nicked and broken four inches above the bud. Most of the buds start growth in the ensuing two weeks.

After a fortnight the stocks are examined, and in the few instances where the buds are still dormant, a ¼-in.-wide ring of bark is removed from the stock about an inch above the dormant bud in order to

---

* The tape used in Jamaica is manufactured by the Resinite Sales Corporation of Santa Barbara, California, U.S.A.

Potting rooted cuttings.
baskets are nearly filled
potting mixture before
cuttings are put in

35. Rooted cuttings with their first flush

(a) Stem-cutting   (b) Single-leaf cutting

36. Storage space for rooted cuttings. The floor is concreted and the roof consists of alternate panels of glass and corrugated sheets

37. Inside propagating she[d] Trinidad. Rooting bins in the ground and baskets of rooted cu[ttings] being hardened off in the foreg[round]

38. Open spray bed with lines of T-jets on both sides

. Bench grafting. In the middle the stock and scion are prepared for grafting and
ɔting. On the left the graft has been sealed with grafting tape. On the right the
stock and scion have united and roots have developed

40. Marcotting: root development in treated shoots

41. Young cocoa under forest trees which have been selectively thinned, Cong

induce activity. Where the bud has failed to take, the stock will be re-budded.

Subsequent treatment consists of staking and tying the buds when they have grown to nine inches in length, and cutting the stock immediately above the budding point when the scion has made about two months' growth. The plants can be potted about two months after this operation, if desired.

If the bud is placed on the stock about four inches above ground-level, the scion can be induced to develop its own roots by earthing up the stock after the scion has developed.

If the bud is placed sufficiently low down on the stock, the possibility of chupons arising is negligible. Seedlings can be raised in the field from seed at stake and used as stocks for budding.

MARCOTTING

By this method rooting is induced on a branch while it is still attached to the tree. It can be employed when a small quantity of material is required. Standard methods for marcotting are well known, and a technique for marcotting is described by Evans in the *Report on Cacao Research, 1945–1951.*

GRAFTING

A system of saddle- or bench-grafting worked out by Evans in Trinidad can be used conveniently where there are facilities for producing rooted cuttings. It is operated as follows: Two cuttings are taken from different trees, one of which is to be the stock and the other the scion. The base of the scion cutting is split and fitted over the wedge-shaped end of the stock. The union is tied with grafting tape and painted with low melting-point paraffin wax. The stock and scion are now treated in the same way as cuttings for rooted cuttings and placed in a propagating-bin.

H

REFERENCES

Archibald, J. E. *The Propagation of Cacao by Cuttings.*

Burchardt, A. "Notes on cacao work at Hacienda Clementina." *Proceedings of 4th Inter-American Cacao Conference* (Guayaquil, June 1952).

Burle, M. L. "A note on rooting cocoa cuttings under plastic." (Cocoa Conf. 1957, 52.)

Cheesman, E. E., and Spencer, G. E. L. "The propagation of cuttings in tropical climates." *Trop. Agric.* (Trinidad, 1936), **13**, 20.

Evans, H. "Investigations on the propagation of cacao." *Trop. Agric.* (Trinidad, 1951), **28**, 147.

Evans, H. "Recent investigations on the propagation of cacao." *Report on Cacao Research 1945–51* (Trinidad, 1953).

McKelvie, A. D. "Rooting cuttings under polythene." (Cocoa Conf. 1957, 51.)

McKelvie, A. D. (1957). "The polythene sheet method of rooting cacao cuttings." *Trop. Agric.* (Trinidad, 1957), **34**, 250.

Murray, D. B., and Bridge, C. J. R. "A comparison of various methods of rooting cuttings." *A Report on Cacao Research, 1955–56* (Trinidad, 1957), 41.

Murray, D. B. "A new technique in the vegetative propagation of cacao." *A Report on Cacao Research, 1953* (Trinidad, 1954), 53.

Nichols, R. "Propagation of cacao in plastic bags." *Nature* (Lond.) (1958), **181**, 580.

Pyke, E. E. "Vegetative propagation of cacao I–V." 1st, 2nd and 3rd Reports on Cacao Research 1931–3 (Trinidad, 1932–4).

Stahel, G. "The multiplication of cacao by leaf cuttings." Bulletin 61, Department Landproefstation van Suriname (1948).

Topper, B. F. "New method of vegetative propagation for cocoa." *World Crops* (1957), **9**, 38. (Cocoa Conf. 1957, 49.)

Chapter IX

THE COCOA PLANTATION (4)

PLANTING AND AFTER-CARE

I. PLANTING IN THE FIELD

Planting at Stake—Planting from Nursery Beds—Planting with Baskets

PLANTING may be done by setting seed "at stake," or by using plants previously grown in nursery beds or in baskets.

PLANTING AT STAKE

Planting seed at stake may suit conditions where cocoa is easy to establish, such as where it can be economically supervised in the field and where pests which attack young cocoa are not too numerous. When holes have been prepared and filled, two or three seeds are planted per stand, an inch or so below the surface and about three inches apart. When grown, the most vigorous plants are retained and the remainder discarded. An important disadvantage of this system is that there are only two or three plants to choose from, whereas a nursery provides a large choice. Plants growing at stake will require to be surrounded by palm fronds or other shading material for the first few months of their growth, if low shade plants such as *Xanthosoma* sp. have not been established previously.

PLANTING FROM NURSERY BEDS

Where the plants are in nursery beds they should be removed in the morning, being eased carefully out of the soil by pressing a garden fork into the bed to a depth of about nine inches, so as to avoid damage to the tap-root in the process of lifting. Where the soil in the bed is compacted, lifting will be made easier by a gentle watering the previous evening. The object is to allow as much soil to remain adhering to the roots as they will carry, except where there is an admixture of clay, when it is advisable to crumble it away from the plants. Plants which have recently developed a new flush are left in the bed until the flush has hardened.

It is desirable to plant the seedlings soon after removing them from the bed, but if they have to be transported some distance they can be wrapped in leaves and put in crates or hampers; fifteen to twenty plants to a container make for convenient handling. In the event of unavoidable delay between lifting and planting, the plants may be kept in good condition by putting them in a shaded place and sprinkling them with water every few hours. Where seedlings have to be kept longer than usual before planting, some of the leaves may be removed, but opinion seems to be divided on the value of this procedure.

PLANTING WITH BASKETS

When planting out in baskets, a hole is made at the planting site deep enough to have the top of the basket at ground level, and wide enough to allow some soil to be rammed firmly around it. The soil around the plant will be levelled off so that it is flush with the ground. If the basket is new, it is advisable to remove the bottom before planting, unless it consists only of a few strands of cane; otherwise it may impede the growth of the tap-root.

Whether the planting is done in prepared sites at stake with un-basketed seedlings or seedlings in baskets, it is extremely important that the soil in the hole is well packed when the plant is installed, and it is advisable to use a ramming-pole for this purpose. Loosely packed soil will compact later and the result will be a saucer effect at ground level; the surrounding soil outside the basket may contract and the soil in the basket dry out. Furthermore, there may be waterlogging around the plant during heavy rains. Also, a plant in loose soil may be more easily blown over. Some planters advocate raising the level of the soil around the plant with a good soil mixture, but this idea is not universally accepted.

Trinidad planters recommend that nursery seedlings should reach a height of two feet before planting in the field; it is important that plants be chosen according to their size, health, and vigour of growth, and not according to their age. Successful growers have stressed the need to use sturdy plants and ruthlessly to discard the mediocre and poorly-grown.

II. PROVISION OF SHADE

*Ground Cover and Temporary Lateral Shade—Permanent
Overhead Shade—Some Functions of Shade—Degree of
Shading Desirable—Species of Trees Suitable—Methods of
Providing Overhead Shade—Establishment Methods in Papua
and New Guinea—Views on Use of Shade in the Congo—
Value of Certain Forest Trees in the Congo*

Under all conditions of cocoa-growing, it is accepted that the
ground should not be left uncovered for any length of time. This
applies to the first stages of preparation of the land and right through
the history of the plantation. Although there is some difference of
opinion as regards the extent to which the cocoa tree needs shade
after it has grown and produced a canopy, there is universal agreement on the need for shade at the seedling stage and in the first few
years of the life of the tree. Shading in various forms is applied as
ground cover and temporary lateral shade and, finally, as permanent
overhead shade.

GROUND COVER AND TEMPORARY LATERAL SHADE

The most satisfactory arrangement is of course to have the overhead shade grown well in advance of planting the cocoa, but where
the forest has been removed and no tree shade has been provided,
some form of ground cover is desirable. Various leguminous plants
such as *Puereria* spp., *Dolichos* spp., *Desmodium* and others, have
been employed as ground cover in oil palm, coconut and rubber
plantations, but are less used in cocoa plantations. With the exception of *Desmodium* they are all creepers and need a great deal of
attention to prevent damage to the young cocoa plants. Shrubby
plants such as *Crotalaria* spp., are much more satisfactory, and
they can serve the purpose of ground and lateral shade. *Crotalaria
anagyroides* is much used in this way in New Guinea. *Erythrina
lithosperma*, "Dadap," cuttings are employed in a similar way in
Western Samoa. *Gliricidia* can also be used for this purpose.

Tannias (*Xanthosoma* spp.) and eddoes (*Colocasia* spp.) are widely
used and so are several species of bananas and plantains. These last
are usually planted in the lines of cocoa trees and can be allowed to
remain in the plantation for some time after it has reached the bearing stage. They have the advantage that they grow quickly, their

shading capacity can be regulated and they provide material for mulching. They also respond readily to manuring and thus their growth can be speeded up, if desired. The roots can be used as food for labourers or sold to offset establishment costs.

The West African farmer usually relies for ground cover on a variety of food crops, such as cocoyams, maize, cassava and plantains. Where cassava is planted near the cocoa, there is a danger of the latter being damaged when the cassava is harvested.

The harvesting of large quantities of food crops from land which is planted to cocoa is not to be recommended, as soil fertility will be lowered, and the practice will be unprofitable in the long run.

PERMANENT OVERHEAD SHADE

The need for permanent shade, the extent to which it should be applied and the circumstances under which it could advantageously be dispensed with altogether, have been much debated. Although a good deal has been learnt about the functions of shade in recent years, and well-founded theories have been put forward to explain some of its influence on the cocoa tree, much still remains to be discovered about its functions under varying conditions of sunshine, humidity and soil.

SOME OF THE FUNCTIONS OF SHADE

Among the more important functions of shade trees are the protection of the organic matter in the surface layer of the soil from the sun. The stems, branches and leaves provide shelter which helps to keep the climate within the plantation equable. Usually, being deeper rooted, shade trees tap soil layers not accessible to the cocoa and bring up nutrients, depositing them on the surface in the form of leaves and branches, and, incidentally, adding large amounts of humus to the surface layer. If the shade trees employed are of an especially deep-rooted type, they, in fact, continue to some degree the functions of the forest in building up organic matter and increasing the nutrient content of the soil surface.

Adams and McKelvie (1955) estimated that a shaded cocoa farm in Ghana derived from forest shade trees per annum approximately two tons of litter per acre, containing 70 lb. nitrogen and 4 lb. phosphorus.

Hardy (1955), discussing Immortelle shade trees in Trinidad, says that the root nodules contain over 4 per cent of nitrogen, leaves 2 to 3 per cent and flowers 3 to 6 per cent. The amount of nitrogen contributed by fall of flowers alone in one year is 20 lb. per acre.

A crop of 500 lb. of cocoa removes 12 lb. of nitrogen per acre. There is therefore a net gain of 7·5 lb., equivalent to nearly 40 lb. of ammonium sulphate fertilizer per acre.

The root system of the shade tree helps to keep the soil open for drainage and aeration and so is of particular value on land which is liable to waterlogging.

DEGREE OF SHADING DESIRABLE

The study of this subject has not yet advanced far enough to make it possible to lay down rules for optimum shading under the different conditions in which cocoa is grown. It is certain that until the function and effect of shading are more fully understood, and the plant breeder has evolved a cocoa tree that will perform satisfactorily with little or no shade, it is generally safer to apply shade to a greater or less degree, unless in any particular locality it is proved to be unnecessary. It has been observed that experienced planters have been able to adjust the degree of shading within a single cocoa field from quite heavy to relatively light shading. This was done by carefully observing the response of the cocoa trees to varying degrees of shading.

In a rich soil where cocoa grows a luxuriant canopy and the ground is well protected, there is a generous deposition of litter, and nutrients are kept in circulation. In a poor soil where the canopy is less luxuriant and the soil is less well protected, there is rapid loss of organic matter and nutrients. There may, therefore, in certain circumstances, be less need for shade on a rich soil than on a poor one.

Shade trees, apart from reducing the light intensity within the plantation, reduce air and soil temperatures and affect atmospheric humidity, but although maximum temperature is depressed, the minimum is not affected. It is possible, especially at high altitudes, that excessive shading might prevent the temperature rising to the level necessary for maximum flushing and fruiting and the proper development of the pods. According to observations by Greenwood and Posnette (1950), flushing was suppressed when the weekly mean of the daily maximum temperature fell below 28·3° C. (83° F.). The findings of these two workers are further confirmed by Adams and McKelvie, who noted that pod growth was slower when the mean daily maximum temperature fell below 28·3°–29·4° C. (83°–85° F.)

Experiments in shading coffee in the Belgian Congo showed that unshaded coffee gave a much higher yield than coffee under shade. In the islands of Hawaii coffee is unshaded but treated with heavy applications of mineral manure, and high yields are obtained. It would be unwise at this stage, however, to conclude that what applies to coffee will apply equally to cocoa. In so far as experimental work has been done in the manuring of cocoa under shade, the findings are that under heavy shade there is less response to fertilizers, but there is a response, particularly to nitrogen, according as the shade is reduced and the light intensity increased. Experience in plantations in Grenada shows that the unshaded cocoa fields give a much greater response to mineral or pen manure than those under shade.

There will undoubtedly be competition for soil nutrients between shade and cocoa trees at certain stages of the growth of the shade tree, but since the shade trees develop their root system with greater ramifications at lower levels than the cocoa tree, their contribution to the surface layer in the form of humus and nutrients will show a balance in favour of the shade trees. On the other hand, where the supply of soil moisture is marginal for cocoa, especially in the dry season, the moisture supply may not be sufficient for both cocoa and shade trees, and it is found that the shade trees usually win in the competition for the moisture available and the cocoa trees suffer. Under such conditions recourse must be had to the maximum use of windbreaks and the minimum of shade.

Grenada is often quoted as a country where cocoa is grown without shade, but here the fields are small and many of them were, previous to the hurricane in 1955, surrounded or partly surrounded by nutmeg trees, or otherwise protected by windbreaks. Furthermore, and still more important from the point of view of shade, the country is hilly, and a large proportion of the plantations are on steep slopes so that they are in shadow for part of the day. Although cultivation and manuring is practised in this island, the yield of cocoa even on good soils is low, so that it is doubtful if Grenada has benefited from abandoning shade. Western Samoa is another country where planters believe in growing cocoa without shade. This practice was probably favoured in the early days as there is a lower incidence of black pod in the absence of shade. Yields of cocoa on some of the fields of the New Zealand Reparation Estates in Samoa vary between 3 and 5 cwt. per acre, a few fields give yields of 7 cwt. per acre, and this on a volcanic soil of a type which is assumed to be highly fertile. Yields on some of these fields were originally about 17 cwt. per acre. It seems doubtful whether a convincing case has been made out for the practice of dispensing with shade in this instance. It is possible that Western Samoa would have maintained a higher level of yields if a number of shade trees were grown with the cocoa, and black pod were kept under control by spraying.

42. Young cocoa growing in the shade of bananas, Grenada

. A mixed plantation of coco-
ts and cocoa in New Guinea

44. A cocoa plantation in Western Samoa with ground cover of Dadap
(*Erythrina lithosperma*)

45. Windbreaks on River Estate, Trinidad: (*Left*) *Dracaena* forming a tall dense
hedge. (*Right*) West Indian Mahogany (*Swietenia mahogani*)

Forest land in Ghana cleared for ~~ting~~ cocoa. A number of forest trees ~~been~~ left as permanent shade. The ~~y~~ams seen in the foreground will provide ground shade

47. Young cocoa growing in partly thinned jungle, Malaya

Young cocoa trees growing under thin-ned forest shade in the Congo

49. A young cocoa plantation at Keravat, New Britain. Shade trees are *Leucaena glauca*

50. Ground shade of Crotalarias planted in advance of cocoa, New Guinea

51. Small farmer's plot of youn; cocoa growing under shade of *Leu caena glauca* in the Gazelle Peninsul

52. Young cocoa growing in plantation with coconuts and bananas, Jamaica

53. Cocoa growing among rubber, Ce

In those countries where cocoa has already been grown for a good many years considerable guidance as regards the degree of shading desirable is available to the new planter, but where planting is to take place in absence of such guidance, the degree of shading is much more difficult to assess. Shading is necessary under all conditions in the first few years of establishing cocoa. In absence of evidence to the contrary, it would be wise to assume that permanent shade is required.

Grass found growing within the plantation indicates insufficient shade. On the other hand certain small plants, such as *Zebrina pendula* in Trinidad, indicate that shading in the plantation is optimal.

TYPES OF TREES SUITABLE AS PERMANENT OVERHEAD SHADE

The type of tree best suited to provide permanent shade is easily described, but it is a less simple matter to find one which combines all the attributes of the ideal tree. This should have a spreading canopy admitting filtered light and broken sunshine, retain its leaves well into the dry season and have a deep-rooting root system to prevent the tree being blown over easily. It should not compete unduly for soil nutrients and moisture. Trees with brittle stems and branches which are liable to be broken by the wind are to be avoided. Some trees are suitable in one country but not in another. For instance, *Leucaena glauca* is much favoured in New Guinea and Indonesia and in some other countries which have a short dry season, but it is unsuitable in countries with a long dry season as under these conditions it seeds profusely and becomes a weed. Trees with small, divided leaves allow penetration by light; trees with dense foliage such as mangoes or colas, cannot be used with advantage. Deciduous trees, which shed their leaves in the dry season, are probably better in the drier climates than evergreens. They drop a dense cover of leaves on the ground which helps to retain the moisture, and transpiration by the shade tree itself is checked at this time of the year. It has been suggested that evergreens are best suited to areas with no marked dry season. Trees which have no thorns on the stems are preferable as they can be climbed for the purpose of controlling the spread of the branches and the density of the foliage. Leguminous trees of a suitable type add to the nitrogen content of the soil, but it is not necessary to limit the choice to leguminous trees if a suitable type is not available. The tree that is perfect in every respect will seldom be found, and a choice must eventually be made from trees that have the greatest number of the desirable qualities.

Trees indigenous to the country are, on the whole, preferable to those which have been introduced, as they are less likely to suffer from pests and diseases. The wide range of trees, such as those of the *Albizzia* spp., and *Erythrina* spp., and trees of similar habit of growth, will usually supply a number of types suitable for trial.

METHODS OF PROVIDING OVERHEAD SHADE

Selective thinning of the high forest has been widely practised in West Africa and recently adopted in Malaya. Here the undergrowth is cleared, a number of trees with suitable canopies are marked for retention and the remainder are felled. Where the forest stand is uniform, this process is fairly easy to apply; but where there is an uneven stand, it is much more difficult to thin out in order to arrive at a suitable degree of shading throughout. It may be necessary to plant a number of quick-growing trees, such as *Musanga smithii*, or a similar type of secondary tree, to occupy the insufficiently shaded areas. These would be replaced later by trees of a more permanent nature. The necessary degree of shading and the number of forest trees to be left would, of course, depend on the judgment of the planter. When the forest is thinned, the canopies of the remaining trees spread out, and further thinning or trimming of the branches may be required. It may take several years before the forest stand has been adjusted in such a way as to provide the desired degree of shading. Treatment of the forest by thinning should be done 9–12 months before the cocoa is due to be planted.

Secondary forest can be treated in a similar manner, and it is, in fact, easier to adjust good secondary forest for cocoa-planting than to adapt high forest for this purpose.

In Papua and New Guinea, cocoa is planted between coconuts (coconuts usually spaced at 30 ft. apart) when these are at least eight years old. Coconuts provide ideal shade where their canopies have developed well, but where there is insufficient development of the canopy, it has been found that supplementary shade of *Leucaena glauca* is necessary. There is no evidence that there is any competition between cocoa and coconuts in Papua and New Guinea. In fact, the view is held that coconuts yield better where they are intercropped with cocoa.

In Ceylon cocoa has been planted among rubber for a number of years. There does not appear to be any competition for nutrients between the two crops, and there is no evidence that there is a transfer of disease from one crop to the other. Rubber at a normal stand does, however, tend to overshade the cocoa.

Where the forest is to be cleared completely, and overhead shade is to be established, it is desirable that the shade trees should be planted twelve months ahead of the cocoa. Unless the forest is to be burned, planting of shade could take place when the undergrowth has been removed and the forest has been felled sufficiently to permit of lining. The damage done to shade seedlings during the felling of the remaining forest will be negligible.

The spacing of shade trees will depend mainly on the size of the canopy which the tree to be used will develop. It is better to plant too many than too few, as they can easily be thinned to the required density as occasion demands.

The trees in most general use for planting as overhead shade are *Erythrina* spp., *Albizzia* spp., *Peltophorum* spp., and *Leucaena* spp. The forest tree, *Terminalia superba*, in addition to being favoured in the Congo as a tree to be left *in situ* when the forest is thinned, is also planted to provide shade.

In the past there was too great a tendency to regard "permanent" shade as really permanent. Shade trees grew to a great size and there was no attempt to control their growth. When they fell they did much damage to the cocoa trees. An example of this is to be seen in Trinidad, where for many years *Erythrina poeppigiana* was used almost exclusively at higher altitudes and *Erythrina glauca* at lower levels. Both of these types of trees grew to a considerable size and developed large canopies, but they had the disadvantage that they carried thorns on their stems which made climbing to control their growth difficult. In recent years the former have developed a "broom" disease, believed to be due to a fungus, and many of the trees have died. *E. glauca*, under wet conditions, suffers seriously from a bark-destroying fungus, *Calostilbe striipora*. One diseased tree in the course of its fall has destroyed as many as sixteen cocoa trees.

The tendency in the future will be to use trees which respond to quite severe trimming in order to prevent the shade becoming too large, and also to ensure that the degree of shading is maintained at the proper level. Trees without thorns on the stems are of course to be preferred. *Erythrina lithosperma*, which goes under the name of "Dadap," is a useful shade tree, some varieties of which have no thorns on their stems.

Van Hall, quoting from Lock, gives an interesting description of shade management in Ceylon. The shade used was *Erythrina lithosperma*, "Dadap," and was preferred on account of its rapid growth, luxuriant foliage, absence of thorns and because it could be lopped twice a year. The gist of the description is as follows: Large cuttings

of dadap which will develop in a year or two into fair-sized trees are
planted between young cocoa plants in the same line. The number
of shade trees at this stage will be the same as that of the cocoa
plants. When the canopies of the dadaps have developed so that
they meet, the thinning process begins and continues until the stands
are forty-five feet apart (the cocoa spacing is 15 ft. by 15 ft.), a stage
which is reached in about five years after the original planting. At
this stage a young dadap-cutting is planted in the square of old
dadaps to take the place of these when they have outgrown their
greatest usefulness. The cutting down of dadaps, together with the
periodic lopping of branches, supplies a great amount of material to
enrich the soil.

Where it has been decided that the shading is too dense and thinning is required, this is best done in stages and very gradually. The
removal of a great deal of the overhead shade in one operation will
upset the growth of the cocoa tree and also make it liable to pests,
such as an attack of thrips.

METHODS OF ESTABLISHING SHADE IN PAPUA AND NEW GUINEA

In Australian New Guinea cocoa has been successfully interplanted in coconut plantations, the spacing of the coconuts being
30 ft. by 30 ft., and that of the cocoa 15 ft. by 15 ft. As the cocoa
is planted not less than eight or ten years after the coconuts, the
palm fronds give suitable shade.

In *The Papua and New Guinea Agricultural Journal* for October
1954, Mr. F. C. Henderson has written on "Cacao as a Crop for
the Owner-Manager in Papua and New Guinea." *Crotalaria anagyroides* and *Tephrosia candida* are, he states, the two temporary
shade plants most common; *Leucaena glauca* is the most widely
used permanent shade, and sometimes *Albizzia* spp. and *Peltophorum
inerme* are also employed for this purpose. In Papua and New
Guinea it is customary to cut and burn the forest completely in
preparing the land for planting.

A number of shade combinations and planting methods are recommended. In all, the first step is for the labourers to prepare the seed
bed by hoeing a continuous strip twelve to eighteen inches wide
straight across the field over the open cocoa holes.

METHOD I
Temporary Shade: *Crotalaria anagyroides*.
Permanent Shade: *Leucaena glauca*.
Crotalaria seed is dibbled in the prepared beds in a continuous

line three feet to six feet on each side of the cocoa hole. *Leucaena* seed is planted through the remainder of the beds between the holes joining up with the *Crotalaria*.

METHOD II

Temporary Shade: *Crotalaria anagyroides.*
Permanent Shade: *Leucaena glauca.*

Crotalaria is dibbled in in a continuous line from cocoa hole to cocoa hole. Seed of *Leucaena* is planted with the *Crotalaria* in the mid-section between the holes.

METHOD III

Temporary Shade: *Crotalaria anagyroides.*
Permanent Shade: *Leucaena glauca.*

Established from rooted seedlings or cuttings. This is the same as Method II except that the *Leucaena* is established by planting three to five rooted seedlings three feet to four feet high, of finger thickness, instead of seed. Cuttings may be used but the strike of these is uncertain. *Leucaena* seedlings are hardy and can be pulled out of the ground, topped with a knife, dropped into holes made with a pointed stick, and the round firmed around them. They will strike readily.

The advantage of Methods II and III over Method I is that a quick coverage is obtained over the whole area and so maintenance costs are reduced. However, Method III is applicable only when ample supplies of *Crotalaria* seed are available.

METHOD IV

Temporary Shade: A mixture of *Crotalaria anagyroides* and *Tephrosia candida.*

Permanent Shade: *Leucaena, Albizzia, Erythrina* or *Peltophorum.*

This is the same as Method I but 25 per cent *Tephrosia* seed is added to the *Crotalaria*. The advantages gained are:

(i) the temporary shade lasts longer as the *Tephrosia* carries on after the *Crotalaria* dies out;

(ii) *Tephrosia*, being woody, holds the *Crotalaria* and prevents its being blown over by the wind.

Where large species of permanent shade are used they are spaced 30 ft. to 45 ft. apart, and do not give adequate shade for some time. Hence it is essential, where these are used, to add *Tephrosia* to the temporary shade mixture in order to carry the temporary shade until the permanent shade is established.

METHOD V

Leucaena glauca as Temporary and Permanent Shade.

Leucaena glauca can be used as both temporary and permanent shade. The seed is dibbled in in a continuous line from cocoa hole to cocoa hole. It grows in a hedge and is continuously reduced until at maturity only one to three plants have been allowed to persist between the cocoa holes to form the permanent shade.

The planting of cocoa is delayed by this method as the *Leucaena* is rarely sufficiently advanced in under six months to give adequate shade to the cocoa seedlings. This method is used where temporary shade seed is difficult to obtain.

It should be mentioned here that Mr. F. C. Henderson, who has made a careful study of cocoa culture in various parts of Papua and New Guinea, is opposed to the idea of planting cocoa in thinned forest. He believes in removing the forest entirely.

VIEWS ON THE USE OF SHADE IN LUKOLELA PLANTATIONS IN THE CONGO

In a paper prepared by Monsieur M. L. Poncin, General Manager of the Lukolela Plantations, and read at the Cocoa Conference in London in 1957, shading of cocoa on this estate, based on thirty-five years' experience, is discussed.

The estate is situated along the banks of the River Congo, 1 degree north of the equator.

"From the standpoint of pedology, the plantation is on a heavy clay soil, yellow-ochre ranging in some places to red-ochre in colour. This overlies a deposit of hydrated iron oxides the concretions of which have coalesced in places to form large lumps that are often visible on the surface. The sub-soil is a white, plastic, impermeable clay which is visible on the surface in the low-lying areas, when it then has a profile typical of a gley.

"The following are the chemical constants of one of the good soils:

pH generally 4·5 to 5·5, sometimes 6·5.

R_2O_3 1–3 M.E./100 g.

P_2O_5 1–3 mg/100 g.

Exchangeable bases 3·5–8 M.E./100 g.

Fine earth 50 to 60 per cent (top-soil), 60 to 90 per cent (sub-soil).

Concretions 50 to 70 per cent (sub-soil).

"The red-ochre areas with concretions are the richest and possess pH values up to 6–9; exchangeable bases, 16·3; P_2O_5, 4·1.

"We must emphasize one of the characteristics of Lukolela

Plantations which is caused by the nature of the soil and which surprises all visitors: the tap-roots of our cocoa trees are no more than 90 centimetres long; they are usually branched and end in nodules. Our shading policy derives partly from this handicap.

"Lukolela has an equatorial climate and a rainfall of between 1,400 and 1,600 mm. [approximately 55 and 63 in.] per year.

"Both the temperature and the relative humidity are remarkably high. There are two more or less distinct peaks in the rainfall which occur during the equinoctial seasons. There is no really dry season, but two and sometimes three months (June, July and August) are relatively dry."

Light. Poncin quotes Professor G. Lemee, Professor of Science at Strasbourg University, who has carried out research at the Centre Agronomique at Bengerville and says, "Knowledge of the influence of light and water supply on carbon dioxide assimilation by the cocoa tree, together with that of the water balance within the tree, constitutes a fundamental basis for the proper solution of the shading problem."

Lemee observed that, "During the damp, cloudy season, the rate of assimilation, under varying intensities of light, is at a maximum in full light . . . but that, as the light intensity increases, the increase in the assimilation rate becomes less and less marked until at light intensities exceeding 25 per cent of full sunlight it becomes negligible.

"On the other hand, during the dry season strong sunshine reduces the rte of assimilation. During this period, optimum assimilation occurs in conditions of medium light intensity; below this optimum level insufficiency of light becomes a limiting factor, while above it deficiency of moisture from insufficient protection is likewise a limiting factor.

"Consequently, if it is true that a reduction in light intensity is not *per se* a desirable factor in shading, it should not be overlooked that carbon dioxide assimilation increases very little when the amount of light exceeds 25 to 50 per cent, and particularly that conditions differ in places where the dry season can be long and severe."

Air Humidity. Hygrometer readings are nearly always over 80 per cent, but Poncin points out that during periods of severe drought the beneficial influence of large shade trees on air humidity is important. He emphasizes that humidity does not increase the incidence of disease where the estate is well managed.

Soil Humidity and Temperature. Poncin stresses the fact that shading protects the soil from drying out and prevents excessive temperatures developing in the upper layers, and goes on to say:

"For the sake of completeness, let us recall, as so many others have already done, that above 26° C., a rise in temperature of one degree entails an increase in the loss of nitrogen in the soil from 40 to 50 kg. per hectare per year, and that in the Belgian Congo it has been established that as much as 1,000 kg. of nitrogen per hectare are lost annually from unprotected soils.

"In all fairness the point which we are considering ought to be stated in another way. Assuming a flourishing plantation you had established, would the cocoa trees be capable of protecting the soil and of creating a micro-climate capable of ensuring their culture in perpetuity?

"Without doubt the answer is in the affirmative, so long as the physical and chemical constants of the soil are excellent and provided that no serious climatic, mycological or entomological change occurs."

Regulation of Metabolism and Organic and Mineral Nutrition. "The opponents of shading sometimes emphasize the competition for nutrition and water which it is likely to involve. There is some truth in this, and some tree species are clearly harmful to cocoa. The grower must, therefore, choose carefully among the species available to him and take local experience into account. This point will be dealt with later in a section on establishing shade.

"But, in so far as shade trees are compatible with cocoa, it is certain that the part they play in the regulation of metabolism and in providing organic and mineral matter is most valuable to the maintenance of soil fertility.

"In the absence of organic manure, which is virtually unobtainable on a large scale, the waste matter of all kinds provided by shade trees helps to compensate for what is extracted from the soil by the cocoa beans."

Protection against Certain Pests and Competitive Sun-loving Plants. Poncin mentions that capsids, especially the *Sahlbergella* species, thrive more readily in the absence of shade, and thrips are also fond of light. Most of the weeds, particularly grasses, which have a deleterious effect on cocoa are usually found where the ground is inadequately shaded.

The Management of Shade. It is the practice in Lukolela to allow the forest growth to spring up between the rows of young cocoa because it is maintained that it is more important to shade the base of the young plants than to shade the foliage. This forest growth is of course kept under control so that it does not interfere with the growth of the cocoa. A few forest trees are allowed to grow on as shade trees.

At the end of the first year there is a preliminary thinning of tall

54. Cocoa harvest in West Africa. Pods being opened with a small machete

55. Building a fermenting heap; the beans are being placed on plantain leaves, West Africa

56. Covering a completed heap with plantain leaves which are held in place with pieces of wood, West Africa

57. Cocoa drying on mats in Ghana

shade trees, some being felled and some being treated with arboricide. Poisoning of forest trees with arboricide has the advantage
that it acts slowly and thus gradually increases the light. At the end
of the second year the undergrowth between the lines of cocoa is
uprooted and spread around the base of the cocoa trees, and those
trees which are to provide shade are left. It is emphasized that the
forest growth should be controlled so as not to restrict the lateral
growth of the cocoa trees. As the shade trees grow they are given
constant attention and cut back, and the canopy is adjusted to provide what is considered to be optimum light in the plantation.
Where there is sloping ground exposed to desiccating winds, two
levels of shade are favoured, the lower level being well above the
tops of the cocoa trees. The degree of light entering the plantation
is increased as the cocoa trees grow older. Poncin postulates two
signs which can be taken as evidence of over-shading, namely, lack
of vigour and absence of new leaves, and an inadequate yield from
a tree of a given age.

Treatment of an Inadequately Shaded Plantation. He suggests that
where shade is inadequate, cover crops should be planted. He has
found that the woody leguminous plant *Flemingia* has given good
results at Lukolela and he prefers it to any of the herbaceous plants.
It is said to grow almost anywhere and does not appear to compete
with cocoa for moisture during the dry season. In inadequately
shaded land, where *Terminalia* or *Ficus* do not grow well, but where
the soil is moderately good, *Hevea* has been used.

Comment on M. Poncin's Experience and Views. The above gives
the experience and views of a highly successful planter who has
brought a great deal of skill to bear on his enterprise. In addition
to benefiting from the success and failure resulting from various
measures undertaken for the improvement of cultural techniques, he
has kept abreast with experimental work on cocoa and has put the
results to practical use.

AN ASSESSMENT OF THE VALUE OF CERTAIN FOREST TREES IN THE
CONGO

Monsieur M. Poncin comments as follows in regard to certain
forest trees at Lukolela Estates:

"*Artificially planted Indigenous Shade Trees.* It is sufficient to say
for the time being that it is unreasonable, on the pretext of providing
uniform spacing, to fell a good indigenous tree only to replant the
same species later.

I

"We are therefore in favour of *preserved natural shade.*

"*Incompatible Trees.* Experience has led us to reject various trees. After the terrible drought of 1942, it was very noticeable that cocoa trees had died mostly under certain kinds of tree, while they had survived under others. Here is a list of a few incompatible trees:

> *Celtis mildbraedii*
> *Drypetes gossweileri*
> *Lannea welwitchii*
> *Macrolobium coeruleum*
> *Macrodesmis sp.*
> *Pentaclethra macrophylla*
> *Piptadenia africana*
> *Plagiostyles africana*
> *Strombosia grandifolia*

"We rule out certain other trees because they are hosts for various pests:

> *Cola brunelii* (undoubtedly the source of *Sahlbergella* in our area)
> *Cola acuminata* (*Sahlbergella*)
> *Cola sp.*   ,,
> *Sterculia becquaertii*   ,,
> *Annonidium manii*   ,,
> *Ceiba pentandra*   ,,
> *Bosqueai angolensis* (*Corticium*)

It is also wise to avoid *Cola* species and members of the families Sterculiaceae and Bombacaceae because they are suspected of being carriers of the swollen shoot virus.

"We have further noticed that certain trees depress the yield of cocoa when they reach old age:

> *Milletia versicolor* (which we had spread everywhere by means of cuttings)
> *Albizzia ealaensis*
> *Pseudospondias microcarpa*
> *Myrianthus arboreus*

"There is still a great deal to be discovered and proved in this field. Once the problems of shading are studied, it is easy to attribute all kinds of failure in cocoa growing to this cause, and to hasten to add names to the list of incompatible trees without any real justification."

Mr. H. R. Lancaster, a director of the Huileries du Congo Belge, has assessed a number of these trees as follows:

Good Shade	*Croton mubango*
	Ficus spp.
	Trema guineensis
	Phyllanthus discoideus
	Ricinodendron africanum
	Pterocarpus soyauxii
	Fagara macrophylla
	Macaranga spinosa
	Alstonia congensis
	Picnanthus kombo
Poor Shade	*Myrianthus arboreus*
	Turreanthus africana
	Uapaca guineensis
	Panda oleosa
	Diospyros spp.
	Strombosia spp.
	Strombosiopsis spp.
	Calloncoba welwithii
	Calloncoba glauca
	Annonidium manii
	Acioa spp.
	Allanblackia floribunda
	Desplatzia dewevrii
Incompatible Trees	*Isoberlinia seretii*
	Macrolobium dewevrii
	Barteria fistuloza (fourmis)
	Uapaca guineensis
	Myrianthus arboreus
	Ceiba pentandra
	Cola spp.

Musanga smithii has been found useful as shade for young cocoa. It is only regarded as secondary shade and should be removed when permanent shade is established. It is subject to attack by *Epicamtoptera* spp., which eat the foliage in the dry season when the shade is most required.

Croton mubango is a shade tree especially favoured at Mokaria as it has a particularly good canopy giving the filtered light effect required for cocoa, but at Lukolela this tree is less favoured.

III. WINDBREAKS

*Necessity for Protection from Wind—Degree of Effectiveness
—West Indian Practice*

NECESSITY FOR PROTECTION FROM WIND

Windbreaks must be planted after careful study of the prevailing winds. Cocoa trees react unfavourably to cold or drying winds which may blow at certain seasons of the year, and they also suffer when exposed to periodic gales from the sea. The provision of windbreaks is as necessary under certain conditions as the provision of shade or drainage. In West Africa, large areas of cocoa died off when the forest which protected the cocoa from wind was removed in the course of annual food-crop farming.

In the normal course of clearing the forest for planting, the underbrush is removed, and even where shade trees are planted there may be conditions where, just above ground level, there is little to obstruct drying winds from sweeping through the plantation. In conditions like these a windbreak is of especial value and it can have an important function in maintaining atmospheric humidity and an equable temperature.

DEGREE OF EFFECTIVENESS

A barrier consisting of a high hedge formed with a single line of trees, with lower-growing trees between the taller ones, will provide the maximum shelter for the greatest area. It should be so planned as to allow the wind to pass through; it must not form an "impenetrable wall" over which the wind will glide and strike the field with force on the leeside. There is no advantage in having a wide belt of trees; a windbreak of one to three trees deep will give protection for a greater distance on the leeside than one which, for instance, is fifty yards deep.

The extent to which a windbreak formed by a hedge of trees will provide protection on the leeward side and on the windward side and the distance on either side for which the protection will be effective, has been the subject of study in a number of countries. The degree of protection provided will be dependent on a number of factors, the more important being the penetrability of the barrier and the direction and velocity of the wind. A fairly good windbreak may reduce wind velocity by 15 to 20 per cent, and even by as much as 30 to 40 per cent where a barrier is well placed. The distance on the leeward side for which protection will be provided may extend from 20 to 30 times the height of the barrier, and on the windward side for from two to five times its height.

Windbreaks are normally grown on the boundaries of the estate or along the edge of fields, but sometimes it may be necessary to have windbreaks within fields, especially where these are large or the contour of the land makes it desirable.

WEST INDIAN PRACTICE

In Grenada and Trinidad some estates have provided windbreaks with trees forming two storeys, the upper one being formed by mango (*Mangifera indica*) or galba (*Calophyllum antillanum*), and the lower one, which fills the spaces between the trunks of the taller trees, by *Hibiscus* or *Dracaena*. The latter forms a hedge which grows to a height of twenty feet or more. Other trees used in these two countries as windbreaks are sapodilla (*Achras sapota*), West Indian mahogany (*Swietenia mahogani*), cloves (*Eugenia aromatica*), Barbados almond (*Terminalia catappa*), and cashew nut (*Anacardium occidentale*).

It is not always sufficient to provide windbreaks around the outside of large plantations. It may be necessary also to have windbreaks within them to temper the wind in sections which would otherwise be unduly exposed.

It is important that the trees used as windbreaks should be deep-rooted and not easily blown over. In deciding the extent to which trees of economic value for their timber or fruit should be chosen, first consideration will have to be given to their suitability for providing shelter, and the avoidance of those which may attract pests.

IV. AFTER-CARE

Attention Required in Early Stages—Later Stages—Pest and Disease Control—Shaping and Pruning—Rooted Cuttings

The operations involved in after-care of newly-planted cocoa vary greatly with the climate and the methods adopted in growing it.

ATTENTION REQUIRED IN EARLY STAGES

Light hoeing around the young seedlings encourages the spread of the feeding roots. The extent to which weeding is required will depend on the amount of shade in the plantation and on the local rainfall. It is important to emphasize the necessity for hand-weeding the area immediately around the young plants, in advance of the general cutlassing of the weeds throughout the farm. Labourers swinging cutlasses are very apt to sever the stems of young plants or injure them to such an extent that they become diseased and die. In this way many trees in plantations have been lost in the first few years of establishment, and, as complete supervision of the labour is impossible, the only safeguard is weeding by hand in the immediate vicinity of the cocoa.

During the twenty-four to thirty months after planting, some young trees will have become casualties, and these will have to be replaced. Shade will have to be trimmed back and adjusted so as to allow the proper amount of light to reach the cocoa, and missing shade trees must be supplied.

Removal of chupons and shaping of the young cocoa trees will need particular attention during the first few years.

DRAINS

Drains require to be cleaned and the drainage system enlarged according to the needs of different parts of the estate. The fork is a better implement than the spade for cleaning drains as labourers are inclined to smooth over the sides of the drains, with the spade, and thereby impede the flow of water into the drain. The débris from the drains can be left in heaps for a time to decay before it is applied to the trees. Where such débris is highly acid it is improved by having some lime mixed with it.

The road system should be extended, and attention to culverts and road surfaces should be part of the general development of the plantation.

LATER STAGES

Except in those countries where cultivation is common practice, such as Grenada and Ceylon, deep-forking or digging of the soil near the plant is not recommended. Where deep cultivation is the rule from the beginning, the plants develop a deeper root system, but sudden deep cultivation of a plantation previously uncultivated would be disastrous. The periodic application of heavy dressings of farmyard manure or compost is at present confined to a few countries only. The average planter would not resort to manuring unless he had satisfied himself by tentative experiment, or unless properly laid-out experimental trials indicated that manuring was profitable.

PEST AND DISEASE CONTROL

Control of pests and diseases will take a certain amount of time. Rats, monkeys, squirrels and parrots can all be troublesome where they are numerous. The planter may require to have recourse to trapping, shooting and poisoning, in order to reduce their number. Beetles which bore into the stems or cut the bark of the young plants will have to be hand-picked or sprayed. Black pods resulting from *Phytophthora* fungus should be removed early to reduce spread into cushions. Cankered wood will have to be removed, and wounds and exposed areas of the stem treated with antiseptic dressing or paint. Where witches' broom is present, the brooms must be removed as frequently as recommended by authorities who have made careful studies on the spot.

Mere sanitation alone may not eliminate pests and diseases, but it is accepted that a high standard of sanitation greatly reduces the incidence of many of these and is more economic than relative neglect.

SHAPING AND PRUNING

The main objects of pruning are to remove unwanted growth and train the trees to the desired shape. The aim in shaping is to produce a well-balanced framework on which the fruit may be borne. The manner in which the cocoa tree grows is described on page 8 under "Habit of Growth." This tells how three to five branches fan out from the terminal bud of the seedling plant, and the first decision on shaping relates to the number of these branches to be left on the tree. Three well-spaced branches make for a good tree, but there are occasions when it may be desirable to leave four such branches at the jorquette in order to get a balanced tree. It will be found that some of the fan branches grow much more strongly than others, and, where possible, the weaker ones would be removed. After the fan branches have developed at the jorquette, chupons emerge from the stem and grow upwards parallel to the main stem. It is common for a chupon to emerge just below the jorquette which will grow upwards until it jorquettes in its turn. A chupon will again arise at the second point of jorquetting and this process of growth may be repeated four or five times after the first chupon arises. The fan branches on the lower stem of a tree developed in this way will atrophy and fall off.

On most types of cocoa the first jorquette takes place about three to four and a half feet from the ground. The second important decision on shaping has to be made when the first chupon emerges. If the height of the plant from ground level to the jorquette is considered satisfactory, then the chupon is suppressed, as are chupons emerging subsequently. On the other hand, if it is considered that a longer stem is desired, the first chupon can be allowed to develop and ramify or jorquette, and the fan branches and the canopy will develop from this point, any further development of chupons being suppressed.

In peasant farming in West Africa it is customary to allow the chupons to grow, and as a result the cocoa plant grows into a tall tree, often thin and spindly. This method was partly the outcome of growing cocoa at very close spacing so that the canopy closed in early and excluded capsids, and ensured a minimum stand after heavy casualties in the early years of growth. Now that there are means of keeping capsids under control, the necessity for such close planting will not apply.

It is argued by some that there is virtue in growing a tall tree in that it provides a large area of stem on which pods will grow. It is standard practice in all parts of the world where cocoa is grown under careful management to control chupon growth at the point where the seedling forms the jorquette. If a somewhat longer stem is desired, a chupon is allowed to grow and jorquette, further chupon growth being controlled from that time onwards. It has been argued that Amelonado cocoa requires different treatment from Trinitarios and other types of cocoa. This would seem to be a fallacy, as some of the highest yields from cocoa in West Africa, obtained from the S.P.R.O. Estate at Gangoa, in the Ivory Coast, were from trees which had chupon growth suppressed.

Where growth is controlled at the first or second jorquette, the fan stems will thicken as the tree matures, and these and their branches will provide adequate stem surface for the growth of pods.

Certain types of Upper Amazon cocoa may require different treatment from that described above. The method of shaping to be adopted must suit the habit of growth of the tree.

EXCESSIVE PRUNING

The various methods and systems of pruning cocoa have as yet had little or no attention from the scientist, so that the only guidance available is the experience of successful planters. The skilful use of the pruning-knife to regulate vegetative growth will induce greater crop yield, but rash and unskilful pruning can give the trees a severe set-back. Excessive and sustained pruning and cutting back may bring about stagnation of growth with consequent reduction in yield, and induce abnormal chupon growth from the main stem. It may also induce excessive flushing and make the tree more susceptible to insect attack.

FREQUENCY OF TREATMENT

Some planters favour undertaking main pruning operations on mature trees at intervals of two years, while others are in favour of annual treatment in the dry season. Yet other experienced planters consider that light pruning should be performed annually, and that heavy pruning should be done only once or twice in the lifetime of a tree, or when the trees have been neglected and fail to produce new wood. Certain planters adopt the plan of careful pruning of 25 per cent of the plantation annually.

UNWANTED AND WANTED CHUPONS

Some trees are prone to produce chupons readily from the main stem—more especially some types of Amazon cocoa. These growths, which are variously known as chupons, watershoots, suckers, or gourmandizers, are best removed while they are still tender and can be rubbed off with the fingers.

Trees which have become senile or damaged will usually send up chupons from the base. These chupons may have their origin in the main roots of the parent tree. A convenient method of renewing an old or unsatisfactory tree is to allow a chupon to grow from the base. When this has developed, the original stem is cut out. Earthing up to the base of the chupon will ensure that it forms its own roost.

Where good planting material is available an unsatisfactory tree would preferably be replaced by a new plant.

SHAPING IN RELATION TO SPACING, ETC.

A tree with a somewhat spreading habit is preferable to one with an upright habit, especially where there is the danger of fungi being carried from the pods above to the pods below. Where trees are close together, fan branches will have to be cut back in order to prevent overlapping and permit access to the plantation between the rows. The pruning and shaping of trees which are planted 8 ft. by 8 ft., or 9 ft. by 9 ft., will obviously differ from those planted, say, 15 ft. by 15 ft. Where conditions are humid and the sky is much overcast for long periods it may be desirable to open the canopy by thinning, to admit light and discourage the growth of fungi. Trees growing in a moist, loose soil may become top-heavy and fall over during a storm unless the canopy is thinned.

Neal Fahey of Trinidad recommends light pruning and the removal of thin and whippy branches in plantations at higher levels on exposed hillsides; this may also apply to trees in drier areas. He maintains that trees growing in a "parasol" shape are best suited to dry conditions.

ROOTED CUTTINGS OR VEGETATIVELY PROPAGATED MATERIAL FROM FAN GROWTH

The shape and manner of growth of a young plant grown from seed differs from that of a rooted or budded fan cutting. The shaping and pruning of a fan cutting is different from that of a seedling. A fan cutting divides at low level and produces a large number of branches. These should be reduced to three or four of the more vigorous distributed over the main stem.

Sooner or later chupons will be produced, and if one of these is allowed to grow, it will eventually dominate all other growth and produce a plant which has all the characteristics of a seedling. Some planters like to retain the rooted-cutting type of growth, while others prefer to develop chupons as soon as possible in order to have a tree of the seedling-tree shape.

REFERENCES

Cocoa, Chocolate and Confectionery Alliance Report of Cocoa Conference, London, 1955.

Greenwood, F., and Posnette, A. F. "Growth flushes of cacao." *Jour. hort. Sci.*, **25**, 194 (April, 1950).

Hall, C. J. J. van. *Cacao* (2nd edition, 1932).

Henderson, F. C. "Cacao as a crop for the owner-manager in Papua and New Guinea." *The Papua and New Guinea Agricultural Journal*, October 1954.

Poncin, M. L. "The use of shade at Lukolela Plantations" (Cocoa Conference, 1957, 281).

Chapter X

THE COCOA PLANTATION (5)

PREPARATION OF THE CROP FOR MARKET

I. HARVESTING

Precautions to be Observed—Labour Required

In countries with a well-defined dry season of several months the main harvest usually begins at the end of the wet season and continues in the first few months of the dry season, with possibly a minor harvest during the first months of the following wet season.

PRECAUTIONS TO BE OBSERVED

Harvesting consists of picking and breaking the ripe pods, removing the beans and transporting them to the fermentary. Labourers new to the work may require some instruction on how to distinguish ripe pods, but after some practice they can do so quite readily. Most pods assume a distinctive colour when ripe. For instance, green-podded Amelonado turns yellow, and red pods usually turn an orange or near-orange colour. These changes are slow and the pod will remain in a suitable state for harvesting for two or three weeks.

The fruit is borne on cushions on the stem of the tree. These may cease to bear if damaged, so it is most important that the harvesting tools should be sharp and so shaped that the cushions cannot be injured, as a damaged cushion can provide a point of entry for fungi. In many parts of the world the machete is the usual harvesting implement, but a sharp knife is better, and very careful planters use secateurs. A long-handled knife which can cut with both an upward and a downward thrust is required for pods above a certain level. The pod stem should be cut close to the tree, the thickened jointed portion being left attached to the cushion. This stump drops off later, leaving a well-healed scar which is impervious to fungi.

It is important that only ripe pods be picked; under-ripe pods may not have sufficient sugar in the pulp for successful fermentation, which is the next operation. On the other hand, over-ripe pods tend to become dry, and germination of the beans may be induced.

124

It must be emphasized that beans from diseased pods should not be fermented with the healthy ones. Very often such beans are infected with mould, which may cause breakdown of the testa and allow other moulds to enter.

LABOUR REQUIRED

Labourers employed on harvesting should be on "daily pay" rather than on "task" or contract, as there is the possibility of the trees being damaged and of unripe pods being harvested, if the operation is rushed.

The number of labourers naturally depends on the number of trees and the weight of the crop. Neal Fahey of Trinidad suggests the following division of labour for harvesting: a gang in charge of an overseer would consist of 5 men picking, 2 to 6 gathering pods into small heaps, 3 to 5 collecting the small heaps into large heaps. There are also women who usually lift the pods by sticking the point of a light cutlass into them and flicking them into a basket. One man is engaged in cutting the pods open, and four women extract the beans, generally using a wooden spatula, because when large quantities of beans are dealt with, the juices from the fresh beans may be "hard on the hands."

The pods are usually opened by cutting the husk with a knife or machete, but by this method a proportion of the beans may be damaged and rendered susceptible to attack by insects and mould. It is preferable to open the pods with a wooden mallet or by striking two pods together.

It is common practice to harvest one day, and break the pods and transport the beans to the fermentary on the following morning.

II. FERMENTATION

Experimental Work—Purple Beans—The Fermenting-house —Fermenting-boxes—Fermentation—A New Approach— Observing Progress—Causes of Unsuccessful Fermentation —Equipment: Cleanliness—Fermentation of Different Types of Cocoa—Handling Small Quantities

EXPERIMENTAL WORK ON FERMENTATION

In Trinidad research into the various processes involved in fermentation has been going on at the Imperial College and at the Colonial Microbiological Research Institute, and in Ghana at the West African Cocoa Research Institute.

Significant contributions have also been made by members of the staff of Cadbury Brothers Ltd., both in the Bournville Laboratories and in the field. Attention has been directed towards (1) developing methods whereby small quantities of beans can be fermented; (2) studying factors which affect the success of large-scale fermentations, and (3) investigating the physical and chemical changes involved in fermentation.

For laboratory studies, and sometimes for the plant breeder as well, it is useful to be able to ferment the beans from one or two pods, and methods are available to do this. Earlier hopes that it was only necessary to control the temperature of fermentation have proved unfounded, and it is important to control the *p*H of the beans as well.

A fermentation vessel has been designed for the use of the planter or plant breeder who wishes to ferment small quantities, say, the beans from 150–500 pods. This is useful when it is desired to assess the value of cocoa from a small number of selected trees. It is possible to ferment as little as 20 lb. of wet cocoa in a basket if adequate care is taken, but variations are liable to arise in the course of successive fermentations. These must be avoided when confirmation of the flavour of the samples is required, and for accurate reproducible results the use of the small fermentation vessel is recommended.

The standard fermenting-box used in the experiments was 3 ft. × 3 ft. × 3 ft., and it was usually loaded with 400–500 lb. of wet beans, the mass being first turned after two days and then two days later.

It was noted that during fermentation in boxes there was some variation in temperature within the mass. Near the top of the box— apart of course from the actual surface layer—it was likely to be several degrees higher than in the lower part.

In beans fermenting in heaps, variations are much greater. Indeed, unless great care is taken they can be of such magnitude as to cast doubts on the value of the heap method if fermented cocoa of really even quality is to be produced.

Other experiments of interest to plantation owners were also carried out. In one, cocoa pods were broken and the wet beans transported by lorry for about fifty miles. They were then allowed to stand overnight before being put into the fermenting-boxes. This had no adverse effect on the course of fermentation or on the flavour of the finished beans. In another experiment, 3,000 pods were kept for a week after harvesting, then broken and the beans fermented. Again no adverse effects were found. Several hundred pods, however, had to be discarded because of the development of mould in the beans during the week the pods were on the ground.

The use of the term fermentation, although well established, is not entirely satisfactory. Breakdown of the pulp is a true fermentation, but reactions in the cotyledon are not.

It had been common practice on certain estates in Trinidad to leave cocoa in the pods for a week or more after harvesting. This was said to be "Venezuelan practice." Dr. Howat notes: "Hancock reports that in Trinidad storing of the pods for a week resulted in a rapid rise in temperature to 55° C. instead of a long period at 37° C. during subsequent fermentation." A comparison shows that the percentage of dry beans recovered from a given quantity of wet beans depends upon the variety. Typical out-turns are: Amelonado 44 per cent, Amazon 38 per cent.

PURPLE BEANS

In recent years an increasing proportion of under-fermented purple beans has come on the market. They vary from bright purple with a "cheesy" texture to dull purple with an open texture like that of a well-fermented bean.

A high proportion of purple beans may result if the beans have been fermented for too short a period, if the fermenting mass does not reach or is not maintained at the right temperature or if unripe beans are included in the mass.

Some producers try to reduce the number of purple beans simply by fermenting for a longer period, but this may easily lead to over-fermentation.

While it is usual to expect high-quality manufactured chocolate from beans of a good brown colour, brown beans can be produced by methods other than fermentation. Fermentation, however, is the only way of producing the precursors of the true chocolate flavour, and dependence on visual examination alone is not a sufficient test of good preparation.

THE FERMENTING-HOUSE

On organized plantations fermentation is carried out in properly designed and equipped buildings, though well-fermented cocoa can be produced by more primitive methods.

The fermenting-house is usually an oblong building, and may be some 24 ft. long by 21 ft. wide, with a row of fermenting-boxes on each side, and a passage down the middle. A wide space between the eaves of the roof and the top of the wall on the lee side of the house permits a free movement of air and the escape of gases emanating from the fermenting cocoa.

A substantial house for the process would consist of concrete walls and a roof of aluminium sheeting. As the juices which run off from the fermenting cocoa are corrosive, it is desirable to have the fittings made of wood or other resistant materials. Flooring will last longer if the tiles and cement are acid-resisting.

FERMENTING-BOXES

Fermenting- or sweat-boxes are usually of inch-thick planks, and so constructed that the planks fit into slots so that they can be slipped out when it is desired to transfer the cocoa from one box to the next, or to vary the size of the box, or to wash the planks. Where nails are used, they are inserted in such a way that they do not come in contact with the beans as these may become stained by contact with metal. The boxes should be made of durable wood, such as *Chlorophora excelsa*, *Carapa guianensis*, or *Hieronyma caribaea*. Three-eighth-inch holes about six inches apart in the bottom of the box allow the liquid to drain away in the process of fermentation.

The dimensions of the boxes may range between 3 ft. deep by 5 ft. by 4 ft. and 3 ft. deep by 9 ft. by 6 ft. It is generally accepted that the depth of fresh cocoa should not exceed three feet for good fermentation, and as wet cocoa weighs about 50 lb. per cubic foot, a box 5 ft. long by 4 ft. wide would take some 3,000 lb. of cocoa. It is difficult to ferment quantities of less than 300 to 400 lb. of wet cocoa, but quite large amounts can be fermented at one time in containers of a suitable size, provided there is not too great a depth of cocoa.

Much labour will be saved if the house is built lengthwise down a steep slope, with the fermenting-boxes arranged in steps down the side, the top of each successive box being level with the bottom of the preceding one. The cocoa can thus be easily transferred from one box to the next by simply removing a few planks from the front.

The number of fermenting-boxes and the capacity of the drying facilities should be sufficient to cope with the crop of an estate at the time of maximum harvest.

Lining of fermenting-boxes. On the estates of the Huileries du Congo Belge, experiments have been conducted on the lining of fermenting-boxes with certain materials. The most satisfactory result was obtained with a lining of aluminium sheet. These estates now use this sheet for lining the last two of the seven boxes used in fermentation. It is claimed that this improves the quality of the dried cocoa, and the beans are less subject to mould. This company gets a premium for quality when the cocoa is sold in European markets.

58. Fermentary, Venezuela

60. McKinnon Drier

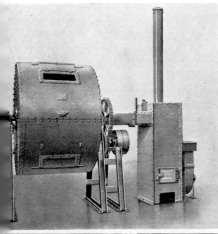

59. The inside of the fermenting-house shown in Fig. 63, showing the seven sweat boxes

61. Baskets for carrying cocoa on mule-back, Bahia

62. Mule-load of cocoa arriving at fermenting house, Bahia

63. A fermenting-house in the Congo. It is built on a slope to reduce labour handling cocoa

64. Drying-sheds on an estate in Trinidad. The roof of each shed is in two parts wh run on rails

65. Trays outside drying-house at Lukolela, Congo

FERMENTATION

The routine of fermenting cocoa is simple. Fresh beans are emptied into fermenting-boxes and then they are covered with banana leaves several layers thick. In some places it is customary to line the sides of the boxes with banana leaves and even to line the bottom. As far as the sides of the boxes are concerned, this practice is hardly necessary unless the wood is thin, and extra insulating material is required to retain heat. Lining the bottom is quite definitely undesirable unless adequate care is taken to ensure that there are holes pierced in the leaves for aeration of the beans and for drainage. After forty-eight hours, the mass should have developed sufficient heat, and it is then mixed and turned into another box. The second turning will take place after a further period of forty-eight hours. During turning, the temperature will drop and it is desirable that the operation should be done as quickly as possible. Although the frequency with which the cocoa is turned in the box varies according to the views of the planter as to what gives the best result, Dr. Howat considers two turnings adequate under the conditions in which he carried out numerous experiments on a commercial scale in West Africa. Amelonado cocoa is usually fully fermented in six to six-and-a-half days. Planters in Trinidad have found that a longer period is necessary for fermenting some of the Forastero-type selections.

The fermenting-boxes should be sheltered from draughts and wind which would delay or prevent the proper rise in temperature. At the same time it is important to ensure that there is some movement of the air round the boxes for aeration of the beans and for the removal of carbon dioxide. Mixing must be done thoroughly when changing from one box to another, otherwise some of the beans will be underfermented. During turning and handling of the cocoa in the boxes, beans which adhere to each other should be separated, foreign matter should be removed and beans which are diseased or otherwise defective should be discarded.

A NEW APPROACH TO THE FERMENTATION OF COCOA

H. W. S. Allison and T. A. Rohan conducted some interesting experiments in West Africa on fermentation of Amelonado cocoa. This new technique was based on their experience that the cocoa beans in the surface layer of the standard fermenting-box are killed within twenty-four hours. In other words, the process of fermentation proceeds more rapidly in the upper four inches of the fermenting-box.

K

Trays of the dimensions four feet by three feet and four inches deep, with slatted bottom, were used. The trays were filled with 200 lb. of wet cocoa beans and stacked on a rack. The distance between the trays was from six to twelve inches. A close-fitting cover of banana leaves and sacking was placed over the top of the tray. Successful results were obtained with five-tray stacks; stacks of up to twelve trays containing 1200 lb. of wet cocoa, gave good results.

It was found that Amelonado cocoa could be fermented in two to three days by this method. The cocoa was not mixed on the trays.

By arranging the wet cocoa on the tray so that only half the available space is taken up during fermentation, the beans can be spread over the whole tray after fermentation, thus making it possible to dry the cocoa on the same tray.

OBSERVING PROGRESS

The development of fermentation can be roughly tested throughout the period. The temperature at different stages can be estimated by plunging the arm into the fermenting mass, and the progress of the operation can be judged by cutting through a few beans, noting the degree of change in colour, the gradual separating out of the laminae of the cotyledons and the change from a bitter to a milder taste. The deep blue or purple of the fresh Forastero gradually changes to a lighter colour, and when fermentation is complete the kernel is readily detached from the seed-coat and the kernel itself can be easily broken up. When dry, the well-fermented bean will show an even break if both ends are held between the fingers and it is snapped through the middle.

CAUSES OF UNSUCCESSFUL FERMENTATION

There are occasions when the fermentation of a consignment of cocoa may go wrong. Some of the predisposing factors are the presence of over-ripe or under-ripe beans, or beans affected by *Phytophthora palmivora*, beans which have dried out by being too long in the pod after harvesting, or which have got wet during a rainstorm while being transported from the field.

If the season changes from being humid and warm to being dry and chilly at night, the period of fermentation may have to be slightly extended.

EQUIPMENT : CLEANLINESS

Wooden shovels have been much used in the past to transfer cocoa from one box to another, as the sharp edge of the ordinary metal shovel would damage the beans. In Western Samoa, square-mouthed metal shovels with a strip of steel welded on to the lip are found to be satisfactory, especially if thoroughly washed after use. During the operation of turning and mixing, the cocoa must be picked over, and foreign matter, the placenta, and diseased beans which may have found their way into the mass, must be removed. The fermenting-boxes must be washed and scrubbed from time to time.

FERMENTATION OF DIFFERENT TYPES OF COCOA

Fermentation of Amelonado or Criollo cocoas is carried out on similar lines, the former taking anything from six to eight days, and the latter two to five days; but the even and satisfactory fermentation of mixed samples of Trinitarios, and of hybrids which tend variously towards Amelonado and Criollo types, is difficult. It is necessary to keep Amelonado and Criollo types apart during harvesting and ferment them separately. In a number of countries where the first introduction was Criollo, followed later by Forastero, the mixture is often uneven. The only thing that can be done here is to compromise and find out by experiment what type of fermentation is best suited to the greater bulk of the particular mixture being dealt with. In the course of time, by means of vegetative propagation and later by breeding, the mixed cocoas of today may be converted to a high-grade uniform type.

HANDLING SMALL QUANTITIES

There are occasions when harvestings are not sufficiently large to undergo fermentation by themselves. These small lots should be put in a container which is well insulated to enable the small mass to generate the necessary heat. They should not be added to larger parcels of cocoa which have already undergone partial fermentation, but should be fermented by themselves throughout. When dealing with these small quantities it will be necessary to stir and mix the mass in the same container, as less heat will be lost in this way than if the cocoa is transferred to another container for the purpose of turning.

III. DRYING AND STORAGE

Sun-drying—Artificial Drying—Types of Driers and Methods of Drying—Testing for Dryness—Polythene Liners and Cocoa Bags—Storage

SUN-DRYING

In countries where the main harvest takes place chiefly in the dry season it is usual to dry cocoa in the sun. The beans are transferred from the fermenting-boxes and spread on drying-floors or trays. In order to expose them fully to the sun, they are raked over with a wooden rake—usually a piece of board fixed on a long handle.

Where the midday sun is strong, it may be necessary to cover the cocoa with mats for about two hours in order to prevent too-rapid drying and crinkling of the seed coat. Mats are also usually held in readiness for spreading over the cocoa in case of rain.

A convenient arrangement for getting the trays under cover at night or during rain-showers is to have them fitted with wheels to run on rails, so that they can easily be pushed under a roof when necessary. Alternatively, a roof can be arranged so that it slides to-and-fro over the trays.

During the time the cocoa is drying it is continually picked over to remove foreign matter and immature and defective beans, and to separate beans which are sticking together.

The period of sun-drying may take from one to two weeks, depending on the weather. The depth of the beans on the drying-floor should not be such as to make the process of drying unduly protracted. A rough idea as to the drying-space required may be gained from the fact that 112 lb. of wet cocoa requires $5\frac{1}{2}$ square feet of drying-space. In humid climates it is desirable, at the start of the operation, to spread the beans in a thin layer on the drying-floor, and to increase the thickness as the cocoa becomes drier.

Where concrete floors are used for drying they are covered with mats to insulate the beans from the cement, and also to make for better drying. It is inevitable that in gathering up the cocoa from a concrete floor a certain amount of grit will be swept up also, and this in any form is extremely objectionable. Although machinery is used to extract foreign matter at an early stage in manufacture, there is the danger that some may be incorporated in a foodstuff and also that the machinery may suffer damage.

ARTIFICIAL DRYING

Where conditions are suitable, a combination of sun-drying and artificial drying may be applied. Most people favour at least one day of sun-drying before artificial drying begins.

This is the traditional view. Experiments have been conducted in recent years to investigate the effect of artificial drying on flavour, and they have shown that quick drying is not detrimental to quality.

Howat, Powell and Wood used a Chula drier in West Africa. This drier, normally used for copra, was adapted for cocoa by arranging a number of trays in the drying-chamber. Air heated by passing over flues and the outside of an oil-fired furnace was blown through the beans. In the experiments, the beans from one fermentation were divided into two parts, one part being dried in the sun, the other in the Chula drier. Hot-air temperatures up to 80° C. were used, and at this temperature the drying time was 15 hours. Subsequent tasting tests on chocolate made from the two lots of beans revealed no consistent differences.

Similar experiments in Surinam yielded the same results.

THE BÜTTNER DRIER

The firm of Huileries du Congo Belge, which is growing cocoa on a large scale in the Congo, has adopted the Büttner Drier as the standard plant for large-scale drying on their estates. It is manufactured by the firm of Büttner-Werk of Germany and is designed on the lines of similar plants for drying vegetables in temperate climates. It is also used for drying cocoa in São Tomé and in Fernando Po.

The main features of this plant are a vertical cylinder through which 298 trays, each about 39 inches square, are conveyed on an endless chain. The trays, bearing a layer of wet beans two inches thick, are carried from the lower level up an incline and fed into the top of the cylinder. They move gradually round and emerge at the bottom. Hot air is provided by steam-heated pipes and blown by a turbine situated centrally. The chamber enclosed by the cylinder is divided into three separate zones—top, middle and bottom—and the temperature can be adjusted separately. Thermometers are conveniently placed to indicate the temperature in each zone. A diesel engine provides the power for operating the turbine and the endless chain, and a wood-fired boiler generates the steam for heating the pipes.

The drier, with all trays fully charged, will hold 9 tons of wet beans and a period of 16 hours is required for drying. The plant is, of course, kept in continuous operation and the attendants work in shifts.

An attractive feature of this type of drier is the fact that it can be very economically operated. Two men loading and one man attending to the boiler are all the labour required. The occasional attention of an engineer is necessary to keep the plant in good working condition.

COCOA-DRYING ON THE LUKOLELA ESTATES

The Lukolela Estates in the Belgian Congo have arrangements for fermenting and drying which are interesting in that they represent the routine followed in a large and carefully supervised organization. The cocoa is an Amelonado type, and the drying process is partly sun-drying and partly artificial drying.

The drying-house is a long building at each end of which there is an outside furnace connected with lines of piping which run on floor level to a chimney at the opposite end. The obvious virtue of having two furnaces, one at each end of the building, is that it gives a better distribution of heat than where the furnace is at one end only.

Two sets of rails run from outside right across the full width of the inside of the building, each at different levels, the lower set being 5½ feet above the hot pipes. Each set of rails takes ten trays, and the drying-house can accommodate eighty trays at a time. There are air outlets on the ridge of the drying-house.

A drying-tray is 12½ ft. long by 8½ ft. wide and 8 in. deep, and the base consists of a wire mesh which prevents the beans from dropping through. For the first day of sun-drying, the wire base is covered with a mat so that the fresh cocoa does not come in contact with the metal, and by evening the mat is removed, as being no longer necessary.

The following are the consecutive steps taken in the processes of fermentation and drying at Lukolela. The pods are picked on Monday. On Tuesday they are broken and the beans carried to the fermentary. The fermenting-boxes are arranged in batteries of seven. The cocoa is fermented for about seven days, but remains for forty-eight hours in the first box. This provides a spare box for fresh cocoa on the following day and makes for more economical use of the equipment. The cocoa is put in the fermenting-box at 2 p.m. and after going through the usual treatment is removed at 6 a.m. on the following Tuesday. It is spread thickly on a large wooden tray, rubbed over to remove adhering matter, and then placed on the drying-tray in a layer 2 cms. deep.

By the second day of drying, the depth is increased to 4 cms., and on the third and last day to 8 cms. The cocoa is sun-dried in the daytime, as far as possible, and the trays are pushed into the drying-house at night.

The usual time taken at Lukolela, when it is possible to combine sun-drying and artificial drying, is three days. The plant is capable of turning out 10,000 lb. of dry cocoa per day.

The cocoa from Lukolela gets a premium for its good quality.

THE MARTIN DRIER

The Martin (hot-air) drier has also given good results. Three of these driers have been built on the New Zealand Reparation Estates in Western Samoa (see Fig. 3). The largest Martin drier has a drying-platform which measures 45 ft. by 25 ft. and can take a maximum load of 11,200 lb. of fermented cocoa spread out in a layer two

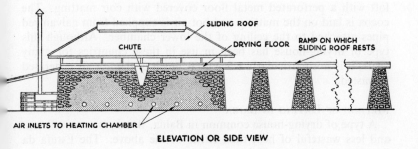

FIG. 3

THE MARTIN DRIER

inches deep. It takes twenty hours to dry the cocoa fully on the Martin drier, though it should be mentioned that on these estates the cocoa is washed before drying.

METHOD OF DRYING IN THE CAMEROONS

When the Germans held estates in the Cameroons, they installed drying-houses which contained a large oblong platform, usually covered with slates, with a furnace at one end and a chimney at the other. The floor is heated by an arrangement of flues which traverse the area under the floor between the furnace and the chimney. The wet cocoa beans are put directly on to the slates and have to be constantly pushed backwards and forwards to prevent them from being scorched on the hot floor.

METHOD OF DRYING IN CEYLON AND JAVA

The drying-house in most common use in Ceylon and Java has a loft with a perforated metal floor covered with coir matting. The cocoa is laid on the matting and hot air is supplied from galvanized pipes attached to the ceiling of the lower chamber. Although this type of drying-house has been in use in these countries for many years, it is not particularly efficient as much of the hot air generated is wasted.

METHOD OF DRYING IN BAHIA

A type of drying-house common in Bahia, Brazil, is more efficient and less wasteful of heat than either of the above. The Estufa da Balaco is an oblong building consisting of two chambers, divided by a partition through which three to six tiers of rails, one above the other, run the whole length of the building.

One chamber is heated by a large pipe or cylinder which is supported just above floor level, and traverses the bottom of the chamber in a " U " shape; there is a furnace at one end of the pipe and a chimney at the other.

The other chamber is used for loading and unloading the trays. Trays of 10 ft. square, or 10 ft. by 15 ft., with wire mesh or expanded metal bases, are loaded with cocoa in layers one to two inches deep and pushed through the oblong doors of the partition into the drying-chamber. The doors, being hinged on their upper edges, flap to the closed position on being released.

The temperature in the drying-chamber is regulated by controlling the fire and adjusting the flue which penetrates the wall just above ground level.

A drying-house of this type with two rows of five tiers of trays

. Tray with wire mesh base
ady for loading. The door
rough which the trays will
 pushed along the rails into
e drying chamber is in the
background, Bahia

67. This picture shows the
arrangements of rails
which pass through the
partition to carry the trays
into the drying chamber,
Bahia

68. One lot of trays with
wet cocoa is entering the
drier at the top, another
is emerging with dry cocoa
at the bottom

69. Drying-platform, w
sliding roof and drying tr
at two levels which can
slid under the drying p
form, Bahia

70. Raised drying floor with sliding
roof. The beans are gathered in rows
to allow the floor to be dried by the
sun; when the floor is dry the rows
will be split and the cocoa spread on
the dry surface

71. Prefabricated equipment for use
by African farmers, Ivory Coast

. Cocoa growing under
ade of mixed forest
trees in Ghana

. Exploitation of forest
d; maize being grown
after felling forest

74. Young cocoa on Vanua Levu, Fiji

75. A farmer among his young cocoa trees, Western Province, Ghana. The shade consists of plantains, cocoyams and some forest trees

76. A farmer unrolling his drying mats in the morning

would accommodate some 4,000 lb. of dry cocoa. If the cocoa had some preliminary drying on trays in the open, the process would be completed in the chamber in 24 hours.

An improved model of a drying-house of the above design has been built by the firm of Wildberger at Belmonte in Bahia. This house has a drying-chamber at each end, and a chamber in the middle where the trays from the drying-chamber at either end can be accommodated alternately for loading or unloading. The heat is regulated by controlling the furnace and adjusting a regulator in a flue at the top of the building.

THE SAMOAN DRIER

A cocoa drier which is particularly suited to the needs of small communities, smallholders or small estates, has been recently evolved as a result of some experimental work at Bournville. It has been named "The Samoan Drier," as it is modelled on a drier in use in Western Samoa. In the wet climate of the Southern Cameroons, where it has been extensively used, it has proved satisfactory.

Its advantages are that it can be built at low cost with materials which are usually obtainable even in remote areas; its construction, maintenance and operation require the minimum of skill; there is no danger of the beans being contaminated by smoke.

The drier consists of a metal flue with a chimney fitted at the end; a drying-platform is built over the flue, and the area between the platform and the flue enclosed by a wall to contain the hot air; a roof which is extended to provide space for fermenting-boxes and dry wood. It is convenient to build it on gently sloping ground to permit of easy drainage.

The flue can be made from six tar or oil drums, with bases and lids cut from all but one which is to be used next to the chimney. The ends of the drums are fitted one a few inches inside the other, and riveted. This operation can be rendered easier by making horizontal cuts in the edge of the drum which is to enclose the edge of the drum next to it, so that the edge can be prised inwards. A smoke-tight joint can be made by covering the junction of the drums with asbestos tape three to four inches wide, held in position by a four- to five-inches-wide iron-metal strip which is secured with angle iron and bolts. In the absence of a suitable iron-metal strip, the asbestos can be covered with a strip of aluminium sheet and held in position with two strands of wire. Aluminium strip and wire are more convenient to use where the drums are not quite circular, or are of slightly different diameters.

The flue constructed as above is laid in a three-feet-deep trench which has been lined with mud blocks, concrete or bricks. The floor of the trench is sloped gently upwards so that the chimney end is one foot higher than the end at which the fire will be applied. If the flue is raised slightly off the floor of the trench by resting it on concrete blocks its efficiency will be improved.

The chimney can be made from two galvanized iron or aluminium sheets, riveted end to end, and rolled into a cylinder, and a cowl fitted at one end. Alternatively it can be made of drums of suitable diameter, built into a cylinder in the same way as is described for the construction of the flue. It is important that the cross-sectional area of the chimney should not be less than one-tenth of the cross-sectional area of the flue. For example, where the flue is made from drums of 22 in. diameter, a chimney of 9 in. diameter will be satisfactory. A hole is cut in the end drum of the flue and the chimney is fitted into it and held in position with putty.

A drying-platform is built over the flue. A framework made from 4 in. by 2 in. timbers, supported on eight uprights, which can be extended to support the roof, is erected to support the platform 4 ft. above the flue at the firing end and about 3 ft. 6 in. at the chimney end. Cross-members of 3 in. by 2 in., spaced 15 in. apart, are fixed to the frame, which will carry the mats on which the cocoa beans will rest for drying. Mats, made from the main stem of palm fronds cut in strips and laced together with fibre, will provide a suitable surface on which to dry the cocoa. A drying-surface can be made from wooden laths laid side by side on the framework, but wooden laths contract with the heat and mucilage, and small beans get stuck between them. This does not happen to the same extent with mats, and they have the advantage that they can be easily removed and washed. If the strips of fronds are too widely spaced, two layers of mats can be laid on the framework and this will reduce to negligible amounts the material that will fall into the trench below.

The space between the flue and the drying-platform is enclosed by a wall, thus forming a chamber to contain the hot air. Asbestos sheet makes a good insulating wall. Other materials can be used, such as aluminium or corrugated iron sheets, and concrete or mud blocks or mud. It is desirable to have an easily-removed panel or door at the end of the wall to provide access to the chamber.

Roofing may consist of mats made from palm leaves or other material available locally, or aluminium or corrugated iron sheet. It is important to remember that inflammable roofing material and the woodwork of the building should be sufficiently far away from the chimney to ensure that there is no danger of fire. Where mats are used for roofing, the chimney can be passed through a sheet of aluminium or sheet iron fixed to the ridge of the roof. This will normally be extended to provide accommodation for fermenting-boxes and a supply of dry wood for fuel. It is desirable to store the dried cocoa in a separate building.

A piece of expanded metal, about 4 ft. long, is placed inside the first drum of the flue on which the logs for the fire rest. A sheet of asbestos or metal placed over the entrance to the flue can be used as a damper to control the rate of burning of the wood and regulate the temperature of the chamber. A temperature of between 60° C. and 70° C. makes for good drying conditions. Temperatures approaching 80° C. and upwards are liable to produce brittle beans. It is an advantage to have a thermometer fitted.

Wet cocoa is spread on the drying-platform to a depth of about 2 in. The beans are raked over from time to time to ensure evenness of drying. A drier of the above dimensions will turn out batches of 500 lb. to 600 lb. of dry cocoa, in 40 to 44 hours.

The trench in which the flue rests has to be swept after each lot of cocoa has been removed from the platform, as it is inevitable that a certain amount of dried pulp and broken beans will have fallen through the mats and will form combustible material.

The diagrams reproduced to illustrate the construction of the drier are those used for an experimental drier at Bournville, and the dimensions do not correspond in all respects with the one described above. They do, however, provide a guide for construction of driers of this type. It is probable that with further experience improvements will be effected in building driers of this kind.

MACHINES FOR DRYING COCOA

The most widely-used machines for drying cocoa are usually in the form of a revolving cylinder into which hot air is forced. Two well-known makes which work on this principle are the McKinnon and the Gordon.

Messrs. McKinnon, of Spring Gardens Iron Works, Aberdeen, give the following particulars of their machine:

Diameter and Length of Cylinder	ft.	7×6	6×6	6×4	5×4	5×3
Capacity of Wet Cocoa beans per charge	lb.	7,000	5,000	3,300	2,250	1,700
Power Required (Cylinder)	b.h.p.	2	1½	1¼	1	1
Power Required (Fan)	b.h.p.	3	2¼	1¾	1	¾
Gross Weight	cwt.	78	58	47	41	35
Shipping Weight freight tons		5·6	4·9	3·1	2·6	2·6
Oil Fuel Consumption	gal./hr.	2·1	1·6	1·1	0·75	0·58

Drier Dimensions	Loading Charge		Capacity per Compartment	
	cubic ft.	cubic decimetres (litres)	cubic ft.	cubic decimetres (litres)
7′ 0″ × 6′ 0″ (2134 × 1829 m/m)	176	4984	44	1246
6′ 0″ × 6′ 0″ (1829 × 1829 m/m)	124	3512	31	878
6′ 0″ × 4′ 0″ (1829 × 1219 m/m)	82	2320	20·5	580
5′ 0″ × 4′ 0″ (1524 × 1219 m/m)	56	1584	14	396
5′ 0″ × 3′ 0″ (1524 × 914 m/m)	42	1188	10·5	297

The time required for drying may be from 10 to 30 hours, depending on the amount of moisture in the beans at the time of loading. Freshly fermented beans must undergo several hours of drying before being placed in the drier as the mucilage on the beans would clog the air-holes in the cylinder. The usual procedure is to rake the beans on a drying-floor in the sun before putting them in the rotary drier.

The manufacturers stress the desirability of slow drying, as the beans become lustreless and brittle if they are dried too quickly. Instructions for getting the best results are issued with the machine by the makers.

TESTING FOR DRYNESS

A simple and practical method of testing for dryness is to take a handful of beans, press them hard, and if the shells crackle the sample is dry. A more accurate test is to cut through the bean with a knife, when it will be found that the cotyledons will separate easily if dry. A method much used by brokers is to press the bean end-wise on a hard surface. If the bean is well fermented and dry, it will crumble. The moisture content of dried cocoa should be about 6 per cent and should never be as high as 8 per cent.

Cocoa beans undergo a loss of between 55 per cent and 64 per cent in weight in the process of fermenting and drying.

When the beans vary considerably in size, grading into two or three sizes may be desirable. Where this has to be done on a large scale, power-driven mechanical graders are used.

POLYTHENE LINERS AND COCOA BAGS

It was shown many years ago by Dade that the critical moisture content of cocoa beans is about 8 per cent and that above this level moulds can develop. Cocoa beans are hygroscopic, and in an atmosphere whose relative humidity is in excess of 80 per cent their equilibrium moisture content is over 8 per cent.

In 1958 Dr. B. D. Powell and Mr. G. A. R. Wood conducted experiments in the Cameroons on the uptake of moisture and its prevention.

The climate in the southern Cameroons is very humid and the relative humidity inside a store was found to be on average over 82 per cent, and under these conditions the moisture content of cocoa rose from 4·5 per cent to 7·5 per cent in 30 days. To prevent moisture uptake, polythene liners inside the cocoa bags were used and the moisture content of beans in lined bags rose by only 0·3 per cent in 30 days.

The size of the liners was 30 inches by 60 inches, rather larger in size than the standard cocoa bag, the length being sufficient to make it possible to secure the mouth of the liner with string, or fold it over, before the top of the cocoa bag was sewn. The gauge of the polythene used was 150 and 300; the cost of these liners in the Cameroons was 10d. and 1s. 7d. respectively.

The moisture uptake with both gauges of polythene sheet was similar. The sheet in lined bags stood up to normal conditions of handling during loading and unloading. It is of course essential that the cocoa be thoroughly dry before it is placed in lined bags.

Polythene liners have been used for some time for the protection of foodstuffs such as coffee, tea, flour and other products where it is desirable to prevent the uptake of moisture. This method of keeping cocoa beans in good condition, and reducing the possibility of their becoming mouldy, promises to be of importance where cocoa has to be stored for any length of time under very humid conditions.

STORAGE

Cocoa readily absorbs flavours and aromas, so drying equipment used for other crops, such as copra, is to be avoided. When certain simple forms of driers are used it is essential that the smoke from the driers does not come in contact with the cocoa at any stage of the drying process. Similarly, during storage cocoa must be kept apart from other products the flavour of which it would readily absorb. If the floor on which the cocoa is to be stored is of concrete, wooden dunnage, six inches thick, should be used to insulate the cocoa from the floor.

The fermented, dried cocoa beans are the "raw cocoa" of commerce and are bagged and shipped in this condition for manufacture.

Most estates do not store their dry beans for any length of time but transport them for sale or shipment within a few weeks of drying.
The following are standard weights of full bags in certain countries :

		lb.
Ghana and Nigeria..	..	140
Bahia ..	..	132
Trinidad and Grenada	..	165 or 200
Ceylon, Java, and Samoa	..	112

REFERENCES

Allison, H. W. S., and Rohan, T. A. "A new approach to the fermentation of West African Amelonado cocoa." *Trop. Agric.* (Trinidad, 1938), **35**, 279.

Brown, H. B. "Changes observed in cocoa due to fermentation and their relation to the chocolate flavour." (Cocoa Conference, 1957, 165.)

Bridgland, L. A., and Friend, R. J. "Experiments and observations on cocoa fermentation in New Guinea." (Cocoa Conference, 1957, 177.)

Cadbury Bros. Ltd. *The Samoan Cocoa Drier.* 1957.

Campbell, L. E. "The aims of plant-breeding and the preparation and quality of cocoa." (Cocoa Conference, 1947.)

Eden, D. R., and Edwards, W. L. "Cocoa plantation management in Western Samoa." South Pacific Commission (1952).

Forsyth, W. G. C. "Purple beans." (Cocoa Conference, 1953, 32).

Forsyth, W. G. C., and Quesnel, V. C. "Cacao polyphenolic substances: (4) The anthocyanin pigments." *Biochem. J.* (1957), **65**, 177.

Forsyth, W. G. C. "Cacao polyphenolic substances: (1) Fractionation of the fresh bean; (2) Changes during fermentation; (3) Separation and estimation on paper chromatograms." *Biochem. J.* (1952), **51**, 511, 516. *Biochem. J.* (1955), **60**, 108.

Howat, G. R., Powell, B. D., and Wood, G. A. R. "Experiments on cocoa drying and fermentation in West Africa." *Trop. Agric.* (Trinidad, 1957), **34**, 249.

Howat, G. R. "Fermentation and Drying—Research in the Field." (Cocoa Conference, 1957, 190.)

Howat, G. R., Powell, B. D., and Wood, G. A. R. "Experiments on cocoa fermentation in West Africa." *J. Sci. Food Agric.* (1957), **8**, 65.

Knapp, A. W. *Cacao Fermentation* (John Bale, Sons and Curnow, London, 1937).

Koch, J. "Schokalade—Aroma und Geschmack." *Gordian* (1955), **55**, 17.

Montserin, B. G. "Processing of cacao for the market." *Bulletin Dep. Agric.* (Trinidad, 1952), 3.

Nierinckx, G., and Jennen, A. "Etude de la qualité du cacao." *Bull. Agric. Congo Belge* (1952), **43**, 273.

Palma, M. *The Processing of Fresh Cacao Seed.* (Rockwood and Co., New York, 1951).

Quesnel, V. C. "Curing cocoa in the laboratory." (Cocoa Conference, 1957, 150.)

Rohan, T. A. "Polyphenols and quality in West African Amelonado cocoa." (Cocoa Conference, 1957, 157.)

Rohan, T. A. "Observations on the fermentation of West African Amelonado cocoa." (Cocoa Conference, 1957, 203.)

Rombouts, J. E. "Observations on the microflora of fermenting cacao beans in Trinidad." *Proc. Soc. appl. Bact.* (1952), **15**, 103.

Rombouts, J. E. "Cacao yeasts." *Trop. Agric.* (Trinidad, 1953), **30**, 34.

Rombouts, J. E. "Cacao yeasts." *Trop. Agric.* (Trinidad, 1953), **30,** 34.

de Vos, L. "Artificial drying of cocoa." *Bull. No.* 73, *Landbw. Proefst.* Surinam. 1956.

Wadsworth, R. V. and Howat, G. R. "Cocoa fermentation." *Nature* (Lond.) (1954), **174,** 392.

Wadsworth, R. V. "The quality of raw cocoa as it affects the manufacturer." *Trop. Agric.* (Trinidad, 1955), **32,** 1.

Witt, K. W. de. "Studies on the small-scale fermentation of cacao. II. The conditions of fermentation." *Rept. Cacao Res.* (Trinidad, 1952), 56.

Wood, G. A. R. "Artificial drying of cocoa." (Cocoa Conference, 1957, 212.) See also Appendix V: Cocoa Fermentation.

77. Young clonal trees planted in gaps in a cocoa field to replace missing trees or poor bearers

78. Rehabilitation. Young trees growing under mixed shade

79. Marking out nursery for planting cocoa see␣

80. Cocoa nurseries in Ghana. Seedlings in baskets, shaded by a roof of spli␣ bamboo

Chapter

REHABILITATION OF THE COCOA
PLANTATION

*Aim of Rehabilitation and Processes Involved—Conditions
under which Rehabilitation would be Profitable—Comparison
of Rehabilitation with Replanting*

IN his studies of the cocoa industry in Trinidad, Professor C. Y. Shephard concluded that there was a strong case for extensive rehabilitation of many estates in that island.

He based his conclusion on the fact that although many planters would replace trees that had died, they would never cut out a tree that was a poor bearer and put a better one in its place. He pointed out that young cocoa trees, planted here and there throughout the estate to replace dead trees, did not grow well as the immediate environment was unsuitable for them. Although a tree on good soil may live for a hundred years or more, and give a good yield through-out that period, few live to that age, and the casualty rate is high under the old system of attention and management. Not more than 10 per cent of trees of the original planting would be found in a sixty-year-old plantation. A large proportion of trees had died off and were replaced by others that did not thrive, and of those that survived a proportion were poor specimens. Analysis of the crop-ping of fields of certain estates on good soils showed that 25 per cent of the cocoa trees gave 60 per cent of the total output. Similar analysis on poor soils showed that 25 per cent of the trees gave 80 per cent of the output. The replacements on the poor soils did not reach the level of yield of the original trees.

AIM OF REHABILITATION AND PROCESSES INVOLVED

Shephard says that the aims of rehabilitation should be to raise the average yield of the poor bearing area to that of the best. This would be done in two phases: first, by replacing the trees con-sidered incapable of earning a profit; secondly, by replacing the trees that give a lower yield than could be expected from the replacements.

L   145

FIRST YEAR

A plan of implementing a scheme of rehabilitation is outlined by Shephard on the following lines. The first phase would be spread over five years. In the first year the fields would be divided into convenient areas for treatment. After the main crop had set, the trees would be examined by walking along between the rows and marking those to be removed with a blaze one foot long at waist height. The planter would apply certain standards to guide him as to which trees to cut out and which to retain. The number of pods borne per tree and the pod value would be important criteria of the value of the tree. Trees showing particular susceptibility to disease and those badly damaged or otherwise unsatisfactory would be marked for removal.

SECOND YEAR

The second year would be devoted mainly to pruning all but the blazed trees in the dry season, and the planting of shade and windbreaks. This would enable the ground shade to develop sufficiently before the time came to plant the cocoa.

THIRD YEAR

During the wet season of the third year the drainage system of the field would be overhauled, casualties in shade and windbreaks would be replaced and the blazed trees cut out. Cocoa would be planted and fertilizers applied, and their use continued annually at the end of the dry season until the trees came into bearing.

FOURTH YEAR

The trees pruned in the previous season should receive further attention in the fourth year, chupons and surplus fans being removed, and the trees trimmed so that they acquire a satisfactory shape. Casualties among the cocoa plants and young plants which have made unsatisfactory growth should be replaced. After this year it will be uneconomic to replace casualties as their growth will be unsatisfactory. From this time onwards blank spaces resulting from the death of cocoa plants should be filled by planting ground shade and permanent shade.

FIFTH YEAR

By the fifth year of the first phase of rehabilitation the rooted cuttings will have been in the field for nearly two years and they should be pruned so as to leave three or four stems. Ringweeding of the young plants will precede general cutlassing of the weeds.

COMPLETION OF THE FIRST PHASE

The above would complete the first phase of rehabilitation of a particular field, and the assumption is that other fields on the estate in need of rehabilitation would be in their first to fourth year of treatment. There would be a temporary loss of yield in the fields under treatment due to the cutting-out of a certain number of trees and the setback which follows pruning. This loss would, however, soon be made up by the improved yield from the pruned trees and, in due course, from those planted during rehabilitation. Some revenue might be derived from temporary shade if this were composed of an economic crop.

SECOND PHASE AND FOLLOW-UP

Having completed the first phase of rehabilitation the planter should turn to the second phase which consists of going back to the first section of the field to be treated and repeating the process previously carried out. There will, of course, be much less to do during this phase, and when it is completed the yielding capacity of the field should be considerably increased.

The above is a resumé of what might be called the accepted, classical method of rehabilitation as evolved by Shephard, who contends that rehabilitation should not finish with the completion of the second phase but be a continuous routine practice. The amount of work to be done in successive cycles would be progressively less.

CONDITIONS UNDER WHICH REHABILITATION WOULD BE PROFITABLE

A field must be above a certain level of fertility if it is to be worth the cost of rehabilitation. The increased returns that would be derived from rehabilitating a field of mediocre fertility would not show a profit and might show a loss. Since Shephard first developed his theories about rehabilitation, they have been tested on plantations. Some of the most experienced and discerning planters incline to the belief that rehabilitation is only worth while where the bulk of the trees are in good condition and yielding well, and only a small proportion of the trees are missing or have to be cut out. Where a large proportion of the trees are missing or are due for replacement, it is much more economical and profitable to cut out all the trees and make the plantation anew.

MAINTAINING HIGH-YIELDING CAPACITY

Apart from any major operations of rehabilitation, the technique described above for the replacement of low-yielding trees could be applied with advantage to a cocoa plantation soon after it has come to the bearing stage. Removal and replacement of unsatisfactory trees could be continued as a routine throughout the history of the plantation.

COMPARISON OF REHABILITATION WITH REPLANTING

Dr. A. L. Jolly, lecturing at the Inter-American Institute of Sciences at Turrialba in 1956, pointed out that rehabilitation was invented by Shephard in the days when seedlings only were available, the technique for the raising of rooted cuttings not having been developed. Under this system of rehabilitation some 30–40 per cent of the sites, which included blank sites and sites of poor bearers, would be planted, the theoretical loss in yield being only 10 per cent. The planter would be able to retain his best trees, yielding anything from 75 to 90 per cent of the total yield, and concentrate on the remaining 30–40 per cent of the cocoa stands in the field. He would be able to lavish enough care on this area to ensure that the supplies would be well established. While this theory is attractive, experience has demonstrated that in practice it has drawbacks. It is difficult to get young plants to thrive in competition with and under the overshading effect of established cocoa trees. Reduction of the shading effect would mean mutilation of a number of the good standing trees and consequent reduction of their yield. There is also the difficulty of adjusting the temporary shade at frequent intervals around the young plant. Furthermore, as the supplies will be dispersed throughout the field, they will be expensive to supervise in relation to their numbers, and some may get overlooked. If bananas or other saleable crops are planted for temporary shade, harvesting will be expensive.

Where all the cocoa is cut out, the field should be prepared throughout in a uniform manner with temporary and permanent shade and windbreaks. The shade can be adjusted to the advantage of the young cocoa and for the suppression of weeds, a matter which is difficult and often impossible under rehabilitation. The growth of young cocoa trees is relatively uniform and the cost of supervision in relation to their number is much less than under rehabilitation.

The most important consideration in complete replanting is the higher cost. Although rehabilitation might be more expensive in relation to the area under treatment, only a portion of the field would be undergoing the early stages of treatment in any one year. In replanting there is complete loss of revenue from cocoa. In the days when even seedling cocoa was not selected with any great degree of skill, seedlings took ten years to reach a profitable yield and at least fifteen years to repay planting costs.

Under modern conditions, there are several factors which operate in favour of complete cutting out and replanting as opposed to rehabilitation. Good planting material comes into bearing and gives an economic yield at a much earlier stage than seedlings did in the past. Returns for capital invested are realized sooner and the capital can also be paid off at an earlier date. Although the costs are higher, the returns are greater on account of the higher price of cocoa. Jolly goes on to point out that the difference in capital requirement for replanting as compared with rehabilitation is not as great in practice as might be expected. A programme of replanting undertaken three years ago indicates that labour costs are 50 per cent higher than those of rehabilitation. He quotes a particular case of replanting where the yield of a temporary shade of bananas was quite profitable, the revenue being 315 Trinidad dollars per acre in the first four years. This represented 65 per cent of the gross planting costs of this particular field.

REFERENCES

Shephard, C. Y. "The Cacao Industry of Trinidad: Some Aspects. III. The Examination of the Effects of Soil Type and Age on Yield" (*I.C.T.A.*, Trinidad, 1937).

Chapter XII

PESTS AND DISEASES*

Means of Control Now Available—Pests of Major Importance: Capsids—Other Pests—Virus Diseases—Fungus and Other Diseases—Defoliation of Extremities—Deterioration of the Cotyledon—Epiphytes and Parasitic Plants—Spraying Methods and Formulations

MEANS OF CONTROL NOW AVAILABLE

COCOA and other tree crops grown on a large scale in the tropics are subject to a number of pests and diseases the incidence of which has at times given cause for alarm. It must, however, be strongly emphasized that cocoa is no more prone to these than are such crops as, for instance, rubber and tea. A large proportion of the rubber and tea plantations have been administered by progressive plantation companies who appreciated that these industries must be supported by adequate research. Cocoa, on the other hand, during its process of evolution from a stage of comparative insignificance to one of considerable importance in world economy, has been mainly a crop of the smallholder or peasant farmer. The inauguration of research to cater for the needs of cocoa and find the means of providing economic methods of combating the pests and diseases has been of comparatively recent development.

The tardy provision of research in West Africa, for example, was to a great extent responsible for the spread of virus, the devastation caused by capsids and the annual losses through black pod. Of recent years, however, the greater awareness of Departments of Agriculture, the assistance given by the specialist personnel of certain chemical manufacturers, and the provision of research have secured the industry against the troubles which threatened it from 1936 onwards.

The attention which has been focused on pests and diseases of cocoa from 1945 onwards, especially in West Africa, has created in some quarters the mistaken view that the industry in this part of the world is on the decline, might indeed be reduced within a short time

* It should be noted that of the diseases discussed in this chapter, only a few occur in any one country; only a very few are of economic importance in any country, and for these an effective means of control has been found.

to one of minor importance, and that major production of raw cocoa would once again be dependent on the Americas. How mistaken that view has been is demonstrated by the fact that every country in West Africa, from Sierra Leone to the Congo, has increased its capacity as a cocoa producer, and the average annual output during the next ten years will be greater than that during any decade since the crop was first introduced.

There is now a remedy which can be economically applied for every major pest and disease of cocoa. Under the conditions of care and management which a company would normally apply to its plantations, pest and disease control is a straightforward matter of routine; even virus disease, which has rightly been given so much prominence in the past, can be kept under control. Where cocoa is grown by a multitude of peasant owners, the process is less simple. The success of the measures to protect the trees is dependent on the efficiency and the energy with which Departments of Agriculture encourage the farmers to give the necessary attention to their cocoa farms.

Various methods are employed to bring pests and diseases under control or to mitigate their attack. Chemicals are mainly used in the form of liquid sprays, dusts and fumigants, and for painting on the trees. Biological control of certain pests of cocoa has been used with limited success.

PESTS OF MAJOR IMPORTANCE: CAPSIDS

Capsids are a pest of cocoa in West Africa, Java, Ceylon and New Guinea, and in South America.

Capsids in West Africa

The two species which cause most of the damage, *Sahlbergella singularis*, which is about half an inch long and speckled brown in colour, and *Distantiella theobroma*, which is the same size but considerably darker in colour, have caused great havoc in the past, particularly in Nigeria, Ghana and the Ivory Coast. In some other countries of West Africa they are not of serious importance.

The life histories of these two capsids are similar. The eggs are laid on twigs, pods, or pod-stalks, and are inserted inside the tissues. The wingless nymphs hatch out after 12 to 18 days, and the nymphal stage lasts for an average of 25 days, after which time the winged adult appears. The adult female begins laying eggs about a week later and continues to do so for the rest of her life, which may last for as long as six weeks.

Both nymphs and adults feed on cocoa, confining themselves to pods and young shoots and preferring pods to chupons and chupons to fans. Both species attack young plants and old trees, although *D. theobroma* prefers young seedlings and *S. singularis* is commoner on mature trees.

When feeding, the capsid thrusts its mouth-parts into the tissues of the plant. It then injects its poisonous saliva, which probably

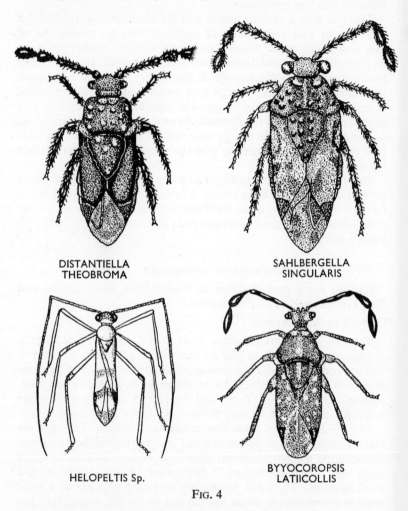

DISTANTIELLA
THEOBROMA

SAHLBERGELLA
SINGULARIS

HELOPELTIS Sp.

BYYOCOROPSIS
LATIICOLLIS

FIG. 4

FOUR SPECIES OF CAPSIDS WHICH ATTACK COCOA IN WEST AFRICA
The bottom left figure is magnified 3 times, the others are magnified 4 times.

81. Low-pressure spraying with Gammexane using Motoblo sprayer for control of capsids in Ghana

A young cocoa tree which has been severely damaged by capsids

83. Capsids on young green stem. The lower insect is an adult, the other two are nymphs. There are two capsid lesions on the stem

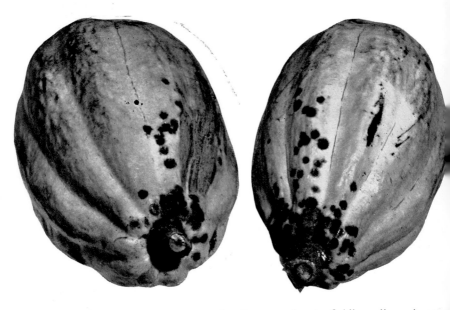

84. Capsid attack on cocoa pods. Damage due to *Sahlbergella* and *Distantiella*

85. Capsid attack on cocoa pods. Damage due to *Helopeltis*

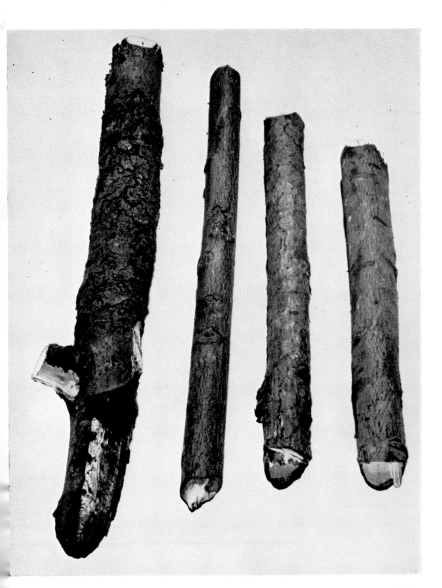

86. Stems damaged by capsids.
(*Left to right*): old cankered stem;
healed capsid lesions; "hammer
knock" condition due to feeding
by capsids; healthy stem

87. A branch from a cocoa tree
which has been attacked by capsids and subsequently invaded by
a fungus, as indicated by the dark
discoloration

88. Nest of Enxerto ant (*Azteca papaensis*), Bahia

89. Control of capsids, Congo. A hand-operated machine—
Le Mistral—which is used for dusting cocoa

assists in the extraction of the plant's sap. Each feeding-puncture, of which a capsid will make 24 to 36 in a day, becomes a dark brown or black spot, which frequently becomes infected with a fungus.

This fungus, *Calonectria rigidiuscula*, is often found in the region of capsid damage, and the view was held that attack was almost invariably consequent on the injury sustained by the tissues of the plant by capsids. Recent work by D. Kay casts doubt on this contention.

S. singularis is parasitized by a wasp-like insect, *Euphorus sahlbergella*. The degree of parasitism may rise as high as 30 per cent at certain times of the year, but this does not prevent the number of *S. singularis* from increasing. The parasite might effect better control if it were not itself parasitized. No parasite of *D. theobroma* has so far been found.

During the crop season when there are many pods on the trees, the capsids will feed on them and the pods become speckled with black spots. Pods, however, are rarely so seriously damaged that they have to be discarded.

The capsids increase in number during the harvesting period, after which they move to the canopy of the cocoa trees and feed on young shoots; this may result in widespread damage known as capsid "blast."

Capsid attack on young cocoa occurs when it is two to three feet high. The damage inflicted may kill off the young flushes, and subsequent flushes may be similarly injured; thus the development of the plant can be delayed by several years, or the plant may even be killed.

Unless measures are taken to suppress it, the insect will continue to attack the young flushes of the tree throughout its growth.

Capsid "pockets" occur where the fall of a forest tree has damaged the cocoa trees and these respond by producing young shoots which, in turn, are heavily attacked. The die-back so caused is followed by the growth of more young shoots which are in turn attacked. The cycle will continue until the trees are weakened and die out, but all the time more trees are being exposed to capsid attack, thereby enlarging the pocket.

INSECTICIDES USED WITH SUCCESS

The use of DDT, for painting the axils of the branches where the capsids were known to rest, gave satisfactory control with young cocoa. This method, apart from being laborious and expensive, could only be used on young trees while the branches were still within the reach of the operator. It has now been superseded by the use of sprayers which apply the insecticide either directly or as a fine mist, which can be projected to the tops of even quite high trees. Experiments were carried out with different types of insecticide, and a BHC in a purified form, known as "Gammalin" in the United Kingdom and as "Lindane" in the United States, gave very good results and could be mixed with water in a form which is convenient to apply. Further experiments with insecticides indicate that Aldrin may also be a useful spray against capsids.

In the past, the adoption of sprays on a grand scale for the control of capsids was impeded on account of the enormous quantities of water that would be involved. As supplies are not everywhere available where cocoa is grown, especially in the dry season, this difficulty presented what seemed to be an insuperable barrier. Even if there had been a satisfactory spray, the cost of transporting water over long distances would have rendered the treatment of cocoa in this way uneconomic. It was fortunate that the discovery of effective sprays was closely followed by the discovery of a new method of application, namely, Low Volume Spraying, which only requires a relatively small quantity of water. The insecticide applied by low volume sprayers is of course more concentrated, but the mixture is deposited on the plant in fine droplets. These evaporate quickly, leaving a solid deposit which does not injure the tissue of the tree.

Following on a good deal of experimental work, Ghana adopted two types of machine for spraying. The first is hand-operated, fitted with a lance and trigger control by which the application of the spray is regulated. The cost is within the reach of the farmer of modest means and can be employed in treating young cocoa and also mature cocoa where the capsid attack is not extensive. For large-scale spraying, a power-driven machine is used. A small two-stroke engine, using petrol fuel, supplies the power to drive a fan which impels air at high velocity through the tube or lance. The insecticide mixture emerges through a nozzle designed to convert it into a fine mist. Machines of this type, operated by a gang of labourers trained for the work, can treat from thirty to fifty acres in a day. The area covered is mainly dependent on having a water supply within convenient reach. In practice, two operators are employed for each of the five machines, in order that the operator is relieved after each round of spraying. An extra machine with one operator is usually kept in reserve to take the place of a machine which may go out of action. The gang walks in line through the cocoa farm, each operator eight paces from the other. Ghana is spraying some 700,000 acres of mature cocoa badly damaged by capsids. This area will be given two sprayings, the second being applied four weeks after the first. The treatment will be applied twice a year. Previous trials indicate that it will give general control.

STANDARDS ADOPTED IN GHANA FOR CAPSID CONTROL

Based on experience of considerable experimental work, including spraying on a field scale, the Department of Agriculture in Ghana has now adopted the following as standard practice:

Low volume spraying with Motoblo is done during the months of June and July at intervals of four weeks. The concentration for the first spraying is one pint of Gammalin 20 (that is 4 oz. of Gamma BHC toxicant) in five gallons of water per acre. In the second spraying only half a pint of Gammalin 20 (that is 2 oz. of Gamma BHC toxicant) in five gallons of water per acre is used. A similar treatment is given during November and December. Where there is a high proportion of large trees, the amount of mixture applied may have to be increased to 10 gallons per acre.

In the case of high-volume spraying where the farmer is using the Mysto sprayer, 112 c.c. of Gammalin 20 is used in one gallon of water for the first spraying, and 28 c.c. per gallon of water in the second spraying.

There is no evidence that spraying in these quantities interferes with the process of pollination.

SPRAYING-MACHINES

Of the number of hand-operated machines in West Africa, the Mysto pneumatic sprayer is the most widely used. The container, which is made in cylinder or knapsack form, is of brass sheet and electrically welded. Both forms are fitted for shoulder straps. It is manufactured by Messrs. W. T. French and Son, Limited, Mysto Works, Browning Street, Birmingham.

A machine which has been tested and found satisfactory in the West African Cocoa Research Institute is the Leo-Colibri No. 8. This is a pressure-retaining pneumatic knapsack sprayer fitted with a 13-ft. bamboo lance. With high working pressure—up to 110 lb. per square inch—and low-volume nozzle, the insecticide is applied as a fine mist which drifts through the canopy.

The Motoblo mist sprayer is a motorized machine, shoulder-mounted, with a two-stroke motor. It weighs 31 lb. when empty, and the lance can be fitted with a variety of diffusing heads. This appliance may be used for high- or low-volume spraying, and is an adaptation of a machine widely used for spraying vines on the

Continent. It is manufactured in the United Kingdom by the Kent Engineering and Foundry Limited, Tovil, Kent, and is the machine adopted by the Department of Agriculture in Ghana for low-volume spraying of capsids on a large scale.

M. de Bellfroid, owner of the Lukolela Estates in the Congo, succeeded in keeping capsids under control with the use of the Mistral Duster. This consisted of small hand-operated bellows fitted with a tin container for the insecticide, and a two-and-a-half-foot long delivery tube. One of the insecticides which gave good results with this duster was "Solvexane," which contains 2·2 per cent gamma isomer of benzene hexachloride, about half a pound being used per acre per month. The labour costs in keeping capsids under control by this method at Lukolela are quite low.

Capsids in Other Countries

Comparatively recently, a capsid species, *Bryocoropsis laticollis*, has been found on cocoa. In Ghana it was first recorded in 1939. In Nigeria the same species has been seen on plants other than cocoa; it appears to be moving from its original host to cocoa and may become a major pest. At present it is relatively harmless, the damage being almost entirely confined to the pods.

Species of *Helopeltis* are about the same size as the other capsids, but have a slender yellowish body and long thin antennae and legs.

Members of this genus are found on a variety of plants throughout West and Central Africa. On cocoa, *Helopeltis* feeds almost exclusively on the pods and a heavy attack on young pods may prevent their maturing. The feeding-punctures on older pods cause little direct damage, but may lead to subsequent attack by fungi.

Various *Helopeltis* species cause much damage in Java and Ceylon. They attack pods, shoots, and leaf-stalks. Young pods may be badly damaged if heavily attacked, and young shoots may be killed.

The numbers of the insect vary considerably with the season, being very numerous in the wet season and almost negligible in the dry.

In New Guinea cocoa was first planted at least fifty years ago but capsid damage was not experienced until 1949. The species found in the territory of New Guinea belong to the genera *Parabryocoropsis* and *Pseudodoniella*. They primarily attack pods and, as these insects are much more plentiful than they are in West Africa, the amount of mechanical damage is considerable. This is greatly increased by the entry of other insects into the capsid lesions, and, what is of greater importance, by the entry of a fungus, *Gloeosporium* species.

This causes most damage during the wet season when the main crop is on the trees.

In some districts of Ecuador a capsid, which is known locally as "mosquilla," causes serious damage to pods. Two species, *Monalonion atratum* and *M. dissimulatum*, are found.

Another species of the same genus (*M. xanthophilum*) attacks cocoa in Brazil, where the local name for it is "chupança do cacáu."

Control methods are as described for West Africa.

OTHER PESTS

THRIPS

This small insect (*Selenothrips rubrocinctus*) is a serious pest of cocoa in the West Indies, São Tomé, and certain South American countries. It also occurs in West Africa and has been reported from New Guinea, but it rarely causes serious damage in either of these countries.

FIG. 5
SELENOTHRIPS
RUBROCINCTUS
Greatly magnified

The cocoa thrips is small, only 1–1½ mm. long. The adults are black, but the nymphs are yellow with a red band across the base of the abdomen.

Thrips live on a wide range of host plants, being very common on cashew trees. On cocoa trees they live on the underside of the leaves where their eggs are laid and where large colonies of nymphs are to be found. They pierce the leaf-cells and suck the sap; this damages the outer layer of the leaf, which becomes silvered. R. G. Fennah writes: "The nymphs carry the abdomen curved upward, with a drop of clear fluid poised on the hairs at its apex. This is periodically released and drops on the leaf surface where it dries to form a brownish spot. The speckling caused by the presence of many such dots on the partially dried or silvered tissue is characteristic of thrips injury."

The damaged leaves will die if the attack is severe, and trees may be defoliated. A severely attacked tree will respond by flushing and the young flushes may in turn be attacked. Repeated attacks may kill a tree.

In Surinam, attacks by thrips were followed by damage by a fungus (*Diplodia*), which the weakened trees were unable to resist.

Pods are also attacked. They are not damaged, but become discoloured, turning a dirty brown colour, which makes it difficult to determine when the pods are ripe.

Unhealthy trees suffer most from thrips attack. It was found in Trinidad that severe attacks were associated with rapid falls in soil moisture content, coupled with high atmospheric humidity; the severity of the damage was enhanced by the low potash status of the soil. Over-exposure to wind or sun has been thought to be an important cause of thrips attack, and some fields of the clone I.C.S. 1 which were planted without shade have suffered severely from thrips.

It might be expected that thrips would be prevalent in West Africa, but they are not common. This may be due to the fact that the numbers of the insect are kept in check by the hymenopterous parasite, *Dasyscapus parvipennis*. At times the proportion of parasitized thrips has reached 80 per cent. This insect was introduced into Trinidad in the hope that it would control thrips there but it has not become established.

Severe outbreaks of thrips can be controlled by spraying with nicotine. Bordeaux mixture, when sprayed on to the leaves, acts as a repellent but does not kill the insects.

In many outbreaks certain trees escape damage and appear to be resistant to thrips. Search for resistant trees was undertaken in Trinidad and a tree known as RT 18, which is also a good commercial type, was selected. This selection was included in a clonal trial at River Estate, but it did not yield well under the conditions there.

ANTS

One of the worst pests of cocoa in Brazil is the "enxerto" ant (*Azteca paraensis* var. *bondari*), which has become a serious menace during the past twenty-five years.

It makes its nest in the epiphytes on the cocoa trees, the pods and shoots of which it gnaws to provide further nest-material. This in itself causes some damage to the trees, but the ants also protect mealybugs (*Pseudococcus citri*) and scale insects, which suck sap from the trees and weaken them.

The epiphytes, too, cause harm by interfering with the flowering of the trees. Individually, the epiphytes, ants, and mealybugs would do little damage to the cocoa trees, but in association with one another they create a serious problem.

Another species of ant (*Azteca chartifex*), almost equally important, also protects aphids, scales, and mealybugs, and makes nests out of material from pods and shoots. Two others, *Crematogaster* sp. and *Solenopsis* sp., the fire ant, cause similar damage and attend similar insects. The last-named has a very painful sting which causes difficulties in harvesting. It is reported that these ants can be controlled by spraying with gammexane.

In other parts of South America and the West Indies damage by ants is localized and sporadic, the "parasol" ants (*Atta cephalotes*) being the most serious. They make very large nests to which they carry large quantities of leaves and small branches. They can be destroyed by pouring carbon bisulphide or a 2 per cent solution of chlordane down the holes of the nests; carbon bisulphide acts as a fumigant, but is highly inflammable.

MEALYBUGS, APHIDS, AND SCALE INSECTS

Apart from their importance as vectors of virus diseases of cocoa, mealybugs are occasionally found in large enough numbers to become a primary pest. Aphids and scale insects have also been reported as troublesome. These insects suck the sap from the tree, and may cause a considerable drain on it when they occur in large numbers.

In Ghana the aphid *Toxoptera coffeae* is sometimes troublesome. This small insect is dark brown to black in colour and attacks young shoots and leaves. The leaves become curled and later they may harden and fall off. The aphids are attended by small black ants, *Pheidole* sp., and others. Control measures are rarely necessary.

In Fiji aphids (*Aphis gossypii*) are normally found on young shoots and leaves. Mealybugs (*Pseudococcus citri*) attack young pods also and may cause withering of the pod, malformation, or delayed ripening.

LEAF-EATING BEETLES

Beetles belonging to the families Chrysomelidae and Scarabeidae cause serious damage to young plants in some countries.

The genus *Adoretus* occurs in West Africa, Java, Ceylon, Fiji, and Samoa. These beetles feed on young flushes during the night, making numerous holes in the leaves, thereby checking growth.

In Samoa young plants are protected by a ring of stones built around them up to a height of one foot or more, but beetle attack occurs as soon as the plants emerge above the stones.

In some countries leaf-eating beetles appear suddenly and cause serious damage. Spraying the young plants with DDT emulsion or lead arsenate will control them, but it must be done as soon as the first damage is detected.

MOTHS

Several moths attack the leaves and shoots of cocoa trees.

In New Guinea a moth, *Pansepta teleturga*, has recently been found attacking cocoa. The larvae feed under a webbing of frass and consume large areas of bark; this may lead to the death of the branches and even of whole trees when colonies of larvae are at work. No method of control has been evolved.

In Fiji and the New Hebrides the caterpillars of the moth *Adoxophyes fasciculana* attack the leaves, and in Ghana and Nigeria a small green Tineid moth, *Earias biplaga*, attacks leaf buds and young leaves, and has damaged chupons from coppiced stumps.

Cocoa Moth

This moth (*Acrocercops cramerella*) is a major pest in Java. The eggs are usually laid in the furrows of the pods and, after hatching out, the larvae burrow through the pod wall and live in the pod, making tunnels in the pulp. Although they do not attack the beans, both the yield and the quality of the cocoa are reduced.

Only one method of control has been successful. Complete removal of all pods, ripe and unripe, once a year, thereby breaking the life-cycle, has provided a certain degree of control, but the moth has alternative hosts, such as the cola tree (*Cola acuminata*) and the numbers of the moth build up again after a few months.

This moth also occurs in Dutch New Guinea. In both countries it has been observed that smooth-podded Amelonado trees are less susceptible to attack.

Cocoa Pod Borer

This small Noctuid moth (*Characoma stictograpta*) is found in Ghana, where it is a minor pest. It flies at night and lays its eggs at the stalk end of the pod. The larvae tunnel in the pod and produce a brown sticky mass of frass between the pod and the trunk. The damage is not serious but the wound provides an entry for fungi.

Longicorn Beetles

These fairly large beetles belong to the family Cerambycidae, members of which are to be found in most cocoa-growing countries, where they are pests of varying importance. Where they cause considerable damage control measures can be taken. The life histories of these species of beetles, and the damage caused by them, are similar, so one of them is dealt with in detail and the distinctive features of others will be described.

Cocoa Beetle

This fairly large Longicorn beetle (*Steirastoma breve*) causes considerable damage to cocoa plantations in Trinidad, Grenada, and some South American countries.

The adult beetles are black, nearly one inch in length, and have two long antennae.

The adult female makes holes in the bark in which she lays her eggs, and then seals the holes. After hatching, the larvae feed under the bark, making tunnels in the wood. They feed for two or three months before pupating, and in that time the tunnels may go right round a branch, thereby ring-barking it. As the eggs are often laid near the fork of a tree and sometimes on the main stem, serious damage may result.

FIG. 6
STEIRASTOMA BREVE
Slightly magnified

Young trees, especially those between three and five years old, suffer most from beetle damage, though trees vary considerably in the extent to which they are attacked. Beetle damage was surveyed at River Estate, where it was found that certain clones suffered much less damage than others.

The adult beetles gnaw the bark of the young branches. Normally this causes purely superficial damage and it is unusual for it to be deep enough to be serious. The control measure most commonly employed is to collect the adult beetles by hand. They are fairly easily caught and large numbers may be destroyed, but it is doubtful whether the method provides effective control.

The beetle has a number of other host plants, some of them related to cocoa. This fact was made use of twenty or thirty years ago when it was the practice to lay traps—branches of other host plants—in which the beetle was expected to lay its eggs. These were usually placed close to the cocoa trees and were collected at intervals and burnt. This practice died out during the years of depression and has not been revived.

Parasites and predators exist but they appear to have little effect on the beetle population.

Spraying with lead arsenate is probably the best method of control. This can be confined to those parts of the young trees, such as the main stem and large branches, that are most likely to be affected.

OTHER LONGICORN BEETLES

In Java the beetle *Glenea novemguttata* is a serious pest. It is about half an inch in length and causes the same type of damage as has been described above.

Another member of the same genus, *G. aluensis*, has been reported

M

from New Guinea. It became troublesome after the last war owing to the neglect of plantations, but it appears to be a less serious pest now that the plantations have returned to a normal degree of cleanliness.

Various members of the genus *Monohammus* occur in New Guinea, where they are minor pests. In New Hebrides *M. holotephrus* attacks the trunks and large branches of the tree and therefore causes more serious damage.

Various Longicorn beetles have been found on cocoa in West Africa. Members of the genera *Tragocephala*, *Mallodon*, and *Glenea* occur in Ghana, but all are minor pests.

WEEVIL BORER

This insect (*Pantorhytes plutus*) ranks as a major pest of cocoa in New Guinea. During its larval and adult life, which extends over two years, it bores into the wood and causes extensive damage. The adults also cause considerable damage by chewing the soft bark of young shoots.

TERMITES

Termites have been reported as a minor pest in West Africa, Ceylon, Java, Samoa, New Guinea, New Hebrides, and Grenada.

Termites normally attack dead wood. They enter cocoa trees through wounds and will follow up damage caused by other insects or fungi. Considerable damage by termites has been reported from the New Hebrides where it prevents the healing of wounds, which consequently become enlarged. The trees may even be killed.

Attack by termites can be minimized by the removal of dead wood, by avoiding damage by machetes, by the killing of the queen in the termite nests by fumigants, and by maintaining control of other pests and diseases; in other words, by good estate sanitation.

FOREST FAUNA

Animals and birds can constitute a major menace to a cocoa industry, and they can be particularly troublesome where the crop is introduced for the first time, or the area planted is small in relation to the population of the cocoa-loving fauna. When a crop, palatable to animals or birds, is introduced to a country, it is inevitable that it will be heavily attacked until such time as the fauna is reduced or the amount of the crop grown is so extensive that the depredations of these pests are no longer of economic importance.

In certain districts of Sierra Leone the monkey population has increased to the detriment of the cocoa industry. Conditions which have given rise to this situation are: the killing-off of leopards which are their natural enemies, the fact that monkeys are not generally killed for food, and that there is a high proportion of fruit-bearing secondary forest providing food for them. Organized drives killed upwards of 14,000 monkeys in six days in one district. In the absence of periodic drives to reduce the monkey population, cocoa-planting there would be uneconomic. Rats and squirrels are a peren-nial trouble to cocoa. They are usually the most serious menace where it is first introduced to an area, and they are a constant trouble even where it has been grown for many years. On the occasion of a severe and prolonged drought which resulted in a short-age of food crops in the cocoa zone of Bahia, rats consumed large quantities of cocoa pods. Their numbers were reduced by destroying their nests which were generally in trees. Rats and squirrels are des-tructive to the mid-crop in West Africa as there are few alternative crops available at this time. In addition to eating the cocoa on the trees they also remove the seed planted in the cocoa farms to such an extent that it is general practice to plant seedlings earlier in the season and postpone the planting of seed until September, when the supply of alternative food is plentiful. Parrots are usually the most troublesome birds; woodpeckers can also cause a great deal of damage. Apart from direct losses caused by forest fauna in eating the crop, much indirect harm can be done by damaging the cocoa pods and making them vulnerable to fungus attack. As regards the smaller animals and birds, shooting, trapping, snaring and poison-ing are the main ways of keeping down their numbers.

VIRUS DISEASES

There are a number of virus diseases of cocoa, among them those in the "swollen shoot" group of West Africa which have been of major concern because of their destructiveness. Similar, or possibly identical, diseases have been described from Trinidad and Ceylon. All these viruses show leaf pattern symptoms of various types at some stage, but these symptoms may be evanescent and sometimes difficult to detect. The swollen shoot symptom, which is shown by only some of the virus types, is characteristic. None of these viruses is sap-transmissible, but all can be transmitted by grafting or bud-ding. The vectors chiefly concerned are mealybugs, principally *Pseudococcus njalensis* Laing, *P. citri* Risso and *Ferrisia virgata* Ckll., but some of the viruses are transmitted by *Paraputo ritchei* Laing and various species of *Pseudococcus*. All types of virus seem to have long latent periods in adult trees which in some cases may extend to two years. This can complicate control methods. A number of alternate hosts of the West African viruses are known, chiefly members of the families *Bombacaceae* and *Sterculiaceae*, of which a number are wild in West Africa. Some of the mild strains of virus can protect against some of the severe and lethal types.

Control measures have been directed along three main lines— eliminating infected trees and with them the reservoir of virus; eliminating or severely limiting the vectors; conferring immunity by breeding or by cross-inoculation.

Control by removal of infected trees, with or without their contacts which may carry the virus in latent form, led in West Africa to very extensive and elaborate surveys of the swollen shoot group of viruses, campaigns for the cutting out of trees and payment of compensation to the cocoa farmers. This control campaign, effective where the percentage of trees infected was not too high, has been a major effort on the part of the Governments of Ghana and Nigeria, both of which have expended very large sums of money annually for this purpose. That the worst forms of this disease have been contained there can be no doubt, though very heavily infected areas could not be saved from devastation. Cutting out of living trees, often still bearing a few pods, could not be other than unpopular with farmers, and it speaks much for the goodwill of the Departments concerned, and for the good sense of the majority of cocoa farmers, that so little opposition to this method of control has been experienced.

Indirect control of the insect vectors has been attempted, but has not developed very far. The mealybugs are subject to attack by a number of parasites, but these are generally not very effective. Attempts at biological control by the introduction of parasites from outside West Africa have been unsuccessful. It may be noted that a virus vector which is not a pest in its own right, to be effective in virus control requires almost complete elimination of the vector since any one individual may effect a transmission. Insecticidal methods can be used on an experimental scale, but are uneconomic for commercial use. Systemic insecticides can be used, but again present serious disadvantages on grounds of cost and toxic hazards. An indirect or third stage method of virus control may develop through control of the ants attendant on the mealybugs and without which they cannot survive. These ants, mostly species of *Crematogaster*, can be controlled by formicides such as dieldrin, and there is a possibility that control by such means may have success. It would, however, have to be used as an adjunct to cutting out of diseased trees for which there is no known cure.

Control by developing immunity or tolerance of the virus in the cocoa tree has been attempted. So far little tolerance has been discerned in any cocoa variety, though there are some distinct differences. These are, however, not large enough to be useful. The creation of artificial tolerance by inoculation with mild types of virus is possible for some of the viruses, but there is a danger that if such a method were used on a large scale a huge reservoir of virulent virus might build up in the cocoa tree, with a risk of subsequent breakdown of the immunity and loss of the trees.

The magnitude of the problem of control of swollen shoot diseases in West Africa can be gauged from figures for Ghana alone, where between 1946 and 1957 a total of some 63 million diseased cocoa trees were removed. To discover these trees on scattered farms in the forest entailed mapping some 124,000 farms and cost, in compensation to farmers alone, over £7,000,000. In Nigeria similar efforts were made, though in general the disease appears to have been less destructive than it has been in Ghana.

FUNGUS AND OTHER DISEASES

Phytophthora palmivora

This and similar fungi cause Black pod (known as Brown pod in Brazil) and can affect the pod, stem and leaves. It occurs to a greater or lesser degree in almost every country where cocoa is grown. The aggregate loss of cocoa due to this disease over a number of years amounts to many thousands of tons. The incidence of the disease varies with the rainfall and the rainfall distribution, and with humidity and temperature, being on the whole higher in countries of greater rainfall. It can be particularly troublesome where cocoa is growing at high altitudes which are subject to prolonged mists during the cropping season.

These fungi attack several other tropical crops, including rubber, coconuts, cotton and citrus.

Pod rot is by far the most important damage caused by *Phytophthora palmivora*, but in some countries the fungus also causes a canker and a chupon wilt. It attacks pods of all ages. In Costa Rica the fungus causes a considerable loss of young cherelles. It will destroy the beans in young pods, but in the case of slight attacks on ripe pods, some of the beans may be saved by frequent harvesting.

The first symptom of black pod infection is a brown spot which appears about five days after infection. This spot rapidly enlarges and darkens until the whole pod is invaded and blackened. Two days after the appearance of the first symptoms, a white web of mycelium and conidia is formed on the surface of the pod, the conidia or spores being the main source of infection. The pod continues to produce spores for about ten days, after which time it will have been invaded by several other fungi which will suppress the *Phytophthora*.

The spores produced on the surface of the pod are spread by raindrops, insects and, possibly, by air currents. Rain falling on an infected pod will carry spores to healthy pods lower down the trunk, and neighbouring pods may be infected. Many types of insects carry spores, spreading the disease from pod to pod and from tree to tree.

The spores germinate when the relative humidity is high. In Costa Rica it has been claimed that free moisture is essential for germination, but in Nigeria it was found that germination takes place when the relative humidity is 95 per cent or more. In Brazil the incidence of attack increases rapidly when the temperature drops as low as 15° C., a temperature which favours persistence of moisture on the pod.

Dade showed that the spread of the disease depends mainly on the relative humidity of the atmosphere. In the cocoa areas of Ghana the relative humidity is high at night, being around 95 to 100 per cent, but during the day there is considerable variation. The disease spreads most rapidly when the relative humidity remains high both day and night. Although the fungus can infect healthy pods, injured pods are attacked more easily and invaded more readily. Prolonged periods of high humidity are liable to cause infection of healthy pods.

Pod infections are often associated with some predisposing factor. Dade analysed the infections on a number of trial plots and found that 5 per cent were due to contact with a diseased pod; a similar percentage followed injury to the pod, and a variable percentage— 5 to 27 per cent—was due to drip; the remainder had no predisposing factor. Most of the injuries were caused by insects, although some were due to knife cuts. Insect injuries were much more numerous in the drier situations, so that infection due to injury was more important where humidity was lower.

Diseased pods on the trees are undoubtedly the main source of infection of other pods, but there is some doubt as to the amount of infection caused by diseased pods or old husks on the ground.

After the fungus has completely invaded the pod it may infect the flower cushion. This may lead to the formation of a local canker in the cushion, which may infect the pods in the next crop.

The canker caused by *P. palmivora* varies in incidence. In many important cocoa-growing countries it is insignificant, but in Trinidad and Ceylon it has caused considerable damage and sometimes has proved fatal to the trees. Damage is also reported from the New Hebrides and Western Samoa. A canker appears as a moist spot on the bark of the stem or on a main branch, and it becomes enlarged to form a dark area which exudes a reddish liquid. The extent of the canker can be seen by removing the bark, whereupon the dark affected part is visible.

The effect of a canker varies greatly from tree to tree. It may develop and spread to such an extent that the tree is killed; on the other hand, the tree may recover, sealing off the canker with a layer of callus. In those countries where there is a dry season of several months, the trees make their best progress towards recovery during the dry months.

Criollo trees are more susceptible to canker than Forastero, hybrids being intermediate in this respect and variable in their susceptibility. As the proportion of Criollo and hybrid trees has decreased in certain countries, the importance of this disease has declined considerably. Cankers rarely, if ever, form spores, so they must originate from infected pods, possibly by way of the pod stalk and flower cushion.

The chupon wilt caused by *P. palmivora* is relatively unimportant, occurring only in Central America where it does little damage.

The value of copper sprays for black pod control has long been known. Its recent wide adoption for the control of black pod fungus in West Africa is largely the result of efforts by the Departments of Agriculture and Plant Protection Limited. The problem of finding a suitable portable machine for spraying or dusting was common to both capsid and fungus control. The machines described for use on capsids can, after adjustment, also be used for the treatment of this fungus.

Carbide Bordeaux is still the spray in most common use. In the wetter parts of the Nigerian cocoa zones and in the Cameroons there is a high incidence of black pod. A 1 per cent Bordeaux mixture (1 lb. copper sulphate, 6 oz. calcium carbide, 10 gallons water) applied once a month for eight months has given a good measure of control in both Nigeria and the Cameroons.

Field trials with 0·1 per cent Perenox applied at monthly intervals, and 1 per cent Bordeaux similarly applied, indicated that the latter was more effective.

In low-volume spraying, Perenox is a good substitute for Bordeaux mixture. In an experiment carried out by the Cameroons Development Corporation in conjunction with Plant Protection Limited, an area of cocoa was treated at the rate of $2\frac{1}{2}$ lb. Perenox in 15 gallons of water per acre per application. The sprayer used was a Kiekens-Dekker-TT-mist-blower. It was pulled by a 4½ h.p. tractor. The disease control was satisfactory.

There are heavy losses from black pod in certain parts of Ghana, although the incidence is not as high as in parts of Nigeria and in the Cameroons. The fungus in Ghana has not responded so readily to the treatments which were successful elsewhere in West Africa. Partial control has been achieved but the results are much less spectacular than those obtained in Ondo, in Nigeria, for instance. W.A.C.R.I., in collaboration with the Ghana Department of Agriculture, continues to experiment with different treatments.

Western Samoa suffers from a high incidence of *Phytophthora* fungus attack on the cocoa crops, and canker of the trees is common. Experimental work carried out in 1954–5 by Harvey C. Smith, mycologist, Department of Scientific and Industrial Research, New Zealand, indicated that control was profitable during the months of heavy cropping. A Friend, 40-gallon, high-volume machine was used and two different sprays were tried, Bordeaux (3–4–50) and Phygon (½–50). The insecticides were applied every three weeks. Good results were obtained, Bordeaux being slightly more effective than Phygon. Further trials in which knapsack (hand-pump operated) and mist-blower (power-operated) machines were used for the application of Bordeaux (3–4–50) mixture at intervals of three weeks gave effective control.

There always have been, and probably always will be, two schools of thought about the best means of controlling *Phytophthora* fungus which attacks the pod. Well-managed estates in Bahia, Brazil, have demonstrated that the incidence of fungus on the pods can be reduced to negligible proportions by careful harvesting and removal of all black pods as soon as the presence of the fungus can be recognized. Weekly harvesting can go a long way towards the reduction of black pods. A high level of control can be attained by a combination of weekly harvesting and spraying. The use of sprays does, of course, lessen the need for very frequent harvesting. It is reasonable to expect that as a measure of control is attained, the number of sprayings can be reduced. In Fernando Po, where spraying with 2 per cent Bordeaux mixture has been normal practice for 24 years, sprayings are limited to three or four a season, depending on the weather. Some trees have shown considerable resistance to attack on the pod and some have shown resistance to attack on the stem or branches. Western Samoa, which has already one very resistant tree, has now set out to select trees showing resistance in both respects. There is little doubt that a careful survey of any large

Cocoa pods affected by black pod. The pod on the left has been affected in two places. The right-hand pod has been completely invaded by fungus

Thread blight. The mycelium of the fungus can be seen on the stem and the back one leaf (M), several dead leaves, typically bicoloured (D), and one hanging by a thread (T)

92. Cocoa pods suffering from *Monilia* disease

93. Witches' broom disease. A lateral fan broom

94. Witches' broom disease. An indurated pod. The black portion is hard and the beans will probably be destroyed

95. Leaf symptoms of swollen shoot

Vein-banding on a young flush. (b) Angular chlorotic spots bordering veins. (c) Interveinal bands. (d) "Pepper and salt" mosaic. (e) Red vein-banding

96. Mealybug tents on a cocoa stem

97. Adults and nymphs of the mealyb
Pseudococcus njalensis

98. A large tented colony of mealybugs on a cocoa pod.
(*Left*): the tent unbroken. (*Right*): the tent broken, showing mealybugs and a

population of cocoa trees would reveal a number with a greater or less degree of resistance in one or both respects.

Spraying is most profitable where a high yield is associated with a high incidence of infection. Below a certain yield and a certain level of infection, spraying will be unprofitable. The conclusion arrived at in Western Samoa in this connection was that spraying is economic when the average number of pods per tree exceeded ten and when the incidence of black pod disease was above 25 per cent.

WITCHES' BROOM DISEASE

This disease is caused by the fungus *Marasmius perniciosus* which is specific to cocoa and some other *Theobroma* species. It is indigenous to South America, probably originating in the Upper Amazon valley from which it has spread to the surrounding cocoa-growing countries—Ecuador, Colombia, Venezuela, Peru and the Guianas. The disease was first studied and the fungus described in Surinam. It did great damage in that country and contributed to the decline of cocoa there.

In 1928 the disease was found in Trinidad and it has since spread further, being found in Tobago in 1939 and in Grenada in 1948. It does not occur in Central America nor in the main cocoa-growing area of Bahia in Brazil, nor is it found outside the New World.

The most obvious symptoms of the disease are the brooms or hypertrophied shoots which are much thicker than healthy shoots and bear many short lateral shoots with undeveloped leaves. Infected flower cushions often form cushion brooms, producing vegetative shoots as well as flowers. Infected flowers have thickened stalks, and occasionally abnormal strawberry-shaped pods are formed but these do not develop to maturity.

The effect of the infection on the growing pod will vary with its age at the time of infection. Cherelles become carrot-shaped and turn black and hard before reaching maturity. Small pods become distorted, the infected side swelling and later turning hard. In both these cases the beans are destroyed. Pods which are even further developed at the time of infection show a hard, blackened area around the point of infection. All the beans in the pod may be damaged, and it is only where pods are nearly ripe when attacked that the beans can be saved.

The disease is spread by spores produced on small mushrooms which develop on dead brooms and infected pods. The spores are released at night, when the atmosphere is nearly saturated with moisture, and are dispersed by air currents. The spores are short-lived, dying within forty-eight hours unless they alight in a place suitable for their development.

Only young developing tissues are attacked. On a vegetative bud the broom appears about six weeks or more after infection, depending on the flushing of the tree, and after a further six to eight weeks the broom dries up and dies. Fruiting bodies will not be formed on a dead broom or infected pod for at least three months, and generally not until five to six months after it has died.

Individually, the small pink mushrooms do not live long, only about three days after reaching maturity, but a large broom may produce as many as thirty mushrooms in a week. Any broom may continue to produce mushrooms for eighteen months, although there is considerable seasonal variation in the numbers of mushrooms formed. The greatest numbers are found in the wet season, and mushroom development ceases in the dry season.

If the disease is uncontrolled, the trees will become covered with hundreds of brooms, and pod losses may rise as high as 70 per cent. Damage is worst in river valleys where conditions are humid but is considerably less on the slopes of the hills. Ridges between valleys may act as natural barriers to the spread of the disease.

Losses can be reduced by the periodical removal of brooms. Brooms are removed along with about six inches of the healthy stem, and diseased cushions are cut out flush with the bark. This should be done at regular intervals of four months; more frequent treatment is unnecessary owing to the time taken for mushrooms to develop. In Trinidad, removal twice a year, in April or May and again in October, is thought to be sufficient. Infected material is destroyed by burning or burying.

Spraying trials have been made, using various fungicides. Although a degree of control has been obtained, the treatment has been uneconomic at normal yields. When a spraying programme can be worked out to control witches' broom and other pod diseases at the same time, this will, of course, reduce the overall costs.

Some years ago the late Dr. Pound made two expeditions to the head-waters of the Amazon, to look for immune or resistant varieties. Many specimens were brought back to Trinidad and tested for resistance. Two of these, SCA 6 and 12, are virtually immune. These clones were propagated and planted fairly widely, but it was found that they produced small beans which might be unacceptable commercially. These clones are now being used in the breeding programme in Trinidad.

Another clone from South America, IMC 67, which appears to be highly resistant to the fungus, is under investigation.

MONILIA DISEASE

This disease (*Monilia roreri*) was first observed in Ecuador in 1914. It is now of major importance in that country, causing an average loss of 40 per cent of pods, and it has also spread to Colombia, Peru, and western Venezuela, being prevalent in wet districts.

The disease affects young pods, but when they reach a certain size they become immune. The first definite symptoms of the disease are seen on pods three to four inches long, which show a slight protuberance and, when cut open, reveal greyish strands. On more mature pods the fungus produces various effects. There may be little external sign of infection except that a few dark spots may be produced or the pod may be covered with a whitish growth. On the Venezuelan or Trinitario type of cocoa, the fungus forms a grey patch surrounded by a white margin. A diseased pod is heavier than a healthy one of the same size, and is more difficult to open. The interior of the pod is enveloped in watery matter and the beans are worthless.

In Ecuador the Cacao Nacional variety appears to be more resistant to the disease than later introductions.

Recent trials in Ecuador have shown that wettable sulphur and zineb—an organic zinc fungicide—are effective in controlling the disease although the most economical frequency and rate of application have yet to be worked out.

MEALY POD

This fungus (*Trachysphaera fructigena*) only occurs in West Africa, whereit attacks coffee as well as cocoa. Pod losses vary from district to district, but are generally less than 1 per cent, although in some districts they may exceed 10 per cent in very wet years.

The first symptom of the disease is a brown area at the point of infection, which rapidly spreads and darkens. Then the surface becomes encrusted with a mealy mass of spores, which is white at first but turns pinkish later. If young pods are attacked they become dry and light, and the beans are rendered useless, but if the pods are attacked at a more mature stage the beans can be saved.

The spores are disseminated by wind and water and will readily attack a damaged pod, but it has not been proved that the fungus can attack healthy pods.

As the spread of the disease is favoured by humid conditions, the control measures include thinning and pruning of the cocoa trees, removal of epiphytes, and weeding and draining which will reduce humidity in the cocoa field. In addition, all infected pods should be removed from the trees.

ANTHRACNOSE

This disease (*Colletotrichum* and allied *Gloeosporium*) is found in many cocoa-growing countries, but it is of little economic importance.

The fungus attacks pods of all ages, forming a brown spot which turns darker and becomes sunken. Pustules of yellow spores are formed in the spots. Young pods may be destroyed, but the beans will not be affected in older pods.

DIPLODIA POD ROT

Botryodiplodia theobromae is a wound parasite and occurs in all cocoa-growing countries. It causes a pod rot which is called diplodia pod rot or brown pod. (This should not be confused with black pod, a quite distinct disease due to *Phytophthora palmivora*.)

The first symptom of diplodia pod rot is a brown spot which turns black and becomes enlarged until the whole pod is invaded. When a pod infected by *B. theobromae* has begun to dry out, large numbers of black spores having the appearance of soot are produced on the surface of the pod, and the beans are destroyed.

In Ghana a condition known as "warty pod" is thought to be caused by a strain of this fungus. Attack by *B. theobromae* can only occur through wounds, which may be caused by insects, squirrels or birds such as woodpeckers. Healthy pods are not attacked. Losses from the disease will be reduced by the control of pests which wound pods, and by removal of infected material.

The fungus also causes a die-back which has been reported from South and Central America, the West Indies, Africa and Asia. A chupon wilt, due to this fungus, occurs in New Guinea.

Die-back occurs on trees which have been weakened by thrips attack, lack of shade or windbreak, poor drainage, drought, or some other cause. Attacks may also occur on trees which have been pruned carelessly. The disease begins at the end of the branches, which dry out and die, the leaves turn yellow and fall off, and the wood discolours and turns grey.

CERATOSTOMELLA WILT

This disease was first reported in 1918 from Ecuador, where it was known as "Mal de machete" as it was associated with cutlass wounds. It has since been reported from several other countries including Colombia, Venezuela, Costa Rica, Mexico and Trinidad. The damage caused by this disease has been increasing in recent years and it is receiving closer study.

Ceratostomella wilt attacks the trunk and main branches and can kill a cocoa tree rapidly. The first symptom is a wilt of the leaves which is followed fairly rapidly by the death of the tree. The leaves, which turn yellow before they die, remain hanging from the branches for several weeks after the tree has died. Examination of the wood shows that the affected parts are discoloured, becoming dark red or red-brown. A pod rot of minor importance is caused by the same fungus and has been reported from several countries.

The disease is caused by *Ceratocystis fimbriata*, though it is better known by its former generic name, *Ceratostomella*. The fungus can only enter the cocoa tree through wounds which may occur naturally or may be caused by man or insects. In Venezuela, cutlass wounds appear to be the chief mode of entry for the fungus, but in Colombia and Ecuador shot-hole borers—*Xyleborus* and *Platypus* species—appear to play an important part in the spread of the disease.

Criollo types are more susceptible than Forastero, and in Ecuador Trinitarios are generally more susceptible than Nacional cocoas, although ICS 95 has proved to be resistant.

In Ecuador, spraying with certain insecticides has been effective in controlling the shot-hole borers and reducing the incidence of the disease, but until the exact role of the shot-hole borers has been determined, this cannot be recommended as a control measure generally.

PINK DISEASE

This disease (*Corticium salmonicolor*) occurs in South America, the West Indies, the Cameroons, Western Samoa, and New Guinea, attacking a wide range of hosts.

The fungus attacks cocoa trees growing under very humid conditions. In New Guinea it is associated with the use of pigeon peas (*Cajanus cajan*) as lateral shade for cocoa. Twigs and small branches become covered with a thin white mycelium which later turns pink and on which the spores are formed. The branches are defoliated and killed, but it is rare for the damage to extend beyond the loss of a few branches.

Attacks are dealt with by removing the affected branches well back from the point of apparent external damage. Incidence of attack may be reduced by improving the drainage in the plantation and adjusting the canopy of the cocoa and shade trees to admit more light. Bordeaux mixture, applied preferably in the dry season, will usually control the disease.

THREAD BLIGHTS

Several species of fungi cause thread blight, a disease which affects many plants in the tropics. In West Africa two species, *Marasmius scandens* and *M. byssicola*, are found. In the West Indies, Brazil, New Guinea, and New Hebrides, *Corticium* species cause thread blights.

In attacks by these fungi, the creamy-white mycelium can be clearly seen as it runs along the twigs and sends out branches to the leaves over the back of which it ramifies in numerous fine threads. The leaves are killed, turn a dark brown colour, and remain suspended from the twigs by a thread of mycelium. The damage does not normally extend beyond the killing of leaves and small branches, though according to reports from the French Cameroons, the trees are sometimes killed.

The incidence of the disease is worst in damp places in the wet season and it normally spreads by contact. It is controlled by removing the infected parts and by copper sprays. Where it occurs frequently, the humidity should be reduced by decreasing the shade or pruning the trees.

Horse-hair blights, the mycelium of which resembles horse-hair, are found on cocoa in several countries, but do no damage.

RED RUST OR ALGAL DISEASE

Three species of algae belonging to the genus *Cephaleuros* cause this disease, which is of minor importance on cocoa. It occurs in Ghana, São Thomé, the Congo, West Indies, Western Samoa, and Brazil.

The symptoms are small, round patches, orange-yellow to rust-red in colour, which are found on the upper surface of the leaves. The injury to the leaves is slight, but young branches also become infected and dark spots are formed on the bark. Only weak, unhealthy trees suffer from this disease so it will not cause any damage where conditions for growth are good. Red rust has been found on young cocoa trees three to four years old, when the temporary shade has been removed and the permanent shade trees are not big enough to shade the young cocoa trees adequately. Sudden changes in the degree of shade weaken the trees and may lead to damage or loss from various pests and diseases.

ROOT DISEASES

Root diseases attack cocoa in most cocoa-growing countries but are generally localized. They cause losses of a few trees from time to time and are encountered most frequently in partly thinned forest or where the forest has recently been removed. The usual symptoms of an attack by a root disease are sudden yellowing and wilting of the leaves, which turn brown and remain on the tree after it has died.

Root diseases are usually spread by root contact, although some of the fungi can also grow through the soil for some distance. It is generally considered, though it is not finally proved, that there is very little spread of root diseases by means of spores.

The most common method adopted for the control of root diseases is to cut down the affected tree and remove and burn both the tree and the stump. An isolation trench, to prevent the spread of the fungus outwards, is dug at least eighteen inches deep round the site of the tree which has been removed. It may be advisable to dig trenches around adjacent trees also, and to extend them in order to provide better drainage in the immediate vicinity of the outbreak.

The more important root diseases are the following:

COLLAR CRACK

The fungus *Armillaria mellea* attacks many trees in temperate and tropical regions and is commonly known as the "Honey Agaric." It causes a serious root disease called "collar crack," which is found in parts of Togoland, the Cameroons, and in São Thomé.

The fungus will attack cocoa trees of all ages and other hosts as well. It infects the tree through the lateral roots and then spreads upwards and downwards attacking the stem and tap-root. On the stem the mycelium of the fungus develops inwards along the medullary rays, then it thickens and exerts great pressure on the trunk of the tree, causing it to crack. The cracks normally extend for three to five feet, but may reach ten feet above the ground. An attack by this fungus is nearly always fatal to the tree. The fungus produces clusters of mushrooms at ground level, which at first are white but turn yellow and finally blacken.

The fungus can spread through the soil from one host to another and it flourishes in damp conditions.

ROOT DISEASES DUE TO *Rosellinia* SPECIES

Three species of the genus *Rosellinia* have been found to attack cocoa, but only one is of any importance. *R. pepo*, or "black root disease," has caused considerable damage to cocoa in the West Indies and has also been reported from Colombia and New Guinea. It attacks many other crops and can be recognized by the smoky-grey mycelium which covers the roots and the white mycelial fans which can be found beneath the bark of the roots.

The disease occurs in patches which spread slowly, although the symptoms may appear suddenly on individual trees. Infected trees should be cut out and the ground should be exposed to the sun.

ROOT DISEASES DUE TO SPECIES OF *Fomes*

Fomes lignosus, the "white root disease," is sometimes found on cocoa in a number of countries. Attacks usually occur after planting on newly cleared land and are worst in damp low-lying areas. The fungus causes the leaves to wither and fall, and this is followed by a general die-back. The soft, white mycelium can be found on the roots, and a black ring can be seen if the trunk is sawn across.

COLLAR ROT

The fungus *Ustulina deusta* (*U. zonata*) has been found in Ghana, but it is more important as a cocoa parasite in the South Pacific, being reported from New Guinea and the New Hebrides. In the latter country it occurs in patches, especially in damp places. The fungus produces hard, grey crusts on the trunk, but there is no external mycelium to be found on the roots. As the fungus spreads by root contact, affected trees should be isolated by digging a ditch two to three feet deep around them, and they should be uprooted.

The following is a report on Cushion Gall by G. A. R. Wood (Cadbury, Bournville, 1959).

CUSHION GALL

"The first report of this disease appears to have come from Colombia where it has been observed in certain areas since 1940 or even earlier. In 1951 it was reported from Costa Rica, Panama and Nicaragua where it is known as 'buba.' More recently it has been found in Surinam where it is called 'yaws,' and a survey made in 1958 also revealed its presence in Trinidad.

"The disease causes hypertrophy of the flower cushions. Large numbers of flower buds are formed, most of which do not open. This growth becomes a spongy dark brown gall which may grow to a diameter of 3 inches or even more. Initially an affected tree will have only a few galls, but after a time all the cushions on the tree from the trunk to the smallest branches will have turned into galls, and, as the attack progresses, the tree becomes less and less productive.

"It has been estimated that in parts of western Nicaragua 25 per cent of the trees have been affected, and on some farms a higher percentage. In most of the other countries from which the disease has been reported, only isolated cases have been found. This was true of Costa Rica a few years ago, but there the disease has apparently been spreading and developing quite rapidly and has become a serious problem requiring close study.

"The cause of Cushion Gall is unknown. The fact that it spreads to all the flower cushions suggests that it becomes systemic; and, furthermore, in Nicaragua, where some affected trees were coppiced, galls appeared on the flower cushions on the young chupons. Examination of the galls has shown the presence of various fungi, bacteria, mites and other insects, but there has been no indication as to which, if any, of these is the cause or vector of the disease.

"The fact that at the Imperial College of Tropical Agriculture most of the affected trees were young trees of Costa Rican clones, suggests that the disease may have been introduced in planting material, but in Trinidad galls have also been seen in cocoa farms.

"In our present ignorance of this disease, it must be regarded as a potential danger to cocoa-growing in the countries mentioned. The only recommendations that can be made with regard to control is that every care should be taken to see that planting material of all types comes from healthy trees."

DEFOLIATION OF THE EXTREMITIES IN COCOA

A condition where the extremities of the branches of the cocoa trees are defoliated is noticeable to a greater or less degree in several countries, particularly where the trees are unshaded or exposed to wind. It occurs in Ceylon and in Western Samoa. In Eastern Nigeria and over considerable areas of the Cameroons it is particularly prevalent, and has been given the name of "leafless twig." Various theories have been put forward as to the cause of this condition. It has been suggested that it may be due to the absence of certain essential minerals in the soil, or may occur in association with high soil acidity which inhibits the uptake of necessary minerals by the tree. Others contend that insect pests or mites are mainly responsible. It seems possible that this form of defoliation may be caused by different agencies in different parts of the world.

Although West achieved a good measure of control of the trouble by the application of Gammalin 20 spray to the trees, the consensus of opinion is that insects are not the primary cause of this condition in the Cameroons. The possibility of its being a physiological condition resulting from a deficiency of manganese or copper in the plant is suggested.

G. Donald and A. L. Wharton, reporting (unpublished work) on the condition of leafless twig in the Cameroons, say:

"The symptoms of this disease on mature cocoa trees have been described by several workers who have visited the Cameroons in the past. The most characteristic features of the disease occur on the fan

N

branches on which the leaves die and absciss in the developing buds, the stipules persist long after the leaves have fallen, the internodes are very short, and many of the axillary buds develop into similarly leafless twigs, forming a type of 'witches' broom'. The apical buds are frequently flexed downwards.

"A similar condition occurs on chupons and seedlings and is descriptively called 'paint brush' disease. The early loss of developing leaves, the retention of the stipules and the shortening of the internodes are features in common between the two conditions, but axillary buds do not normally develop unless the apical bud of the chupon is damaged. In the opinion of the writers the two conditions are possibly expressions of the same disorder."

DETERIORATION OF THE COTYLEDON IN THE POD

This is a condition which occurs infrequently in cocoa beans where the pods appear outwardly healthy. On cutting the bean, it will be found that there are dark stains in the centre of the cotyledon. The tissue of the discoloured portion will be corky and will disintegrate readily. Where the condition is severe, the greater part of the cotyledon may be affected. This disorder is not associated with any pest or disease and the cause would appear to be physiological, possibly due to nutritional imbalance, arising from some aspect of environment.

Criollo type of cocoa seems to be predisposed to this defect. In South America the literature refers to its occurrence in Criollo only. It has been noted in Criollo cocoa in compounds in Malaya, but not in Amelonado type and has been seen in Criollo cocoa in one of the islands in Hawaii, but Amelonado cocoa growing there is unaffected. Again, it is to be found in the hybrid cocoa of Papua and New Guinea and Western Samoa, especially in cocoa that has been much inbred, and in pure Criollo in the Philippine Islands.

EPIPHYTES AND PARASITIC PLANTS

Epiphytes are plants which use other plants for support but do not draw any food from them. They are common on cocoa trees in some countries. They interfere with the flowering of the tree and should be removed.

Mistletoes, on the other hand, are semi-parasitic plants, drawing some of their food from the host plant. They are common on cocoa trees in West Africa and Ceylon, and also occur in the West Indies, where they are known as bird vines, because they have sticky seeds which are disseminated by birds. Mistletoes can be removed by pruning. These plants belong to the family Loranthaceae and their roots penetrate the tissues of the host from which they obtain water and salts; in time this will cause a die-back of the branch above the point at which the mistletoe is attached. If the infestation is heavy, the yield will be reduced.

SPRAYING METHODS AND FORMULATIONS RECOMMENDED IN THE WEST INDIES

The following treatments are recommended for cocoa by Mr. T. E. K. Potter, head of the agricultural department of the firm of Messrs. Geddes Grant Ltd., of Trinidad:

COCOA (PLANTING DISTANCE 12 FT. by 12 FT)

BLACK POD CONTROL

Formulation	To 2 gallons of water add 1½ lb. Perenox plus 3 fl. oz. Agral LN or 1 fl. oz. Agral 90.
Method	Drift spraying in every other row with nozzle adjusted at horizontal for clonal, and 10 per cent above horizontal for seedling cocoa.
Machine	Micronette for pure stands; if interplanted, seedling with young clones, the Motoblo.

COCOA BEETLE CONTROL

Formulation	1 lb. Arsinette in 2 gallons of water plus 3 fl. oz. Agral LN or 1 fl. oz. Agral 90.
Method	Semi-blast spraying directed to base of trunk and branches.
Machine	Motoblo or Micronette.
Rate	2–3 gallons per acre.
N.B.	Operators should use protective gloves, face-shield and respirator.

BLACK POD, MOSS, THRIPS CONTROL

A dual mixture can be applied made up of:

> 1½ lb. Perenox
> ¼ gallon Albolineum
> 1½ pints Didimac 25 Miscible Liquid
> 1½ gallons water

applied at the rate of 4 gallons per acre, at 4-weekly intervals during July–December. Avoid if possible the use of Didimac during flowering for fear of upsetting pollination.

REFERENCES

PESTS

General:
Cohic, F. Extract from the report of a survey made in the New Hebrides. *Cocoa-growing in the New Hebrides*, Appendix 3, D. H. Urquhart (Technical Paper No. 40, South Pacific Commission, 1953).

Dun, G. B. "Pests of cacao in the territory of Papua and New Guinea." "The growing of cacao in Papua and New Guinea," Appendix 2, D. H. Urquhart and R. E. P. Dwyer (Bournville, 1951).

Hall, C. J. J. van. *Cacao* (2nd edition, 1932).

Nicol, J. *Insect Pests of Cacao Trees* (Tafo, 1947).

O'Connor, B. A. "Notes on insect pests of cocoa and coffee in Fiji and other South Pacific Islands." "Cocoa growing in Fiji Islands," Appendix 3, D. H. Urquhart (Technical Paper No. 36, South Pacific Commission, 1952).

Pickles, A. "Pest problems of cocoa cultivation in Trinidad and Tobago" (Cocoa Research Conference, London, 1945).

Capsids:
Annual Reports of West African Cacao Research Institute.

Bellefroid, V. de. "A note on *Sahlbergella singularis*" (Cocoa Conference, London, 1951).

Crowdy, S. H. "Observations on the pathogenicity of *Calonectria rigidiuscula* (Berk & Br.) Sacc. on *Theobroma cacao* L." *Ann. appl. Biol.* (1947), **34**, 45.

Donald, R. G., and Thresh, J. M. "A capsid control experiment in the Western Region of Nigeria." (Cocoa Conference, 1957, 119.)

Dun, G. B. "Notes on cacao capsids in New Guinea" (1953). (Unpublished.)

Fowler, R. L., and Lopez, G. H. "Cacao industry of Ecuador." Foreign Agriculture Report No. 34 (U.S. Department of Agriculture, Washington, D.C., 1949).

Taylor, D. J. "Pest control research at W.A.C.R.I." (Cocoa Conference, 1957, 125.)

Williams, G. "Field observations on the cacao mirids *Sahlbergella singularis* Hagl. and *Distantiella theobroma* (Dist.) in the Gold Coast." *Bull. ent. Res.* (1953), **44**, 101.

Williams, G. "Field observations on the cacao mirids *Sahlbergella singularis* Hagl. and *Distantiella theobroma* (Dist.) in the Gold Coast. Part III. Population fluctuations." *Bull. ent. Res.* (1954), **54**, 723.

Thrips:
Callan, E. M. "Thrips resistance in cacao." *Trop. Agric.* (1943), **20**, 7.

Cotterell, G. S. "The red-banded cacao thrips, *Heliothrips rubrocinctus*, Giard." *Gold Coast Agriculture Year Book* (1927).

Fennah, R. G. "The insect pests of food-crops in the Lesser Antilles" (Depts. of Agric., Windward and Leeward Is., 1947).

Fennah, R. G. "The epidemiology of cacao thrips on cacao in Trinidad." *Rept. Cacao Res. Trin.* 1954, 7.

Hardy, F., "Marginal leaf-scorch of cacao." *6th Annual Report on Cacao Research, 1936* (Trinidad, 1937).

Beetles:

Guppy, R. L., "The life history and control of the cacao beetle." *Bulletin No. 1* (Trinidad Board of Agriculture, 1911).

McKee, R. K. "The incidence of cacao beetle damage to some I.C.S. clones planted at River Estate." *11th Ann. Rep. on Cacao Research, 1941-43* (Trinidad, 1944).

Hammond, P. S. "Capsid control on mature cocoa." *Ghana Farmer*, vol. 1 No. 3.

DISEASES

General:

Briton-Jones, H. R. *The Diseases and Curing of Cacao* (London, 1934).

Bunting, R. H., and Dade, H. A. *Gold Coast Plant Diseases* (London, 1924).

Dadant, R. "Phytopathology of the cocoa tree in the New Hebrides." *Cocoa-growing in the New Hebrides*, Appendix 2, D. H. Urquhart (Technical Paper No. 40, South Pacific Commission, 1953).

Grimaldi, J. "Contribution to the studies of parasitic and saprophytic cryptogams of cocoa in the Cameroons." *Report of 4th meeting of the Inter-American Technical Cacao Committee* (Guayaquil, 1952).

Hall, C. J. J. van. *Cacao* (2nd edition, 1932).

Black Pod:

Bowman, G. F. *The Inter-American Cacao Center at Turrialba, Costa Rica* (Cocoa Conference, London, 1951).

Dade, H. A. "Economic significance of cacao pod diseases and factors determining their incidence and control" (*Bulletin No. 6*, Gold Coast Department of Agriculture, 1927).

Dade, H. A. "The relation between diseased cushions and seasonal outbreak of black pod disease of cacao" (*Gold Coast Department of Agriculture Year Book*, 1927).

Hadland, J. R. G. "A further report on the control of black pod in the Western Region of Nigeria." (Cocoa Conference, 1957, 118.)

McLaughlin, J. H. "Fungicidal control of *Phytophthora palmivora* Bull. on *Theobroma cacao* L. in Costa Rica." *Cacao* (1952), **2**, 1.

Owen, H. "Cacao pod diseases in West Africa." *Ann. appl. Biol.* (1951), **38**, 715.

Smith, Harvey C. *Report on Cocoa Disease in Samoa.*

Thorold, C. A. "Air-borne dispersal of *Phytophthora palmivora* causing black pod disease of *Theobroma cacao*." *Nature* (Lond.), 1952, **170**, 718.

Thorold, C. A. "The control of black pod disease of cocoa in the Western Region of Nigeria" (Cocoa Conference, London, 1953).

Thorold, C. A. "Control of black pod disease (*Phytophthora palmivora*) of cacao by fungicide in the Western Region of Nigeria." *Rept. 5th. Mycol. Conf.* 1954, 97.

Witches' Broom:

Baker, R. E. D. "Witches' broom disease of cacao (a review)." *Report on Cacao Research*, 1945–51 (Trinidad, 1953).

Holliday, P. "A test for resistance to *Marasmius perniciosus* Stahel." *Rept. on Cacao Res.* (Trinidad 1954–55), 50.

Holliday, P. "Further observations on the susceptibility of the Imperial College selections to Witches' broom disease." *Rept. on Cacao Res.* (Trinidad 1955–56), 48.

Holliday, P. "Witches' broom disease of cacao." (Colonial 286, H.M.S.O., 1952).

Monilia Disease:

Fowler, R. L., and Lopez, G. H. "Cacao industry of Ecuador." *Foreign Agriculture Report* No. 34 (U.S. Department of Agriculture, Washington, D.C., 1949).

The fundamental research work on Swollen Shoot is recorded in a series of articles in the *Annals of Applied Biology* under the general title of "Virus Diseases of Cocoa in West Africa" (cited chronologically):

Posnette, A. F. "I, Cacao viruses 1A, 1B, 1C, and 1D," **34**, 388 (1947).

Crowdy, S. H., and Posnette, A. F. "II, Cross-immunity experiments with viruses 1A, 1B, and 1C," **34**, 403 (1947).

Posnette, A. F., and Strickland, A. H. "III, Technique of insect transmission," **35**, 53 (1948).

Goodall, D. W. "IV, Effect of virus infection on growth and water content of cacao seedlings," **36**, 440 (1949).

Goodall, D. W. "V, Alternative host plants," **36**, (1949).

Posnette, A. F., Robertson, N. F., and Todd, J. McA. "V, Alternative host plants," **37**, 229 (1950).

Posnette, A. F., and Robertson, N. F. "VI, Vector investigations," **37**, 363 (1950).

Posnette, A. F. "VII, Virus transmission by different vector species," **37**, 378 (1950).

Posnette, A. F., and Todd, J. McA. "VIII, The search for virus-resistant cacao," **38**, 785 (1951).

Posnette, A. F., and Todd, J. McA. "IX, Strain variation and interference in virus 1A," **43**, 433 (1955).

Other articles include:

Cornwell, P. B. "Movement of the vectors of virus diseases of cacao in Ghana. I. Canopy movement in and between trees." *Bull. ent. Res.* (1958), **49**, 613.

Donald, R. G. "The natural enemies of some Pseudococcidae in the Gold Coast." *J. West Afr. Sci. Assn.* (1956), **4**, 48.

Hanna, A. D., Judenko, E., and Heatherington, W. "The control of *Crematogaster* ants as a means of controlling the mealybugs transmitting the swollen shoot virus disease of cacao in the Gold Coast." *Bull. ent. Res.* (1956), **47**, 219.

Orellana, R. G., and Peiris, J. W. L. "The swollen shoot phase of the virus disease of cocoa in Ceylon." *FAO Plant Protec. Bull.* (1957), **5**, 165.

Peiris, J. W. L. "A virus disease of cocoa in Ceylon." *Trop. Agric.* (Ceylon) (1953), **109**, 135.

Posnette, A. F. "Control measures against swollen shoot virus disease of cacao." *Trop. Agric.* (Trinidad, 1943), **20**, 116.

Posnette, A. F. "Virus research at W.A.C.R.I., Tafo, Gold Coast." *Trop. Agric.* (Trinidad, 1951), **28**, 133.

Renaud, R. "Les maladies à virus du cacaoyer de l'Ouest Afrciain." *L'Agric. trop.* (1954), **9**, 517.

Strickland, A. H., "Coccids attacking cacao in West Africa." *Bulletin of Entomological Research*, **38**, 497 (1947). "The entomology of swollen shoot of cacao. I, The insect species involved, with notes on their biology." *Ibid.*, **41**, 725 (1951). "II, The bionomics of the species involved." *Ibid.*, **42**, 65 (1951).

Todd, J. Mc A. "An indigenous source of swollen shoot disease of cacao." *Nature* (London, 1951), **167**, 952.

The virus diseases of cocoa in Trinidad are described in:

Baker, R. E. D., and Dale, W. T. "Notes on a virus disease of cacao." *Ann. appl. Biol.*, **34**, 60 (1947); "Virus diseases of cacao in Trinidad, II." *Trop. Agric.* (Trinidad, 1947), **24**, 127.

Cope, F. W. "Statistical studies in the effects of virus infection upon yield in clonal cacao." *Rept., Cacao Res., 1945–51* (I.C.T.A., Trinidad, 1953), 126.

Dale, W. T. "Further notes on the spread of virus in a field of clonal cacao in Trinidad." *Rept., Cacao Res., 1945–51* (I.C.T.A., Trinidad, 1953), 130.

Kirkpatrick, T. W. "Insect transmission of cacao virus disease in Trinidad." *Bull. ent. Res.* (1950), **41**, 99; "Cacao virus disease (a review)." *Rept., Cacao Res., 1945–51* (I.C.T.A., Trinidad, 1953), 122.

Posnette, A. F. "Virus diseases of cacao in Trinidad." *Trop. Agric.* (Trinidad 1944), **21**, 105.

Other diseases:

Ciferri, R. "Hollow heart of cocoa beans." *Phytopath.* (1951), **41**, 656.

Crowdy, S. H. "Observations on the pathogenicity of *Calonectria rigidiuscula* (Berk & Br.) Sacc. on *Theobroma cacao*. L." *Ann. appl. Biol.* (1947), **34**, 45.

Humphries, E. C. "Wilt of cocoa fruits." *Ann. Bot. N.S.* (1950), **14**, 149,

Hutchins, L. M. "Current surveys of cushion gall." (7th Inter-American Cacao Conf., Palmira, Colombia, 1958.) Doc. 61.

Kevorkian, A. G. "The cushion gall disease of cacao." *Phytopath.* (1951), **41**, 562.

Malaguti, G. "*Ceratostomella fimbriata* en el cacao de Venezuela." *Acta Cient. Venezol.* (1952), **3**, 94.

McKelvie, A. D. "Cherelle wilt of cacao. I. Pod development and its relation to the wilt." *J. exp. Bot.* (1956), **7**, 252.

Owen, H. "Further observations on the pathogenicity of *Calonectria rigidiuscula* (Berk. & Br.) Sacc. to *Theobroma cacao* L." *Ann. appl. Biol.* (1956), **44**, 307.

Wellman, F. L., and Orellana, R. G. "Buba or cushion gall of cacao in Nicaragua." *FAO Plant Protec. Bull.* (1955), **3**, 71.

Wellman, F. L., and Orellana, R. G. "Buba or cushion gall of cacao in Nicaragua." (5th Inter-American Cacao Conf., Turrialba, 1954). *Trabajos presentados* Vol. I, Doc. 18.

Wood, G. A. R. "Cocoa-growing in Venezuela, Colombia and Ecuador." (1959), 51.

See also the Reports of Cocoa Conferences held by the Colonial Office, L'Office International du Cacao et du Chocolat, and the Cocoa, Chocolate and Confectionery Alliance, London, 1945–53, and the Annual Reports of the West African Cacao Research Institute, Tafo.

Chapter XIII

TYPES OF COCOA REQUIRED, QUALITY AND GRADING

Types of Cocoa required in Manufacture—Quality and Grading—Preparation and Quality—Defective Beans in relation to Quality—Unfermented and Underfermented Beans—Mouldy and Germinated Beans—Damage by Disease and Pests—Grubby Beans—Shrivelled Beans—Importance of Shell Percentage and Bean Size—Definition of Good Cocoa Beans and what to Avoid—Standards set by some Importing Countries—Sampling

THE care and skill with which cocoa beans are fermented and dried in preparation for the market will decide whether they are capable of being processed into palatable cocoa and chocolate. In common with many other vegetable products, the first stages of preparation are vitally important, and if cocoa beans are unskilfully and carelessly treated at the fermenting and drying stage, the damage done cannot be rectified by the manufacturer.

During the 1953–4 cocoa season, manufacturers spent some £250 million on the purchase of raw cocoa; most of this money went to producers and some to their agents. Manufacturers assert, and not unreasonably, that they are entitled to good quality in an article for which they are paying such a high price.

TYPES OF COCOA REQUIRED IN MANUFACTURE

The bulk of the cocoa used in manufacture is of the Forastero type, the best known being Amelonado. This is grown in West Africa and Bahia, and in increasing amounts in many other regions of the tropics. Countries which contemplate growing the crop or expanding the industry are naturally anxious about the type of cocoa to plant. It can be said without reservation that Amelonado will always be acceptable in the markets of the world. It has several advantages from the point of view of the planter. One is that it will come true to type when grown from seed. As uniform cocoa responds to a standard type of fermentation, this is a great advantage at the processing stage. It is less susceptible to most pests and

185

diseases than Criollo and hybrids containing a high proportion of Criollo. Upper Amazon cocoa, introduced to Trinidad and later to West Africa, is similar in character to Amelonado and responds to similar treatment in manufacture.

Criollo was much prized in times past on account of its particular flavour. It was the first to be introduced to Asia and the Pacific; Forastero was a later introduction. In Ceylon and New Guinea, for example, experience has shown that Criollo succumbs to pests and diseases more readily than Forastero or Forastero crosses. Forastero strains are on the increase and Criollos have proportionately decreased over the years. A premium is paid for the better cocoa from Trinidad, Ceylon and Western Samoa, most of which has an admixture of Criollo. In Ceylon, however, there is much picking over and discarding of small beans in order to get a satisfactory sample, and so the premium for flavour is not as great as might appear at first sight.

An estate which grows a mixed lot of cocoa, such as Forastero, Criollo and hybrids of both, is subject to disadvantages. The most important of these is that it is almost impossible to get a satisfactory fermentation due to the fact that the length of time required by each type is different. Where there are marked differences in the size of beans, and where there is a large proportion of small beans which have to be sold at a lower price, the eventual profit will be reduced, especially when the costs of grading and picking have been taken into account.

It has been stated that Criollo is better suited to high altitudes than Forastero, but there appears to be no evidence to support this view. Forastero will grow as well at high altitudes as Criollo.

There is a great deal to be said for growing one type of cocoa, from the point of processing and marketing, as there is normally less wastage in grading. The market for high-flavour cocoas is limited and may become more so. The American market, which is of course the biggest market of all, pays only a very small premium for flavour cocoa.

QUALITY AND GRADING

Most countries with large exports of agricultural produce have formulated grading regulations which classify products according to their quality. By avoiding the export of inferior qualities, it is possible to establish a good reputation in the export market. Buyers know what qualities to expect when purchasing the various grades, and whether or not these grades conform to the regulations of the importing country.

Irrespective of the kind of tree or the type of cocoa from which the raw beans have been derived, the quality eventually depends on the manner of handling during harvesting, processing at the plantation, storage and transportation. There is much wastage of cocoa in producing countries through lack of appreciation of the fact that it is a product which can only be manufactured into edible food if it arrives at the factory in good condition.

When the Americas, apart from Brazil, were the main suppliers of cocoa, the terms "fine" and "quality" were frequently used. These terms usually referred to a particular character or flavour, rather than to the quality of the beans in respect of their size, uniformity, butterfat content, or high standard of preparation. Flavour, as a character, was of more importance in the days when manufacturers had to rely on different flavours to make up a desired blend.

Criollos and allied types were the cocoas with distinctive flavours. Forasteros, of which Amelonado provides the bulk, have a good chocolate flavour. As Brazil and, later, West Africa, both of which grew large quantities of Amelonado, came to supply more and more of world needs, the U.S.A. and the U.K. became accustomed to the use of this basic type of cocoa.

For a time there was a keen general demand for flavour cocoas from the Americas, Ceylon and Java, and high premiums were paid for these for the purpose of blending basic cocoas with them. But as the supply of basic cocoa mounted until it formed the overwhelming bulk of world supplies, flavour cocoas were used mainly to produce the required blends. Again, the increased supplies of basic cocoa coincided with the rise in popularity of milk chocolate for which the mild flavour of Amelonado cocoa is particularly suited. While premiums are still paid for some flavour cocoas, the demand for these is mainly confined to certain European markets, and amounts to between 5 and 10 per cent of all the cocoa produced.

Although the terms "fine" and "quality" are still retained in trade circles, cocoa is now mainly judged on its purity and freedom from defects.

PREPARATION AND QUALITY

The Cocoa, Chocolate and Confectionery Alliance has laid down the following standards for West African cocoa, the essential points of which apply to cocoas from other parts of the world:

PREPARATION

(a) Only beans from clean, well-grown, fully ripe and disease-free pods are to be fermented.

(b) Fermentation of beans from freshly-picked pods should be carried out under the best conditions possible, preferably in lots of not less than 400 lb. wet weight.

(c) During fermentation, the beans should be handled in such a way that the whole batch is evenly fermented (over- and under-fermentation being equally avoided) and adequately aerated.

(d) Drying should be carried out immediately on the completion of the fermentation, and conducted in such a way as to be complete and uniform. At the start, drying should not be too rapid as otherwise the testa shrinks and adheres to the cotyledons.

(e) Drying should be carried out to such an extent as to ensure the keeping qualities of the beans, care being taken that at no stage thereafter they become exposed to moisture or insect infestation.

QUALITY

1. Beans prepared according to the above recommendations should have the following characteristics:

(a) They should be plump and of even size, of not less than 1 gram fermented dry weight.

(b) The shell should be loose and intact.

(c) The cotyledons should be friable, of open texture and chocolate-brown colour. On roasting they should develop the characteristic chocolate flavour.

2. The following characteristics are undesirable:

(a) Beans affected by mould.

(b) Under-fermented beans having violet or slaty cotyledons.

(c) Beans affected by insect attack (weevil, etc.).

(d) Flat, immature, small and broken beans.

(e) Germinated beans.

DEFECTIVE BEANS IN RELATION TO QUALITY

Grading, except where the term is applied to beans of different sizes in a sample, takes into account defects which influence the character and flavour of the finished product. Such defects are: mould, slatiness, grubs (i.e. insects), germination and shrivelling.

Cocoa readily acquires extraneous flavours after drying, and during storage or transit it must be kept apart from other products of strong flavour. A flavour may be acquired in the plantation store or during storage in a dwelling-house. Where the beans become contaminated through contact with copra or with odours from domestic cooking or smoke, the contamination persists and will be detected in the manufactured product.

UNFERMENTED AND UNDERFERMENTED BEANS

Unfermented beans may have been merely dried after removal from the pod, or fresh beans added at a late stage in fermentation. They are usually graded as "slaty," as they are slaty-grey in appearance. The cotyledon is closely packed and leathery, and the shell adheres closely to the cotyledon so that in the factory it is impossible to separate the shell completely from the nib. Unfermented beans do not produce a chocolate flavour on roasting; the fat, which is about 2 per cent less than in fermented beans, is impossible to extract by normal means and extra cocoa butter has to be added in working the mass. The bitter astringent chocolate derived from them is of a blue-grey colour instead of the typical brown associated with good chocolate. They cannot be made into an edible cocoa or chocolate and they are only used for the manufacture of cocoa butter and theobromine.

Underfermented beans are usually the result of one of the following: fermenting of the mass for an insufficiently long period; incomplete mixing of the mass during fermentation; the fact that temperatures attained during fermentation were not sufficiently high.

As such, underfermented beans are not so easily assessed before roasting as are unfermented beans. When they are derived from beans that have been treated in a fermenting-box they are usually purple; the degree to which this colour is evident is a rough guide to the extent of underfermentation. It must be noted, however, that the colour is not an infallible guide. Chocolate prepared from underfermented beans tends to be astringent, depending on the degree of underfermentation, and the chocolate flavour is correspondingly weak.

MOULDY AND GERMINATED BEANS

Mould is a serious defect which may render the beans almost useless for any form of manufacture and will communicate its undesirable characteristics to the rest of the mass in which it is mixed, the unpleasant flavour imparted being evident in the finished chocolate which will be unfit to eat. This is true even when mouldy beans are present in quite small quantities.

A certain amount of light mould on the outer shell may not necessarily affect the cotyledons, but during storage mould in any form is liable to increase. Only two or three kinds of mould are capable of penetrating the shell, and the point of entry is where the radicle would emerge if the bean were to germinate. Possibly the shell is weaker at this point, especially if it has advanced towards germination. Where the more aggressive moulds have penetrated the shell, others will follow.

Apart from objectionable flavours which are impossible to eliminate in the process of manufacture, the fibre of the cocoa is rendered useless, the free fatty acid of the cocoa butter is increased and only after expensive refining can it be converted into an odourless fat for specialized use. Even as little as 4 per cent of mouldy beans in the mass can be detected in the chocolate.

It is normal for beans to carry a certain amount of inoffensive moulds while in the fermenting-box or in the early stages of drying, but these are not usually the moulds that cause damage eventually. The offensive moulds are usually developed during storage under conditions where the necessary precautions are not taken to prevent them. They are particularly liable to occur where the beans have been insufficiently dried, where the moisture content is 8 per cent or over, and where atmospheric humidity is as high as 80 per cent.

To prevent mould it is necessary to provide well-aired stores, to insulate the bags from the floor with layers of wood of adequate thickness and to stack the bags so that they do not touch the walls. It is obvious that it is undesirable to store cocoa for long periods in a humid climate. When this has to be done, the use of polythene liners in the bags should be resorted to. Care should be taken, however, to ensure that the beans are thoroughly dry before being put into the polythene-lined bags.

Germinated beans are, of course, particularly vulnerable to the entry of moulds, and in any sample of cocoa they are usually the worst, or the only ones, affected. They are similarly vulnerable to insect attack. In fact, it can be said that, under normal conditions of handling and storage, a cocoa bean with the shell intact is well protected from moulds or insects.

Beans with broken shells, due to the seed coat being cut when the pod was being opened, or cracked by rough handling after drying, are subject to most of the disadvantages of germinated beans.

Washing of beans during or immediately after fermentation tends to make the shell brittle, and where beans have been much washed a large proportion may get broken in handling the bags during transit. When such consignments are sifted in the factory, there is liable to be an accumulation of broken beans which create a special problem for the manufacturer, as broken beans are difficult to roast and pass through machinery designed for whole beans. Such beans are usually relegated to the manufacture of the less expensive lines of chocolate.

It has been pointed out that an important aspect of broken beans is that they are primarily responsible for the maintenance of the insect population in the cocoa sack, and if germinated and broken beans were eliminated, the insect population would almost disappear.

DAMAGE BY DISEASE AND PESTS

Where pods have been attacked by black pod fungus and the fungus has penetrated the pod wall, some or all of the beans may be affected, and beans which have been attacked by *Phytophthora palmivora* do not ferment properly. The eventual yield of cocoa butter may be only half that of normal beans and it may contain as much as 40 per cent of free fatty acid, and has to be refined before it can be used in any form.

The inclusion of beans which have been partially or severely attacked by fungus in the fermenting mass has the effect of slowing down the process of fermentation and may render satisfactory fermentation impracticable, as such beans have the tendency to hinder the mass from attaining to the correct temperatures, and a high proportion of purple beans may result. Diseased beans, when dry, have a characteristic texture, known in Nigeria as "velvety," and are not accepted for sale in that country. If these beans are manufactured into chocolate, their flavour is akin to that of mouldy beans and is extremely objectionable.

Where parrots, monkeys and squirrels have partially eaten pods, the seeds are susceptible to attack by fungus.

GRUBBY BEANS

There are obvious objections to insects in any form in a foodstuff. Two major pests of stored cocoa are the moth, *Ephestia cautella*, and the beetle, *Araecerus fasciculatus*. The caterpillar of *Ephestia* will not penetrate an unbroken cocoa bean shell but *Araecerus* larvae can do so. Both are insects of the tropics, but the former has adapted itself to life in temperate climates where it is a constant menace to cocoa and other stored food products.

The tobacco beetle, *Lasioderma serricorne*, has in recent years become a pest of increasing importance in West Africa. Prior to 1939 it had been noted on several occasions in cocoa from Nigeria, but not from Ghana. More recently, it has been observed also on a number of occasions in Ghana cocoa.

The infestation probably occurs in the farmer's house or in the broker's store by cross-infestation from other foodstuffs. Infestation may continue to develop after the cocoa has been packed, and larger bulks can progressively become infested as they move to the ports for shipment.

An increased awareness by manufacturers of the undesirability of insect pests in general is leading to an increased attention being paid by exporting countries to problems of insect infestation. It may be necessary in future to subject all affected cocoa to some form of treatment to prevent further development of infestation.

Infestation can be controlled in several ways. The best method is, of course, to pay increased attention to hygiene in brokers' and exporters' stores. In these buildings cleanliness is of prime importance and must receive unremitting care and attention. The spraying of empty stores, railway trucks and other means of transport with some form of insecticide should be matters of routine.

Infested beans must be specially treated. This is best done by fumigation under carefully controlled conditions using either methyl bromide or ethylene oxide. Spraying stacks of stored cocoa with insecticides such as pyrethrum in mineral oil is of value in preventing the spread of infection from an infested bag to a clean one. It seems unlikely, however, that this will prevent the development of infestation in the bags in the centre of the stack.

Infestation can also occur on board ship. Probably much of the infestation which is observed in beans reaching the manufacturer arises from this source and occurs where cocoa is being stored close to other foodstuffs, such as groundnuts. Such cross-infestation is inevitable unless all the foodstuffs carried in the ship have been treated previously.

SHRIVELLED BEANS

Flat, thin, or shrivelled beans, may contain little or no cotyledons and a high percentage of shell.

IMPORTANCE OF SHELL PERCENTAGE AND BEAN SIZE

Even-sized beans are preferred because those differing widely in size are difficult to roast evenly. The shell percentage generally remains constant in beans weighing over 1 gram, but below that weight it rises rapidly. Furthermore, there is much greater variation of shell percentage in beans below 1 gram weight. The shell percentage is lowered by washing, and in cocoa from Ceylon and Western Samoa where cocoa is washed, it may be as low as 8 per

A stab sampler being used to withdraw beans from sealed bags

100. A sample of beans being cut for grading at a buying station in Ghana

101. Samples of cocoa being graded before shipment at Accra

102. Typical samples of beans, West Africa

103. Typical samples of bea
Trinidad

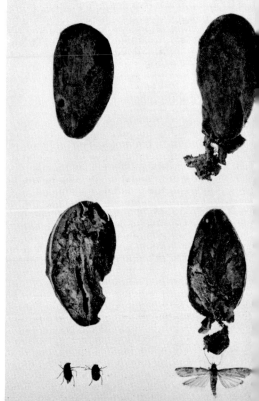

104. Stored cocoa showing external and internal signs of damage by pests. (*Left*) the beetle *Araecerus fasciculatus*. (*Right*) the cocoa moth *Ephestia* sp.

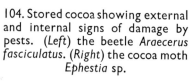

cent. In West Africa the shell percentage of main-crop cocoa is 11 to 12, in the Americas about 14, and may be as high as 16 per cent. When claying was common practice in the West Indies and certain American countries, this added to the weight of the shell, sometimes up to 3 per cent. The earth and dust that collect on the beans in careless handling before bagging, and moulds that may develop later, can give rise to considerable increase in weight of shell, up to 3 per cent in some cases.

The main use of the shell is that of a container for the cocoa nib during transport and storage and it is of practically no value to the manufacturer. It has limited use as a stock feed because of its vitamin D content, but is unsuitable for inclusion in the diet of poultry or young animals because of its theobromine content. Although sometimes used in conjunction with other feeding stuffs for stock, it has, apart from its low nutrient value, the disadvantage that it readily absorbs large quantities of moisture, up to three times its own weight.

The fat content is affected by the bean size. Beans weighing less than 1 gram have a much lower proportion of butter fat than those above that weight. Beans of $\frac{3}{4}$ gram weight have as much as 5 per cent less butter fat than the average bean of 1 gram or over. Since a great part of the chocolate industry is based on the availability of cocoa butter, the amount of fat in the nib is of primary importance. Bean size can, apart from genetic factors, be affected by the season. The mid-crop which develops mainly in the dry season in West Africa has a larger proportion of small beans than the main crop which develops in the wet season. The crop which is harvested in Ghana and Nigeria in May–June is termed "mid-crop" or "light-crop" and the bean weight is below that of the main crop which is harvested in October–January; main-crop beans generally weigh 11 oz. or more per 300 beans. It is sometimes found that where the rainfall has been below normal during the wet season in certain localities the bean size may be below the average for that area.

The shell percentage and bean size are two factors of very considerable economic importance to the manufacturer. Consignments of cocoa with a high shell percentage or an admixture of shrivelled beans with little or no nib or consignments with a large proportion of small beans are much less profitable to manufacture unless they have been bought at a price below that ruling for cocoa of average bean size and shell percentage.

O

Mr. R. V. Wadsworth, formerly Chief Chemist, Cadbury Bros. Ltd., in defining the kind of bean required for manufacture, says:

"The manufacture of cocoa and chocolate requires a cocoa bean which has:

"(i) A brown colour and produces a good, clean, strong chocolate flavour on roasting; in other words, has been well prepared.

"(ii) The lightest shell percentage compatible with protecting cotyledons from breakage; this, as suggested, should be 10 per cent.

"(iii) A high fat content in the cotyledon. Here it is suggested that 60 per cent should be the minimum aimed at by the plant breeder.

"There is no need to emphasize that constancy in these factors is a most desirable quality."

STANDARDS SET BY SOME IMPORTING COUNTRIES

In the U.S.A. there are regulations defining the quality of cocoa to be imported. The United States Pure Food Laws provide that cocoa shall contain not more than 10 per cent mould-plus-weevil, and not more than 5 per cent mould. The New York Cocoa Exchange provides for the following classes:

Class 1. Slatiness not more than 10 per cent and all other defects not more than 8 per cent.

Class 2. Slatiness not more than 10 per cent and all other defects not more than 15 per cent.

Class 3. Slatiness more than 10 per cent but all other defects not more than 8 per cent.

Class 4. Slatiness more than 10 per cent but all other defects not more than 15 per cent.

Cocoa with more than 15 per cent defects other than slatiness is non-tenderable by members.

In the United Kingdom there are no Government restrictions in respect of the quality of imports of cocoa. Cocoa is sold to manufacturers through brokers who belong to associations like the Cocoa Association of London. These have drawn up various types of contracts which, amongst other things, define the quality of the cocoa. Nowadays, cocoa is sold under a type of contract known as A.11. In this the clause defining quality states:

Quality on arrival to be good fermented (or fair fermented); if inferior thereto, a fair allowance, in case of need, is to be made, to be settled by arbitration in London.

Samples from not less than 30 per cent of the sound bags only, weighing approximately not less than 2 kilos, or 4 lb., shall be drawn and sealed promptly at the time of discharge in accordance with Clause 10.

Buyers shall notify Sellers of any claim for inferiority of quality within 28 days of the final day of landing. . . .

The quality stipulated is nearly always "good fermented," for which the limits are 5 per cent defective and 5 per cent slaty. The second grade in the United Kingdom is "fair fermented," with limits of 10 per cent defective and 10 per cent slaty.

In the United States "fair fermented" is the description applied to the Class 1 cocoa already defined—8 per cent defective, 10 per cent slaty.

SAMPLING

Sampling is carried out mainly on large consignments at ports of export or main buying stations. Samples are extracted from a limited number of bags by means of a stab-sampler, and the defects are assessed.

Bulk sampling by this method is an essential and valuable check on bagged cocoa, but it may be deceptive, as odd bags of bad cocoa in a large consignment may be overlooked.

Cocoa sampling cannot approach accuracy unless vast numbers of beans are cut. In West Africa there is often considerable variation in quality between bags and even within individual bags. The "purity" is the percentage of good beans in a sample. A single sample gives a more accurate estimate of the purity of a consignment when the purity is high than when it is low. The estimate is also more reliable when the cocoa is uniform that when it is variable.

Extracts from the Produce Regulations appearing in Appendices IX and X give useful guidance on the framing of such regulations.

REFERENCES

Burton, D. A. J. "The cocoa moth." Cocoa Research Conference, London (1945).

Dade, H. A. "Internal moulding of prepared cocoa." *Gold Coast Dept. of Agric. Year Book* (1928).

The Grading Regulations of Ghana and Nigeria.

Wadsworth, R. V. "The quality of raw cocoa as it affects the manufacturer," *Trop. Agric.* (Jan. 1955), **32**, No. 1.

Waters, H. B. "Errors in sampling cocoa." *Gold Coast Dept. of Agric. Year Book* (1930).

Chapter XIV

WORLD PRODUCTION OF COCOA

Review of Development of Cocoa-planting—Future Expansion—Countries where Further Planting may take place—Development in Ghana—Age Distribution and Output—Influence of Producer Price on Planting—Analysis of some Factors which may Influence Future Production

UNTIL early in the present century the Americas grew most of the cocoa, but the lead was gradually wrested from them by West Africa which has retained its predominant position for the past thirty years. In the past five years Ghana, the Ivory Coast and French Cameroons, and Nigeria, together with the smaller producing countries of West Africa, namely Spanish Guinea, the Congo, São Thomé and Principe, and Brazil in South America accounted for 84 per cent of world production. West African countries alone were responsible for 68 per cent of world output during that period.

REVIEW OF DEVELOPMENT OF COCOA-PLANTING

In common with other tropical crops grown for commercial purposes, cocoa needs suitable conditions of soil and climate and there must be an adequate supply of labour available. These, together with reasonable communications, are basic requirements.

The pattern of cocoa-growing has changed radically in the past sixty years. It was developed first as a commercial crop on individually owned estates. Development by smallholdings took place in the Americas with the liberation of slaves, but planting by companies is a more recent development. The position today is that the growing of cocoa in the important producing territories in West Africa is almost exclusively in the hands of small African farmers. Estates, either company owned or individually owned, are responsible for only a small part of the total production. In Brazil, the bulk of the cocoa is grown by smallholders, but considerable amounts are grown by company-owned and individually owned estates. Elsewhere in the Americas the main production is by medium-sized or large estates, although there is a certain amount of production by smallholders in some of the islands in the Caribbean.

197

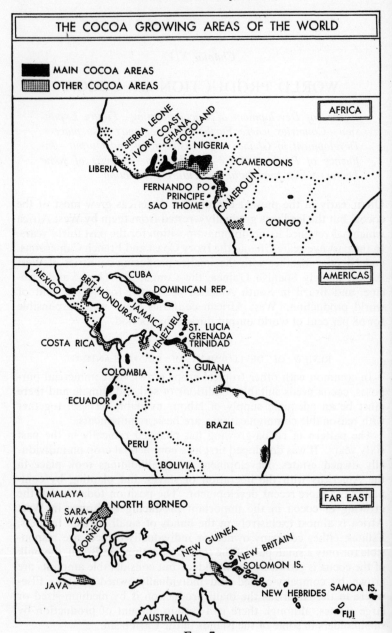

THE COCOA GROWING AREAS OF THE WORLD

■ MAIN COCOA AREAS
▨ OTHER COCOA AREAS

AFRICA

SIERRA LEONE
IVORY COAST
GHANA
TOGOLAND
NIGERIA
LIBERIA
CAMEROONS
FERNANDO PO
PRINCIPE
SAO THOME
CAMEROUN
CONGO

AMERICAS

MEXICO
BRIT. HONDURAS
CUBA
DOMINICAN REP.
JAMAICA
COSTA RICA
VENEZUELA
ST. LUCIA
GRENADA
TRINIDAD
COLOMBIA
GUIANA
ECUADOR
BRAZIL
PERU
BOLIVIA

FAR EAST

MALAYA
SARA-WAK
NORTH BORNEO
BORNEO
NEW GUINEA
NEW BRITAIN
SOLOMON IS.
JAVA
NEW HEBRIDES
SAMOA IS.
FIJI
AUSTRALIA

FIG. 7

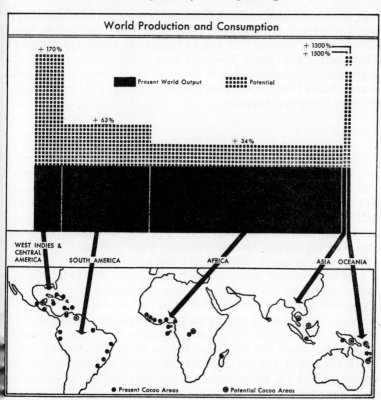

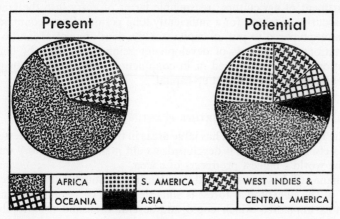

Fig. 8

In Western Samoa, where the industry began as an estate industry, smallholders now produce more than the estates. Similarly, in New Guinea, where previously it was exclusively an estate industry, the inhabitants of the Gazelle Peninsula have of recent years planted up large areas. Developments and trends in Papua and New Guinea indicate that it is only a matter of time before the peasant will become the more important producer.

FUTURE EXPANSION

Large-scale expansion in most countries will, in the future, probably be undertaken by peasant communities and by large companies with substantial capital. Costs have risen so high of recent years that it is difficult for the small man wishing to make a plantation of ten to twenty acres to find the capital necessary to establish his cocoa and subsist until the plantation brings a profitable return. The same applies to the planter who contemplates a few hundred acres.

Peasants who can combine the planting of cocoa with the growing of food crops or cash crops, such as bananas, have little in the way of outlay, apart from the cost of equipment for fermenting and drying. As the cost of these items will have to be met only when the plantation comes into bearing, finding the money need not be difficult.

The extent to which significant planting by companies will take place in the future will depend greatly on the encouragement given by the governments of the countries concerned. Necessary forms of encouragement are the provision of communications; information about the soils and other technical services normally supplied by a department of agriculture; reasonable terms of entry into the land and security of tenure for a sufficiently long period. Some countries are now prepared to put up capital for the development of land by plantations, the process of development being undertaken by corporations locally sponsored or in conjunction with companies who may also be prepared to put up capital.

COUNTRIES WHERE FURTHER PLANTING MAY TAKE PLACE

The French Ivory Coast has large areas in the south-west and lesser areas elsewhere which, if developed, would make that territory one of the world's biggest producers of cocoa.

Ghana still has areas of land for planting, although only a limited part of the unexploited forest is suitable for cocoa. Sufficient land remains unplanted which could add several thousand tons to the present output.

Nigeria has also large areas in the Western Region and some in the Eastern Region still unexploited. The Cameroon has large tracts of land suited for cocoa, especially in Kumba Division.

The Congo, where a high standard of skill is applied to the growing of cocoa, continues to extend the areas under plantations.

In eastern North Borneo there are large tracts of land containing rich volcanic and alluvial soil eminently suited to cocoa. Rainfall is adequate and well distributed; temperatures are suitable. There is exceedingly good growth of cocoa on estates already established. Labour flows freely into this colony from Indonesia. Large-scale development in growing cocoa can be anticipated and North Borneo may well become one of the world's largest producers.

Soil surveys in Malaya indicate that there are large areas of soils with a texture suitable for cocoa. Certain types grow better here than others, and research is going on to decide what is the best type to grow.

The island of New Britain, Bougainville and some of the small islands in this region have been growing cocoa for a number of years. Planting has increased steadily since the war; but the most spectacular increase has been achieved by the peasants of the Gazelle Peninsula who have planted one million trees, mainly through their food farms. There are large areas of land capable of development both on the mainland of Papua-New Guinea and some of the islands. Company planting will expand and there will be a large increase of planting by local tribes, both in the Gazelle Peninsula and, in due course, on the mainland.

Fiji has large areas of land suitable for growing cocoa. Considerable planting may be expected there in due course.

Western Samoa has a large reserve of land as yet untouched, but the need to grow food crops by the rapidly increasing population will eventually set a limit to the area which can be reserved for cocoa. The present annual output is around 4,000 tons and this figure will be increased considerably in the next few years.

Mexico, which has expanded its production in recent years, has further large areas suitable for planting. There is considerable new planting in Costa Rica. Most of the South American countries, including Brazil, are extending their areas under cocoa.

DEVELOPMENT IN GHANA

An analysis of some of the reasons for the slowing down of expansion in Ghana is interesting. Establishing cocoa in Ghana in the early days was a fairly simple and inexpensive process. Forest was cleared, usually within fairly easy reach of the village, and food crops were planted. The land was occupied with food crops for one or two years, and cocoa was planted in the first or second year of farming. The food crops provided the necessary lateral shade, and the weeding and attention given to the other crops were sufficient to enable the cocoa seedlings to establish themselves before the farm was abandoned. Nine to ten years later, the cocoa, having been closely planted, was able to hold its own against the forest growth, and at this stage received attention from the farmer in the form of clearing away the undergrowth and thinning. Cocoa grown in this way took anything from ten to fifteen years to come into bearing, but the cost of establishing it was negligible.

The extra labour, whether employed by the year or as casual labour, was extremely cheap. Some years ago it was common to hire a labourer in the cocoa areas by the year for as little as £5 to £8, with some additions in the form of free farming land and other perquisites.

As time went on, a great part of the area in the Eastern Province of Ghana was planted up in this way and planting spread to Ashanti on similar lines. As land became more difficult to come by in the Eastern Province, people emigrated from there into Ashanti and the Western Province where suitable land was more plentiful.

The planting by groups or individual emigrants was of course on a much smaller scale than that practised by the local farmers who fanned out around the villages of the Eastern Province and in Eastern Ashanti. Most of the areas where this form of expansion took place were remote from large villages, and very often at some distance from roads. Labour here was therefore not readily available. The planting of food crops might or might not be worth while, depending on the accessibility of the site to a motor road.

Thus it will be seen that what might be called the second stage of expanding the cocoa industry in Ghana was and is a much slower process and is also more costly than hitherto.

In more recent years, accessible land has become much scarcer than formerly; the cost of land to the immigrant is higher; labour is scarcer and much more expensive; cost of materials, including cocoa seed, and cocoyam and banana suckers for ground shade, is much higher than previously.

The facilities which made for such rapid expansion in the early stages in the history of the industry in Ghana became less available as time went on. Although planting went on continuously, production, averaged over a number of years, tended to fall slightly rather than to increase. This can be explained by the increased incidence of capsid attack, losses through swollen shoot and heavy losses through black pod in years of unfavourable rainfall. To these influences which limit production may be added the ageing of trees and consequent lowering of yield and the exhaustion of fertility where cocoa was planted on marginal soils.

The conditions which made for rapid expansion of production in Ghana, followed by slowing down of output, apply to the other important producing countries of West Africa and to some extent to Brazil.

AGE DISTRIBUTION IN RELATION TO OUTPUT

It has been stated that cocoa gives its best yield between the ages of 15 to 25 or 30 years. It will, of course, continue to give a high yield for much longer than this on the best soils, but on poor or marginal soils, yield-decline will set in earlier. The history of cocoa-planting indicates that there is a large proportion of the world's cocoa over 30 years old and as a great deal of it is planted on indifferent soils, the yield of a considerable part of the cocoa of the world may be expected to be on the decline. Quite apart from what might be called "natural ageing," premature senility is induced widely by insect attack and to a lesser extent by fungus and virus.

It is self-evident that the cocoa to be reaped during the next five to ten years must come from cocoa already planted. There is not sufficient information on planting which has taken place throughout the world in the past ten years to make it possible to estimate how far new plantings will influence total world production in the near future. In Ghana, where the proportion of new planting is higher than in most other countries, it is estimated that some 33 per cent of the trees are over 30 years old; that 40 per cent are between 15 and 30 years old and 27 per cent are under 15 years old. Estimates of age distribution in Nigeria indicated the percentages of trees in the same age groups to be roughly similar, and the same applies to the Ivory Coast.

The percentages of young cocoa in these three important cocoa-producing countries are reasonably high, and are much higher than are to be found in any of the Americas, with the possible exception of Mexico.

INFLUENCE OF PRODUCER PRICE ON PLANTING

A great deal has been written about the influence of price on planting. While it is certain that a prolonged period of low prices slows down planting throughout the world, a few years of high prices do not lead to an immediate increase in planting. It is equally true that short periods of phenomenally high prices do not necessarily alter the general trend of planting. The greatest stimulus to planting is provided where prices to the producer are maintained at a profitable level for several years.

ANALYSIS OF SOME FACTORS WHICH WILL INFLUENCE FUTURE PRODUCTION

It is not possible to apply statistical methods to estimate future world production year by year, or to estimate the average annual production during the next five or ten years. Even if the areas planted, and the areas which have gone out of production could be estimated with accuracy, it would still be impossible to compute what production should be. Weather is the main factor in influencing high or low outputs. Weather conditions in the large producing countries of West Africa and Brazil may be responsible for raising or lowering world production in any one year by thousands of tons.

A high or unfavourably distributed rainfall may result in a high incidence of black pod and consequently lower output. A low rainfall may operate to the advantage of the crop, as was seen in West Africa in the season of exceptionally low rainfall in 1956–7, when a record crop was harvested. An exceptionally low rainfall may, however, result in a low yield, as has happened in Brazil on one occasion. A low rainfall may also cause a setback to cocoa on the lighter soils.

Increased production will depend on several factors and some of these are:

1. Exploitation of new land.
2. Replanting of land previously in cocoa and the rehabilitation of old plantations.
3. The success with which pests and diseases can be kept under control.
4. The extent to which improvements in cocoa culture can be evolved and adopted. These would include the use of mineral manures, including trace elements, to stimulate increased yields, to maintain yields at profitable levels and to make profitable the use of lands which would otherwise be marginal or unprofitable.
5. The extent to which scientists are able to provide improved plant material, capable of giving good yields and adaptable to a wide range of conditions of soil and climate and not unduly susceptible to pests and diseases.

Considerable areas of land have been planted within the past ten years. There has been some planting in the form of estates but most of it has been by small farmers. A good deal has taken place in Ghana where there is estimated to be about one million acres of new plantings and replanting of areas previously in cocoa. Although considerable advances have been made by farmers in West Africa in the matter of planting and tending their trees in recent years, it is still true that a great deal of the cocoa planted by small farmers in that country will take from ten to fifteen years to come into bearing, so that the full effect of this extensive planting will not be evident for a long time. Furthermore, although measures for pest and disease control are now being extensively employed in Ghana, quite large areas of the cocoa planted during the past ten years will not have had, for instance, the benefit of spraying and will consequently have been set back or killed by capsids. Again, a proportion of the new plantings will have been on poor soil or soil overlying hardpan and will therefore die off. An area approaching 100,000 acres, cut out in the process of controlling virus disease, has to be set off against the net increase of total output. It might be misleading to take figures of estimated new plantings and multiply them by an assumed figure of out-turn of so much per acre in order to arrive at a possible net increase, without giving due weight to the points mentioned above. These reservations apply in a greater or less degree when the effect of new plantings in Nigeria and the Ivory Coast also is being considered.

In the past four years great advances have been made in West Africa in techniques for controlling capsids and reducing losses from black pod. If there is extensive and sustained application of these techniques in the larger producing countries in West Africa, output will be increased by several thousand tons. It must, however, be emphasized that large increases in world output can only be brought about by the extensive, efficient and sustained application of control measures in the main producing countries.

Due to the work of agriculturists, specialists and planters, a great deal has been learned about the effect of environment, but so far none of this knowledge can be applied in a general way to ensure much improved results in cocoa culture. There have been some useful results from the use of mineral manures and trace elements here and there, but these results will not be applied on a sufficiently extensive scale to increase world output for a long time hence.

Plant breeders both in West Africa and Trinidad have had spectacular success in evolving high-yielding strains of cocoa. Again, it must be appreciated that the effect of this work on world output will not be felt for some time to come.

During the past five years 1952–3 to 1956–7, annual world output has averaged 800,000 tons. In this figure is included the record output of nearly 900,000 tons for 1956–7 and would include figures for mid-crops of that season. On the basis of these figures it would seem reasonable to assume that due to the increase in the area under cocoa, and the fact that pest and disease control is now more efficient, an average annual output of 800,000 tons and upwards could be expected in the next five years. However, if reference is made to past figures of world production, such an assumption may be unduly optimistic. For instance, in 1938–9 world output was 787,000 tons, but ten years later, 1947–8, it was 603,000 tons, a matter of 184,000 tons less. In 1950–1 output was 803,000 tons but the following season it was 636,000 tons, a drop of 167,000 tons. The most significant figure of all is the average output for the ten-year period 1941 to 1951 which was 663,500 tons.

It will generally be accepted that the record high output of 1956–7 was due to the coincidence over the whole of West Africa of particular weather conditions which stimulated a high yield. The same was true for Brazil. The importance of weather conditions becomes obvious when the 1956–7 figure of some 900,000 tons is compared with the output in 1951–2, only six years previously, when the world output was 636,000 tons, which is 264,000 tons less. Compared with the output (603,000 tons) for 1947–8 ten years previously, the difference is some 300,000 tons.

The figures for world production in the past five years indicate a definite upward trend, and apart from the fact that the good average out-turn is in part due to a succession of favourable seasons, some of the increase is due to new plantings. Since much of the new planting has taken place within the past ten years, its effect on world output will be more noticeable during the next eight to ten years.

CONCLUSION

In view of the fact that the weather can influence annual output by between 200,000 and 300,000 tons within a few seasons, it would be idle to attempt accurate forecasts of annual world production during, say, the next five years. What can be said with confidence in this connection is that world potential production has increased in recent years, and, as the result of new plantings particularly, there will be a gradual increase in world output in the next ten years. The order of the increases will not be such as to embarrass the manufacturer or the distributor, or depress prices to the level which will make cocoa an unprofitable crop for the producer. Even if world production went up by an average of 100,000 or 150,000 tons per annum during the next ten years, this amount can readily be absorbed in world markets.

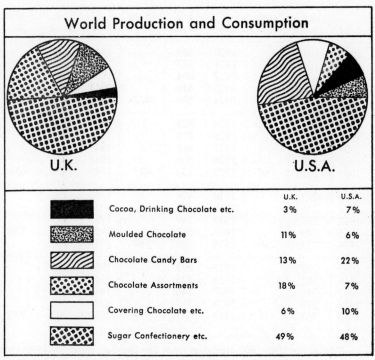

World Production and Consumption

		U.K.	U.S.A.
■	Cocoa, Drinking Chocolate etc.	3%	7%
▨	Moulded Chocolate	11%	6%
▨	Chocolate Candy Bars	13%	22%
▨	Chocolate Assortments	18%	7%
□	Covering Chocolate etc.	6%	10%
▨	Sugar Confectionery etc.	49%	48%

Fig. 9 COCOA PRODUCTS ACCOUNT FOR MORE THAN HALF
OF THE CONFECTIONERY OUTPUT IN UNITED KINGDOM AND U.S.A.

TABLE No. 10

WORLD PRODUCTION OF RAW COCOA

(*in thousand long tons*)

Year	Ann. Prod.	5-year Av.	Year	Ann. Prod.	5-year Av.	Year	Ann. Prod.	5-year Av.
1900	101		1920	369		1940	670	
1901	106		1921	387		1941	654	
1902	125		1922	404		1942	662	
1903	126		1923	449		1943	601	
1904	149	121	1924	500	422	1944	554	628
1905	144		1925	488		1945	614	
1906	147		1926	470		1946	618	
1907	148		1927	481		1947	621	
1908	189		1928	506		1948	603	
1909	201	166	1929	529	495	1949	779	654
1910	217		1930	479		1950	756	
1911	236		1931	524		1951	802	
1912	227		1932	549		1952	635	
1913	249		1933	617		1953	787	750
1914	273	240	1934	580	550	1954	770	
1915	292		1935	691		1955	784	
1916	292		1936	725		1956	833	
1917	343		1937	746		1957	886	
1918	270		1938	717		1958	768	
1919	463	332	1939	787	733	1959	903	835

Figures for 1900–1930 are taken from *The Gordian*; those for 1930–1946 from the paper given by L. A. Byles at the 1951 London Cocoa Conference, and those for 1947–1958 from Gill and Duffus.

105. Imperial College of Tropical Agriculture, Trinidad

106. Cocoa being carried by headload from a farm in Ghana to which there are no roads. Transport in this way may cost a farmer 12s. 6d. per load of 60 lb. to get the cocoa to where it can be collected by motor vehicle

107. West African Cacao Research Institute. Tafo, Ghana

	1954–5		1955–6		1956–7		1957–8		1958–9		Est. 1959–60	
	Production	% of Total	Production	% of Total	Production	% of Total	Production	% of Total	Production	% of Total	Production	% of Total
AFRICA												
Ghana	220	28·1	237	28·5	264	29·9	200	26·5	255	28·3	315	30·8
Nigeria	89	11·4	114	13·7	135	15·3	85	11·2	140	15·6	150	14·7
Ivory Coast	73	9·3	70	8·4	72	8·1	46	6·1	55	6·1	57	5·6
Cameroons	58	7·4	60	7·2	62	7·0	67	8·9	59	6·6	62	6·1
Spanish Guinea	21	2·7	19	2·3	23	2·6	21	2·8	22	2·5	27	2·6
São Thomé and Principe	8	1·0	8	1·0	8	0·9	9	1·2	8	1·0	8	0·8
Togoland	16	2·0	6	0·8	4	0·5	5	0·7	8	0·9	8	0·8
Sierra Leone	2	0·3	2	0·2	2	0·2	3	0·4	3	0·3	3	0·3
Congo	4	0·5	4	0·5	5	0·6	5	0·7	4	0·4	5	0·5
Other Africa	1	0·1	1	0·1	1	0·1	1	0·1	1	0·1	2	0·2
TOTAL: AFRICA	492	62·8	521	62·7	576	65·2	442	58·6	556	61·8	637	62·4
AMERICA												
Brazil	139	17·7	168	20·2	158	17·9	148	19·6	173	19·2	203	19·8
Ecuador	30	3·8	27	3·2	28	3·2	28	3·7	33	3·7	34	3·3
Venezuela	18	2·3	16	1·9	14	1·6	16	2·1	15	1·7	15	1·4
Colombia	15	1·9	15	1·8	14	1·6	15	2·0	19	2·1	19	1·9
Costa Rica	9	1·1	7	0·9	7	0·8	8	1·1	12	1·4	10	1·0
Mexico	12	1·5	14	1·7	14	1·6	17	2·2	16	1·8	17	1·7
Peru	4	0·5	4	0·5	4	0·5	4	0·5	4	0·4	4	0·4
Panama	2	0·3	1	0·1	2	0·2	2	0·3	2	0·2	2	0·2
Bolivia	3	0·4	3	0·4	3	0·3	3	0·4	3	0·3	3	0·3
Other America	2	0·3	2	0·2	2	0·2	2	0·3	2	0·2	2	0·2
TOTAL: AMERICA	234	29·8	257	30·9	246	27·9	243	32·2	279	31·0	309	30·2

TABLE No. 11—*continued*

WORLD PRODUCTION OF RAW COCOA (THOUSAND LONG TONS)

	1954-5		1955-6		1956-7		1957-8		1958-9		Est. 1959-60	
	Production	% of Total	Production	% of Total	Production	% of Total	Production	% of Total	Production	% of Total	Production	% of Total
WEST INDIES												
Dominican Republic	29	3·7	27	3·2	33	3·8	37	4·9	31	3·5	36	3·5
Trinidad and Tobago	8	1·0	9	1·1	8	0·9	9	1·2	8	0·9	7	0·7
Grenada	3	0·4	1	0·1	1	0·1	1	0·1	2	0·2	2	0·2
Jamaica	3	0·4	2	0·2	3	0·3	3	0·4	3	0·2	3	0·3
Cuba	3	0·4	2	0·2	3	0·3	3	0·4	3	0·3	3	0·3
Haiti	2	0·3	2	0·2	2	0·2	2	0·3	2	0·2	2	0·2
Other West Indies	1	0·1	1	0·1	1	0·1	1	0·1	1	0·1	1	0·1
TOTAL: WEST INDIES	49	6·3	44	5·1	51	5·7	56	7·4	49	5·4	54	5·3
ASIA AND OCEANIA												
Ceylon	2	0·3	3	0·4	3	0·3	3	0·4	3	0·3	3	0·3
Indonesia	1	0·1	1	0·1	1	0·1	1	0·1	1	0·1	1	0·1
New Guinea	1	0·1	1	0·1	2	0·2	3	0·4	5	0·6	6	0·6
New Hebrides	1	0·1	1	0·1	1	0·1	1	0·1	1	0·1	1	0·1
Western Samoa	3	0·4	4	0·5	3	0·3	4	0·5	4	0·5	6	0·6
Philippines	1	0·1	1	0·1	2	0·2	2	0·3	2	0·2	4	0·4
TOTAL: ASIA AND OCEANIA	9	1·1	11	1·3	12	1·2	14	1·8	16	1·8	21	2·1
WORLD TOTAL	784	100·0	833	100·0	885	100·0	755	100·0	900	100	1,021	100

TABLE No. 12
WORLD CONSUMPTION OF RAW COCOA (THOUSAND LONG TONS)

	1955		1956		1957		1958		1959		Est. 1960	
	Consumption	% of Total	Consumption	% of Total	Consumption	% of Total	Consumption	% of Total	Consumption	% of Total	Consumption	% of Total
AMERICA												
United States	188	26·6	223	27·9	231	25·8	196	24·6	202	23·8	212	23·6
Canada	13	1·8	14	1·8	14	1·6	12	1·5	12	1·4	13	1·4
Brazil	31	4·4	35	4·4	49	5·5	30	3·7	58	6·8	62	6·9
Argentina	6	0·8	6	0·7	6	0·7	5	0·6	4	0·5	7	0·8
Colombia	26	3·7	23	2·9	24	2·7	24	3·0	25	3·0	25	2·8
Mexico	7	1·0	10	1·2	10	1·1	9	1·1	11	1·3	11	1·2
Dominican Republic	10	1·4	10	1·2	10	1·1	10	1·3	12	1·4	13	1·5
Other America	15	2·1	15	1·9	16	1·8	18	2·3	22	2·6	22	2·5
TOTAL: AMERICA	296	41·9	336	42·0	360	40·2	304	38·1	346	40·8	365	40·7
EUROPE												
United Kingdom	102	14·4	93	11·6	109	12·2	95	11·9	73	8·6	79	8·8
Netherlands	56	7·9	66	8·3	77	8·6	70	8·8	74	8·7	79	8·8
Germany	72	10·2	90	11·3	106	11·8	100	12·6	109	12·9	115	12·9
France	43	6·1	51	6·4	62	6·9	50	6·3	49	5·8	50	5·6
Spain	15	2·1	20	2·5	22	2·5	20	2·5	20	2·3	21	2·4
U.S.S.R.	16	2·3	16	2·0	20	2·2	20	2·5	25	2·9	25	2·8
Switzerland	9	1·3	10	1·2	11	1·2	10	1·3	11	1·3	11	1·2
Sweden	6	0·8	8	1·0	7	0·8	7	0·9	7	0·8	7	0·8
Italy	19	2·7	22	2·8	28	3·1	22	2·8	26	3·0	28	3·1

TABLE No. 12—continued

WORLD CONSUMPTION OF RAW COCOA (THOUSAND LONG TONS)

	1955		1956		1957		1958		1959		Est. 1960	
	Consumption	% of Total	Consumption	% of Total	Consumption	% of Total	Consumption	% of Total	Consumption	% of Total	Consumption	% of Total
EUROPE—*contd.*												
Belgium	8	1·1	9	1·1	10	1·1	9	1·1	9	1·1	10	1·1
Czechoslovakia	4	0·6	5	0·6	6	0·7	6	0·7	10	1·2	11	1·2
Poland	3	0·4	4	0·5	5	0·6	8	1·0	9	1·1	10	1·1
Austria	7	1·0	9	1·1	10	1·1	10	1·3	9	1·1	9	1·0
Denmark	2	0·3	3	0·4	4	0·4	4	0·5	3	0·4	3	0·3
Norway	4	0·6	4	0·5	4	0·4	4	0·5	4	0·5	4	0·4
Hungary	1	0·1	2	0·3	1	0·1	1	0·1	2	0·2	3	0·3
Portugal	1	0·1	1	0·1	1	0·1	1	0·1	1	0·1	1	0·1
Ireland	5	0·7	4	0·5	4	0·4	4	0·5	6	0·7	6	0·7
Other Europe	9	1·3	10	1·2	11	1·2	10	1·3	6	0·7	7	0·8
TOTAL: EUROPE	382	54·1	427	53·4	498	55·6	451	56·7	453	53·4	479	53·4
TOTAL: AUSTRALIA AND OCEANIA	11	1·6	10	1·2	14	1·6	12	1·5	14	1·7	14	1·6
TOTAL: AFRICA	9	1·3	18	2·3	12	1·3	18	2·3	20	2·3	21	2·3
TOTAL: ASIA	8	1·1	9	1·1	12	1·3	11	1·4	15	1·8	18	2·0
WORLD TOTAL	706	100·0	800	100·0	896	100·0	796	100·0	848	100	897	100

TABLE NO. 13

COCOA PROCESSED IN COUNTRY OF ORIGIN
(*Thousand Long Tons*)

	1953	1954	1955	1956	1957	1958 (est.)
Brazil	37	24	31	36	49	30
Colombia	23	22	26	23	24	24
Ghana	14	2	—	6	—	5
Mexico	8	8	7	10	10	9
Dominican Republic	10	11	10	10	10	10
Others	19	20	20	23	27	29
Total	111	87	94	108	120	107

Chapter XV

WORLD CONSUMPTION OF COCOA

Main Consuming Countries—Importance of Price—Difficulties of Forecasting Supply and Demand—Economies in Use of Cocoa in Manufacture—Possibility of Change of Habit of Consumers—Conclusions

MAIN CONSUMING COUNTRIES

OVER three-quarters of the world's raw cocoa is consumed in seven countries. A third of the whole is consumed by the United States, and the United Kingdom, which is next in importance, accounts for one-sixth. Other important consumers are Germany, the Netherlands and France which take 8, 7 and 6 per cent respectively, and, finally, Canada and Colombia, each taking 3 per cent. Europe as a whole takes about 50 per cent of all cocoa beans, American countries take about 45 per cent.

A number of cocoa-producing countries manufacture cocoa beans into various edible products, but processing in producing countries is mainly directed to the manufacture of cocoa butter. The manufacture of cocoa butter in cocoa-growing countries has of late, however, proved less profitable than formerly and many of the cocoa-butter factories have closed down.

IMPORTANCE OF THE PRICE OF RAW COCOA

The future of the cocoa industry in all its aspects eventually depends on the popularity of the products of the cocoa bean with the consumer, and this in turn depends to a considerable degree on the availability of these products to the public at prices competitive with other types of confectionery.

An inadequate supply of raw beans over a period results in an increase in price, and if the increase is unduly great, as reflected in the retail price of the finished product, chocolate is placed at a disadvantage in relation to other types of confectionery. This leads to a decline in demand for raw beans, a drop in their market price, and consequent check to production. Furthermore, following on periods of high prices, manufacturers find ways and means of economizing in the use of cocoa products. From the point of view of the producer

214

the important result that finally emerges is that less cocoa is in demand, and even a normal annual production may give rise to a surplus and a consequent fall in the price of raw cocoa.

DIFFICULTIES OF FORECASTING SUPPLY AND DEMAND

Since world production of raw cocoa ceased to expand in the early forties, the amount of cocoa available to consuming countries is less in relation to population than before the war, and this has led to a keener demand and rise in price.

Apart from a general shortage of cocoa in relation to requirements, there are other factors which influence seasonal upward fluctuations in the price of raw cocoa. The lack of information about the stocks of raw beans on hand at any one time, and therefore the uncertainty about the demand in the immediate future in relation to possible supply creates a problem for the manufacturer. This condition of uncertainty may be remedied in time by the collection and dissemination of accurate information. There is also the impossibility of forecasting the out-turn of crop in the major cocoa-producing countries and the consequent uncertainty about the possible demand for available supplies. In West Africa, the ritual of crop-forecasting begins in late September and is continued at intervals until late December. No technique of forecasting has yet been evolved which can foretell with any accuracy for, say, two months ahead, what the crop will be. "Authoritative" forecasts in Ghana, for instance, made in late September and October, can be wrong by as much as 30,000 tons or more for the main season crop. A forecast of the two crop seasons in Brazil can also be highly inaccurate. A bad season in the main producing countries of West Africa and in Brazil could depress output by as much as 100,000 tons if it occurred within the same twelve months. As the availability of raw cocoa is seasonal, the manufacturer has to buy it while it is on the market, either for his immediate needs or to supplement his stocks, and sometimes he pays a great deal more for what he buys than is justified by the state of the supply. This was illustrated in the violent upward fluctuation of cocoa price in 1953–4. The out-turn of cocoa for that season was 753,000 tons, which was actually above the average of the previous five years, which was 752,000 tons, so that the extremely high prices which ruled for part of this season were not strictly related to an abnormal shortage of cocoa beans.

ECONOMIES IN THE USE OF COCOA IN MANUFACTURE

The eventual effects, at the manufacturing and distributing end, of extremely high-priced cocoa beans, are manifold. Manufacturers may effect economies by adjusting the formula for making chocolate and increase the proportion of other ingredients, thereby using from 10 to 20 per cent less of cocoa beans while still producing the same amount of chocolate confectionery as formerly. The United Kingdom in recent years has used 10 per cent less cocoa material in the manufacture of about normal quantities of chocolate confectionery, but with a lower chocolate content. Some United States manufacturers have economized by reducing the size of the chocolate bar, and increasing the content of nuts and fillers. Although there has been a steady rise in population and in income in the U.S., consumption of cocoa beans was 25 per cent lower in 1955 than in the years 1938 to 1941. This was offset to some extent by an increase in the import of unsweetened cocoa, which rose from 12,000 tons in 1950 to 30,000 tons in 1954. Most of this was used for adding to soft drinks or ice-cream, or for the manufacture of coatings in conjunction with cocoa butter substitutes. The serious trend here from the producer's point of view is the extent to which the manufacturer is economizing in the use of cocoa butter.

POSSIBILITY OF CHANGE OF HABIT OF THE CONSUMER

The most important and lasting repercussion that may result from unduly high prices of cocoa products is that the fashion and habit of the public may change from the consumption of chocolate confectionery to that of other relatively cheaper kinds. When this happens it may take a long time to reinstate the popularity of chocolate in competition with alternatives. Of this, Germany is a striking example. Here, production of confectionery increased from 130,000 tons in 1954 to 144,000 tons in 1955, but there was no corresponding increase in the production of chocolate confectionery. In the United Kingdom production of chocolate products fell from 280,000 tons to 260,000 tons during the same period. In other important consuming countries there has been a similar trend and the consumption of other types of sugar confectionery has increased in relation to chocolate.

The extent to which there will be a sustained or increased demand for chocolate confectionery in the future will be vitally influenced by the price of this product in relation to alternatives. During 1952 to 1953 the price of sugar confectionery in the United Kingdom fell slightly but the price of chocolate rose on average by over 2d.

per lb. Sales of sugar confectionery increased by 133,000 metric tons whereas those of chocolate rose by only 61,000 metric tons.

CONCLUSIONS

While the above analysis of the situation may sound pessimistic, the fact remains that the consumption of cocoa in all its forms is an established habit which will continue as long as there is chocolate available to consume. The continued prosperity of the industry lies in having greater quantities of raw cocoa to manufacture and distribute. The increase in populations with rising incomes must eventually lead to greater consumption. In those countries which at present take 90 per cent of the cocoa beans, the populations will in the normal course increase by about 4·5 per cent and incomes per head will possibly increase by some 10 per cent in the next few years. Should the Soviet Union and her satellites increase their intake substantially, the effect on demand would be very appreciable. The use of cocoa beans in the U.S.S.R. has risen from 10,000 tons during the years 1946 to 1950 to 25,000 tons in 1954. There are many other countries with increasing populations and rising incomes which·are potential markets for cocoa.

The grower is naturally interested in the maintenance of a price which will ensure a profitable margin between costs of production and world price. The prospects are that the demand for raw beans in the foreseeable future will be such as to provide a satisfactory return to the producer.

REFERENCES

Bareau, Paul. *Cocoa—A Crop with a Future* (Cadbury Brothers Ltd., Bournville, 1953).

Cacao, F.A.O. Bulletin 27, Commodity Series.

Cocoa, Chocolate and Confectionery Alliance Reports of Cocoa Conferences (London, 1946, 1949, 1951, and 1953).

Commission on Marketing of West African Cocoa, Cd. 5854 (1938).

Gill and Duffus, *Cocoa Statistics*.

The Main Products of the Overseas Territories: Cocoa. Organization for European Economic Co-operation.

Report of the Cocoa Conference organized by the Cocoa, Chocolate and Confectionery Alliance, 1955.

Report of the Office International du Cacao et du Chocolat held in Amsterdam, April, 1955.

Wadsworth, R. V. "The quality of raw cocoa as it affects the manufacturer," *Trop. Agric.* (Jan. 1955), **32**, No. 1.

Chapter XVI

COCOA MARKETING

*Development of Marketing — Marketing Associations —
Main Markets—Marketing Boards and Subsidiaries—Terminal Markets*

COCOA marketing is the process whereby the ownership of cocoa beans is transferred from the producer to the manufacturer of cocoa and chocolate products.

Until recently, producers sent their cocoa to London and other consuming centres where it was sold by auction. Manufacturers received samples which they roasted, and orders were placed for the particular parcels which suited their recipes. Auctions in their original form were known as "Sales by the Candle" for in those days a lighted candle was set on the auctioneer's desk with pins stuck at intervals down its side. The last bid before the pin fell out secured the parcel.

This was marketing in its simplest form. Both the producers and manufacturers used brokers in London and other established trading centres to look after their respective interests and advise them of market conditions, valuations, etc., for which services they were paid a brokerage.

DEVELOPMENT OF MARKETING

With the growth of more standard grades in the larger producing countries, however, and, allied with it, the greater demand for block chocolate as against chocolate confectionery, less cumbersome methods of marketing gradually came into being.

Thereafter a different method of trading developed. Consequent on increasing production in West Africa and Brazil, manufacturers were able to buy large quantities of cocoa of a standard quality, and were anxious to meet the increased demand and cover their needs for many months ahead, at times even a year.

It was only natural that producers were not willing to commit themselves to selling their cocoa so far ahead, and there developed in the market a class of trader known as a dealer, who was prepared to offer cocoa for the "position" that manufacturers wanted.

It is obvious that no firm would be prepared to run the risks of market fluctuation for long periods.

Terminal markets were therefore opened in London and New York, which enabled dealers to "hedge" their sales. This method of trading has been so finely developed that a producer can at any time find a buyer for any desired portion of his crop even though the cocoa may not yet be on the trees and, on the other hand, a manufacturer can buy his requirements for delivery into his factory at an appointed date. With the rise of the large Marketing Boards in West Africa the importance of the dealer in the world's markets has increased rather than diminished.

MARKETING ASSOCIATIONS

As the business in cocoa grew, bringing new complications, Associations were formed to draw up contracts, regulate disputes and, in general, look after the interests of all those involved in the trade. Such was the Cocoa Association of London, formed in 1926 with a Board of Directors consisting of shippers, producers, manufacturers, brokers and dealers. The rules of the Association are universally known and accepted, and most of the cocoa trade in the world is governed by the Rules of the Cocoa Association of London. The U.S.A. has its own association and rules.

The Cocoa Association of London has several different Contract Forms currently in use to cover the various methods of trading, but the most important ones are Contracts A.11 and A.14, which are used exclusively for West Africa cocoa sold on c.i.f. (cost, insurance and freight) terms and Contract A.14 used for all other cocoa whether sold f.o.b. (free on board), c. and f. (cost and freight) or c.i.f. terms.

In all these Contracts, the seller guarantees that the goods are of the descriptions contracted for and that the weight of cocoa arriving is within a small tolerance of the amount agreed to be shipped.

On arrival, the cocoa is weighed and sampled by independent firms of wharfingers, and buyers and sellers appoint supervisors to check the weights and see that the samples are properly drawn. Should buyers consider the samples are not up to Contract standard, they may claim an allowance from the seller. If the seller does not agree, the matter is settled by arbitration.

MAIN MARKETS

Of world output of raw cocoa, the United States uses over 200,000 tons, the U.K. nearly 100,000, Holland 70,000, France 55,000 and

Germany (Western and Eastern) upwards of 90,000 tons. These figures refer only to grindings of raw cocoa and ignore exports and imports of cocoa butter, cocoa powder and cake. Much of the raw cocoa imported into Holland, for example, is exported in the form of powder and butter. Each of these countries has its own cocoa marketing centre, where internal and international transactions take place. London, for example, deals with 400,000–500,000 tons of cocoa each year, the cocoa finding its way to factories all over the world.

MARKETING BOARDS AND SUBSIDIARIES

In Ghana and Nigeria, there are Government-sponsored Marketing Boards, and sales of cocoa from both countries are made by the Board's subsidiary selling company in London.

Before 1939 some of the cocoa in both the Gold Coast and Nigeria was bought from the farmers by manufacturers who shipped it home, and some by trading firms who sold their purchases on the cocoa markets of the world.

With the advent of the Marketing Boards in 1947–8 the buying organizations of the manufacturers and trading firms became Licensed Buying Agents of the Marketing Boards. All cocoa bought from the farmers is now handed over to the Boards, the price to the farmer being fixed by the Boards and effective for twelve months, as from October 1st. For their requirements of Ghana and Nigerian cocoas, manufacturers must buy from the Board's subsidiary companies in London at the world market price.

It has been the custom of the Board's selling companies to sell the bulk of Ghana and Nigerian cocoa through the London market.

In all other major producing countries there are various Government schemes in force ensuring a minimum price to producers and in the selling of their cocoa to the markets of the world some form of Government price control is operative.

Other cocoas, especially the limited quantities of fine grades, are often sold against samples.

TERMINAL MARKETS

Terminal or futures markets are in existence for a variety of commodities, such as cocoa, sugar, rubber, cotton, wheat, tin and lead.

Briefly, trading takes place in certain quoted months up to twelve months ahead. In London contracts are for multiples of 5 tons, and on the New York market for units of 30,000 lb. Certain specified grades of cocoa at fixed premiums or discounts may be delivered at the seller's option against the contract, when the month of delivery of that contract arrives. Every contract made on the London terminal market is registered with an independent body, the London Produce Clearing House, which guarantees the fulfilment of the contract.

The market's primary function is to act as a hedging medium for operations in raw cocoa. An example of hedging follows.

A dealer sells to a manufacturer a certain type of cocoa for delivery twelve months ahead at a premium of 10s. over the price quoted on the terminal for the same position. At the time of making his sale, he purchases the same quantity of terminal. This purchase of terminal is his hedge and so his position is as follows:

Sale to manufacturer	200s. per cwt.
Purchase of terminal	190s. per cwt.

Having now a sale and purchase he has no worries about whether the market goes up or down. His only interest now is to "undo his hedge," i.e. to purchase the actual cocoa he has to deliver to the manufacturer and sell his terminal at a profitable differential.

The market has in the meantime moved upward and he eventually purchases the cocoa he needs to deliver to the manufacturer at 250s. per cwt., and at the same time sells his terminal at 245s. per cwt.

Thus his final result works out as follows:

Sale to manufacturer	200s.	Purchase of Terminal	190s.
Purchase of cocoa to fulfil sale	250s.	Sale of Terminal	245s.
Loss	50s.	Profit	55s.

Net profit, 5s. per cwt.

From this small illustration can be seen the great safeguard that terminal markets provide in helping the orderly marketing of cocoa with the minimum of risk, particularly in wildly fluctuating markets.

SOIL SURVEYS

THE first requirement for growing cocoa in any part of the world is the availability of a suitable soil.

For a long time past soil surveys have been recognized in the U.S.A. as essential for schemes of land-planning and land-use. New Zealand was among the first of the countries of the British Commonwealth to make use of soil surveys, and they are now being conducted in most British colonial territories. Larger countries may employ their own teams or departments of soil survey, or have survey officers as a division of the Department of Agriculture. Some countries with small Departments of Agriculture and with large extents of territory to survey find it more convenient to employ teams to carry out this work on contract.

SOIL SURVEYS IN GHANA

Ghana was the first country in Africa to form a Division of Soil Surveys within the Department of Agriculture, and this later developed as an independent department under the late C. F. Charter.

The need for assessing the potentialities of the forest zone, especially as regards land suitable for further planting of cocoa, was appreciated by the farmers and Chiefs in Ghana, and in 1948 a grant of £150,000 was made from the funds of the Cocoa Marketing Board to provide the necessary laboratories, buildings, and staff to conduct a soil survey.

It was recognized that in such a relatively undeveloped country, natural regions determined by drainage systems of river basins provided a convenient framework on which soil maps could be based. It was therefore planned to take each drainage basin in turn. The following is an outline of the methods evolved by Charter:

The first step is a preliminary survey to obtain a general idea of the soils, soil associations, and their distribution. Information obtained in regard to communications and sites for possible field bases is noted.

The next two steps are described by C. F. Charter as follows:

Reconnaissance Soil Surveys

Reconnaissance soil surveys are carried out by teams of African assistants taking observations along parallel traverse lines a mile and a

223

quarter apart. A small team of land surveyors marks the starting points of traverse lines, which usually commence along roads or trails, in advance of the reconnaissance teams. These teams consist of six assistants, with one or two spares, and a dozen or so labourers. A reconnaissance team comprises a direction-giver with prismatic compass and ranging poles, who is responsible for the cutting of traverse lines; a distance-measurer supplied with a Gunter's chain, who also keeps a running commentary on the topographical features traversed; a vegetation-recorder who maps the vegetation of a circular area of one-quarter acre at each furlong; and three soil-recorders, one of whom is the team leader, who are equipped with spades, soil chisels, and augers and who, at every furlong, describe inspection holes and collect soil and rock specimens for later examination. Inspection holes are sunk to a depth of four feet and the following data collected for each soil layer observed: thickness; colour; presence or absence of organic matter; texture, that is whether sandy or clayey, based on feel; consistency based on ease of augering, etc.; presence or absence of gravel or concretions, etc., etc.

Detailed Soil Surveys of Sample Strips

Within each soil association mapped by reconnaissance methods, detailed soil surveys are made of representative sample strips measuring two furlongs in width and a mile in length. Traverse lines are run half a furlong apart throughout the length of these strips and observations are taken along these lines and along short offsets at right angles to them so that information can be collected to enable contour, soil, and vegetation maps to be prepared on a scale of ten inches to the mile. In each soil mapped a six-foot profile pit is dug and samples of each layer making up the soil are carefully collected for purposes of correlation and laboratory analysis. This work is performed by detailed soil survey teams which are similarly constituted to those employed on reconnaissance, but their members have additional training and experience, and make use of more advanced techniques.

At the headquarters or main base the soil samples are collected and correlated, and from the information derived from the field, maps are made which show the boundaries of the various soils.

It will be appreciated that a soil survey on this scale requires careful planning. Much detailed work is needed before the final stage is reached where maps are produced on which future land-planning and land-use will be based.

COSTS OF COCOA CULTURE ON ESTATES AND PEASANT FARMS

GENERAL CONSIDERATIONS IN ESTATE COSTING

ON organized cocoa estates both capital cost and recurrent expenditure vary from country to country. Among the controlling factors which vary between countries and even between different parts of the same country are the natural conditions. These include soil fertility, which helps to determine the length of the period a tree takes to come into bearing, and the relative length of the dry season, which dictates whether the crop can be sun-dried or must be dried artificially. This factor also affects weeding costs, which are lower in a country with a long dry season than in one where the dry season is short. Costs of materials and equipment depend, *inter alia*, on the distance they must be transported. Skill in management also enters largely into estate costs.

Production costs per ton are of course related to yield per acre—the higher the yield, the lower the proportionate cost and, naturally, the greater the profit.

Labour varies in efficiency, but the time taken by experienced labourers under supervision is roughly the same for any given task on any plantation. The "man-day," therefore, is a convenient unit for the calculation of labour-costs.

The costs per acre on the peasant farms in West Africa and on peasant small-holdings in other parts of the tropics are of a different order from those on estates. Equipment and buildings for the West African peasant farmer are relatively simple, and the cocoa is mainly harvested in the dry season and sun-dried. Weeding, farm sanitation, and general attention to the cocoa trees are on less intensive lines than are the rule on an estate. The main costs in peasant culture are for labour, some of which may be wholly or partly supplied by the family, or it may be entirely hired.

While capital and recurrent costs per acre are higher on the organized estate than in large- or small-scale peasant culture, the out-turn of cocoa per acre on a good estate is usually greater. For example, the Lukolela estates in the Belgian Congo are intensively tended under careful supervision. They are well provided with good housing for personnel, good buildings for fermenting and drying and with good equipment generally.

225

TABLE No. 14

ESTIMATED LABOUR REQUIREMENTS OF PLANTATION DEVELOPMENT FROM VIRGIN BUSH (AGRICULTURAL OPERATIONS ONLY) FOR OIL PALMS AND RUBBER

Man-days per acre

Oil Palms	Rubber		
Average spacing—30 ft. × 30 ft. triangular = 55 palms to the acre (Planting holes 2½ ft. × 2½ ft.)	Average spacing—22 ft. × 11 ft. = 180 to the acre. (Planting holes 1 ft. × 1 ft.)		
		Seedling Trees	*Budded Grafts*
DEVELOPMENT:			
Survey (initial prospecting) .. 2	Survey (initial prospecting)	2	2
Brushing, felling and lopping 45	Brushing, felling, and lopping	45	45
Lining and holing 8	Lining and holing ..	10	10
Clearing planting lines and paths 23	Clearing planting lines and paths	45	45
Nurseries 22	Nurseries	12	7
Planting 8	Planting	6	6
Cover crops 3	Cover crops	3	3
Sundry labour 9	Sundry labour	8	8
	Add costs for budding ..	—	6
TOTAL DEVELOPMENT .. 120		131	132
MAINTENANCE TO BEARING STAGE: *Per annum*	*Per annum*	*Per annum*	
General weeding 5	General weeding	13	13
Pruning .. —	Pruning	2	2
Replacements.. 3	Replacements.. ..	3	3
Upkeep of paths 3	Upkeep of paths ..	2	2
Control of pests and diseases 2	Control of pests and diseases ..	4	4
Nurseries .. 2	Nurseries	—	—
Sundry labour 5	Sundry labour ..	1	1
		— yrs.	— yrs.
20 × 4 yrs. = 80	25 × 5 = 125	25 × 6 = 150	
TOTAL DAYS .. 200	TOTAL DAYS .. 256	282	

TABLE No. 15

ESTIMATED LABOUR REQUIREMENTS OF PLANTATION DEVELOPMENT FROM VIRGIN BUSH (AGRICULTURAL OPERATIONS ONLY) FOR BANANAS AND COCOA

Bananas	*Cocoa*	
arious spacings, e.g.:	Average spacing—10 ft. × 10 ft. triangular = 500 trees per acre.	
1 ft. × 11 ft. triangular = 415 trees per acre	(Planting holes 1 ft. × 1 ft.)	
2 ft. × 12 ft. triangular = 348 trees per acre	(Planted under natural shade)	
4 ft. × 14 ft. triangular = 256 trees per acre		
(Planting holes 1 ft. × 1 ft.)		
	Stake Planting	*Basket Planting*
ELOPMENT:		
vey 2	Survey 2	2
e cutting 2	Clearing underbush .. 6	6
ling underbush 10	Lining and holing .. 14	14
ing and holing 14	Clearing planting lines	
nting 15	and paths 18	18
al felling 30	Planting 4	18
aring lines 12	Mulching 1½	1½
aining in the field 2	Thinning-out forest shade 8½	8½
dry labour 3		
TOTAL DEVELOPMENT .. 90	54	68
NTENANCE TO ARING STAGE: *Per annum*	*Per annum*	*Per annum*
neral weeding .. 14	General weeding .. 12	12
ning .. 2	Pruning .. ½	½
tilizing .. 1	Replacements.. 1½	1½
	Control of pests and diseases 2	2
	Progressive thinning out of forest shade 5	5
	— yrs.	— yrs.
17 × 1 yr. = 17	21 × 4 = 84	21 × 4 = 84
TOTAL DAYS .. 107	TOTAL DAYS .. 138	152

ESTABLISHING PLANTATION CROPS ON LARGE ESTATES

The estimated man-days per acre for different operations given in the accompanying tables are based on the analysis of plantation records of the land-clearing and development operations for growing the more important crops under a wide range of conditions. These data provide a basis for calculating the costs that may be expected on well-organized estates.

Cocoa is one of the cheaper crops to establish and it also has the advantages that it can be stored in the tropics for a limited period and is easily transported. Bananas are cheaper to establish, it is true, and come into bearing within twelve to fifteen months after planting; on the other hand, they must be put into cool storage or shipped immediately they are picked, and specially constructed ships are required for transporting them to the market.

CAPITAL AND OVERHEAD COSTS ON LARGE ESTATES

The examples given in the foregoing analysis are for labour costs only, and, as examples of costs for large cocoa plantations on the same scale are not available, it may be of interest to quote the distribution of capital costs for a 5,000-acre oil palm plantation. The installations in an oil palm plantation include an expensive mill which would represent 25 per cent of the capital costs, so the figures given below would have to be adjusted according to the type of installation envisaged for fermenting and drying the cocoa.

	per cent
Development and maintenance labour	30
Development and maintenance overheads	25
(Supervision, transport, tools, etc.)	
Housing for senior staff and labourers	32
Stores and other buildings	4
Hospital facilities	3·5
Roads	2
Transport	2·5
Wharfage	1
	100

BELGIAN CONGO

LABOUR COSTS

At the Lukolela estates in the Belgian Congo the method of establishing plantations makes use of existing forest trees for shade, those with a suitable canopy being selected. In the first year the brushwood and felled trees are piled in rows twenty feet apart and lines of cocoa are planted, the plants being spaced ten feet apart between the rows of piled wood. After two years from the time of first planting, the wood has rotted down and further rows of cocoa are planted so that the cocoa trees are finally spaced 10 ft. by 10 ft. throughout.

Operation					Man-days per acre
1st year:					
Marking out the land	..	..	..	..	1
Clearing brushwood ..	..	..	..	..	3
Lining and holing	..	..	..	..	10
Felling and clearing ..	..	..	..	..	62
Nursery work..	..	..	..	..	10
Planting	..	..	..	..	5
					91
2nd year:					
Weeding	..	..	..	..	7
Care of plants	..	..	..	..	2
					9
3rd year:					
Weeding	..	..	..	..	7
Care of trees	..	..	..	..	1
Clearing between the rows ..	..	..	..	7
Lining and holing	..	..	..	..	14
Nursery work..	..	..	..	..	10
Planting	..	..	..	..	2
Thinning and planting shade	..	..	..	1
					42
4th year:					
Weeding	..	..	..	..	13
Care of trees ..	..	..	..	..	12
					25
Total	..	..	..		167

Maintenance of an Established Estate

The following figures from Lukolela estates indicate the cost in man-days per acre for maintaining a mature plantation. The yield is assumed to be about 600 lb. per acre.

Operation						Man-days per acre
4 weedings	..	..	..	..	..	5·3
Harvesting; field sanitation, capsid control, care of cocoa and shade trees	..	..	..	..	18·2
Opening pods..	..	..	..	..	..	3·2
Fermentation and drying	..	..	..	..	2·4
Bagging cocoa	..	..	..	..	..	0·3
Gathering wood for fuel	..	..	..	..	1·1
						30·5

WEST INDIES

REPLANTING OLD ESTATES

The following is an example of the costs of replanting old cocoa fields in Grenada with cocoa plants raised from rooted cuttings. All the old cocoa trees were felled, banana shade was established, but permanent shade trees were not planted. The field was manured with 25 tons of pen manure, which was forked into the soil.

The plants grown from rooted cuttings were provided free by the Government and there are therefore no nursery costs. When women were employed, woman-days have been converted to man-days on the basis of 5 men being equal to 6 women.

Operation	Man-days per acre	
1st year:		
Felling old cocoa trees	18	
Manuring and forking	34	
Lining and holing	13	
Planting temporary shade	17	
Planting cocoa	6	
Draining	20	
Weeding	45	
		153
2nd year:		
Weeding	15	
Supplying and pruning	3	
Adjusting shade	4	
Draining	8	
		30
3rd year:		
Manuring and forking	34	
Weeding	20	
Care of trees	4	
Temporary shade	4	
Draining	8	
		70
4th year:		
Weeding	15	
Pruning and reaping	10	
Temporary shade	4	
Draining	8	
		37
		290

A similar example from Trinidad is given for comparison. Here again the old cocoa trees and immortelles were felled and temporary shade was provided by bananas and tannias. Mineral, and not pen, manure was applied. Immortelles were replanted to provide permanent shade.

Operation		Man-days per acre
1st year:		
Clearing and felling	15	
Lining and holing	12	
Planting temporary shade and immortelles	15	
Planting cocoa	7	
Draining	17	
Weeding	16	
Manuring	3	
	—	85
2nd year:		
Weeding	24	
Care of plants, pruning and supplying ..	17	
Regulating shade	3	
	—	44
3rd and 4th years:		
Weeding	24	
Care of plants	8	
Mulching and regulating shade	7	
Draining	4	
Manuring	3	
	$46 \times 2 = 92$	
	—	
	221	

In these examples from Grenada and Trinidad, the food crops providing the temporary shade and ground cover were partly consumed on the estate and partly sold. The income from food crops helped to offset expenses in the early years.

On one estate in Grenada the whole cost of establishing a cocoa field with clonal plants was repaid at the end of five years, one-third of the income coming from the sale of food crops. The capital outlay cannot always be repaid so quickly. Where the cost of transporting the food crops is high, little or no profit may be derived from their sale.

COSTS AND RETURNS IN THE DUTCH TERRITORY OF SURINAM

In a publication entitled *Developing the Cacao Industry of Surinam*, published by the Department of Agriculture and Planning Board, estimates are made of costs and returns.

All figures are in Surinam florins per hectare. One U.S. dollar equals Sf 1·885.

TABLE No. 16

ANALYSIS OF EXPENSES AND REVENUE
(Per Hectare)

	Sf	1st Year	2nd Year	3rd Year	4th Year	5th Year	6th Year	7th Year	8th Year	9th Year
Expenses	Sf									
Clearing		72								
Improvement of Drainage		50								
Planting shade trees		60		30	30	30	50			
Forking planting sites and beds		42								
Planting bananas		60								
Upkeep of bananas		60								
Cocoa plants (600 plus 10% supplies)			200							
Planting and supplying cocoa			85							
Pruning cocoa				10	20	35	35			
Disease and pest control			15	15	20	40	40			
Thinning shade						20				
Weeding			70	60	50	50				
Upkeep		80					40	150	200	200
Total Expenses	Sf	424	370	115	120	175	165	150	200	200
Revenue										
Bananas	Sf		432	270						
Cacao						60	200	400	600	800
Total Revenue	Sf		432	270		60	200	400	600	800
Gross Profit	Sf	− 424	+ 62	+ 155	− 120	− 115	+ 35	+ 250	+ 400	+ 600
Cumulative Total		− 424	− 362	− 207	− 327	− 442	− 407	− 157	+ 243	

The plantation on which the figures are based was one which was completely cleared and planted with bananas in the first place to provide temporary shade. Bananas harvested in the second and third years gave a gross yield of 9,360 kg. They had to be sold locally at a low price of 7½ cents per kg.

Estimated yields of dry cocoa are:

Year	5th	6th	7th	8th	9th and subsequent years
Kg. per hectare	60	200	400	600	800

In the year in which the calculations were made the value of dry cocoa (after deduction of harvesting costs, preparation and costs of transport) was taken as Sf 1 per kg. (about U.S. dollars 0·23 per lb.).

Expenses per hectare for the first five years would be roughly Sf 1,100. Buildings would cost Sf 60,000. For a 300 ha. plantation the capital involved would be approximately Sf 2,000 per ha.

For a plantation in full bearing the costs and returns per hectare might be:

Income from cocoa		Sf 800
Upkeep	Sf 200	
Overheads	150	
Depreciation at 5% of Sf 1400	70	
		Sf 420
Profit per hectare		Sf 360

ESTIMATED COSTS AND RETURNS ON A SMALL ESTATE IN PAPUA AND NEW GUINEA

In an article entitled "Cacao as a Crop for the Owner-Manager in Papua and New Guinea," in the October, 1954, issue of *The Papua and New Guinea Agricultural Journal*, Mr. Frank Henderson sets out what he considers to be the costs and possible returns on a small plantation of 150 acres of cocoa in the Territory. The units referred to are man-days per acre and Australian pounds.

Total	£22,800
Less Production 4th year	1,500
	£21,300
Plus 4½ per cent Interest 4 years added to Capital	1,917
Total indebtedness end 4th year	£23,217

Running Expenses—Full Bearing

Labour (based on 1 unit at 6s., 93 units per ton cocoa in sto re)	£3,300
Supervision	1,500
Transport	500
Building Maintenance	300
Stores/Supplies (Bags, insecticides, etc.)	1,000
Tools	200
Administrati on	50
Insurance	100
	£6,950
Plus Amortization	2,321
Interest at 4½ per cent	522
Total Running Expen ses	£9,793

Returns

Returns at £300 per ton in Plantation Store	£15,000
Returns at £250 per ton in Plantation Store	12,250

Notes on Budget

1st year	Clearing and planting 100 acres	50 labourers
2nd year	Clearing and planting 50 acres and m ain-tenance of first year's planting	30 labourers
3rd year	Maintenance, completion of buildings, preparation of roads	30 labourers
4th year	Harvesting, maintenance	30 labourers
Full Bearing	Supervision allowance increased to £1,500 per year	40 labourers

To the end of the fourth year, interest charges added to capital.

Fifth year—Interest charges paid only.

Sixth year—From end of sixth year, amortization and interest paid in ten equal instalments.

Full debt amortized fifteen years from commencement of scheme.

Cocoa price quoted for value of produce in store on plantation.

TABLE No. 17

CAPITALIZATION

Years	1	2	3	4
	£	£	£	£
Labour	4,125	2,475	2,475	2,475
(Based on 1 labour unit at 6s.; 100 units clear 1 acre; 25 units plant 1 acre)				
Living Expenses	1,000	1,000	1,000	1,000
House	1,800	—	—	—
Furniture	400	—	—	—
Buildings—				
Labour quarters	750	—	—	—
Stores	100	300	50	—
Drier/Fermentary	—	—	400	—
Tools	400	50	50	50
Transport	1,500	—	—	—
Rent	50	50	50	50
Insurance	100	100	100	100
Transport	200	200	200	200
	£10,425	£4,175	£4,325	£3,875

WEST AFRICA

COSTS UNDER PEASANT CULTURE

Cocoa is established in Ghana in several different ways, three of which may be considered from the point of view of costs.

(*a*) Where the village community or family has cleared land for the purpose of raising food for the family and a surplus for sale, and has planted cocoa in the food farm.

(*b*) Where a farmer secures the right to a considerable area of land for the purpose of establishing a cocoa plantation, the forest is cleared and usually planted with cocoyams as ground cover, and plantains to provide lateral shade for the cocoa for several years. When the forest is cleared and the land hoed, cocoa is planted among the cocoyams and plantains, which are intended to be catch crops and to offset to some extent the cost of establishing the cocoa plantation. This method presupposes that the plantation is either near a road to allow of the cocoyams and plantains being transported to the market by lorry, or not so far away from the road as to make the cost of transporting them by headload prohibitive.

(c) Where an enterprising farmer secures an area of land at some distance from a motorable road, so that the growing of other crops on a large scale for sale would be uneconomic, and cocoa alone is planted. Here there would be less clearing, especially of the large forest trees, as a number of these would be left to shade the cocoa.

Cocoa with Family Food Crops

In considering (a), the economic and social study of the village of Akokoaso in Ghana, made by Beckett in the early 'thirties, in which he investigated labour requirements of cocoa, will be taken as the basis for calculation. He estimated that the annual labour requirements of young farms was 23·8 man-days per acre per annum. This included work on clearing the forest, brushing (weeding and cutting-back of young forest growth), planting and harvesting food crops, and planting cocoa.

The cocoa farms under investigation took ten years to come into bearing, so that total labour requirement for raising the food crops and bringing the cocoa to the bearing stage was 240 man-days per acre.

In this same study, the figures arrived at for labour expended on farms in bearing was 25·8 man-days per acre per annum, made up as follows:

Operation					Man-days per acre per annum
Weeding	..	..	..	..	8·2
Harvesting	..	..	..	..	15·6
Carrying	..	..	..	..	1·4
Sundry	..	..	..	..	0·6
					25·8

These figures could be used in several ways to arrive at the cost of production of one ton of cocoa under the particular conditions which apply at Akokoaso. A great deal of the cocoa of Ghana has been established under these conditions, and it is therefore interesting to make an estimate of what the possible cost per ton might be.

If a generous view is taken and the figure of 240 man-days incurred over the first ten years is charged to cocoa, although it did in fact include food crops as well, we have an average figure of 24 man-days per acre per annum.

The costs in labour are reckoned over a thirty-year period. The cost in man-days during the last twenty years after the cocoa trees have come into bearing would be 25·8 per acre per annum. In order to account for the 24 man-days per annum used in the first ten years, 12 man-days per acre per annum may be added to this 25·8, bringing the cost per acre per annum to 37·8 man-days.

Annual yields of cocoa for a great part of Ghana have been accepted as from 350 to 600 lb. per acre.

If a low average yield of 350 lb. is taken for the twenty-year bearing period, this will make due allowance for the lower yields during the first few years after the cocoa has come into bearing.

At a yield of 350 lb. per acre, it will take 6·4 acres to provide 2,240 lb. (or one ton) of cocoa.

Accordingly, 242 man-days (6·4 × 37·8) would be required to produce a ton of cocoa during the first twenty years of bearing, and at 4s. per day would amount to £48 per ton approximately.

After thirty years, when the labour costs of the first ten non-bearing years had, so to speak, been written off, the labour cost would drop to 165 man-days (25·8 × 6·4) per ton and, at 4s. per day for labour, this would represent £33 per ton.

Now, assuming a higher yield of 500 lb. of cocoa per acre, the cost of producing a ton during the first twenty years would be 4·5 acres × 37·8 man-days × 4s. = £34 approx. On the same basis as before, the cost of producing a ton of cocoa after thirty years would be 4·5 acres × 25·8 man-days × 4s. = £23 approx.

COCOA FARM PLANTED IN LAND PREVIOUSLY IN FOREST, AND PLANTED WITH CATCH-CROPS WHICH PROVIDE GROUND AND LATERAL SHADE

On the basis of method (*b*) the following example gives an indication of the costs and returns which might be expected on a 10-acre cocoa farm over a period of 20 years. The cocoa is established in land where the high forest has been cut down, except for a minimum number of forest trees required to shade the cocoa. Cocoyams and plantains are planted to provide ground and lateral shade.

The 10-acre block on which the figures are based is a third of a 30-acre cocoa farm which is in the process of being established.

The cocoa is planted at stake, spaced at 5 feet by 5 feet apart, three beans being planted at a stand. The plants will be reduced to one at a stand in due course, and it is the intention of the owner to thin out the cocoa to a spacing of 10 ft. by 10 ft. later on. Vacancies will be filled with basketed seedlings. About ten forest trees per acre will be left in the first place to provide shade; these will be thinned to five forest trees per acre when the cocoa is 3–4 years old.

AN EXAMPLE OF THE ORDER OF COSTS OF ESTABLISHING AND MAINTAINING
A TEN-ACRE COCOA FARM IN FOREST COUNTRY IN WESTERN ASHANTI IN
GHANA, FOR TWENTY YEARS, AND THE POSSIBLE RETURNS THEREFROM

Labourers are paid 3s. per day with food supplied, except where otherwise stated.

For the first eight years inclusive the costs would be of the followin order.

	£	s.	d.
1. Partial felling of forest trees and clearing by contract (300 man-days)	45	0	0
2. Purchase of plantain suckers (1,700 at 7s. 6d. per 100)	6	7	6
3. Purchase of cocoyam corms (800 at 6s. per 100)	2	8	0
4. Purchase of 1,800 cocoa pods for seed (at an average of upwards of 35 beans per pod = 50,000 to 55,000 beans to be planted three at a stand. This is equal to three 60 lb. loads of dry cocoa)	12	0	0
5. Planting cocoa (at stake), 17,420 stands, takes 80 man-days	12	0	0
6. Planting 1,700 stands of plantain suckers takes 40 man-days	6	0	0
7. Planting cocoyam corms divided up to plant 6,800 stands takes 80 man-days	12	0	0
8. 1st year, first weeding 8 months after planting—120 man-days	18	0	0
Second weeding 16 months after planting—100 man-days	15	0	0
2nd year, third weeding 22 months after planting—53 man-days	8	0	0
Fourth weeding 28 months after planting—140 man-days	21	0	0
3rd year, fifth weeding 35 months after planting—130 man-days	19	10	0
Sixth weeding 39 months after planting—100 man-days	15	0	0
4th year, seventh weeding 45 months after planting—100 man-days	15	0	0
5th year, eighth weeding after planting—120 man-days	18	0	0
6th–8th year, ninth to fourteenth weeding 64–94 months after planting—600 man-days	90	0	0
9. Share of labourer-caretaker's pay (for four years at £36 for the first year and £48 per annum for three years)	180	0	0
10. Share of erecting mud and wattle house for labourer-caretaker	30	0	0

11. Cost of implements:

	£	s.	d.			
3 felling axes at 12s.	1	16	0			
12 cutlasses at 2s. 6d.	1	10	0			
2 steel files at 3s.		6	0			
3 grinding stones at 2s.		6	0			
				3	18	0

		£529	3	6
Carried forward				

	£	s.	d.
Brought forward	529	3	6
12. Shade-reduction—35 man-days at 6s.	10	10	0
13. Capsid control: 88 gallons of water carried a distance of 2½ miles to farm at 6d. per 4 gallons		11	0
Purchase of subsidized Mysto sprayer	2	0	0
14. Cost of 500 nursery baskets (for vacancies) at 3d. each	6	5	0
15. Share of State fees for land acquisition (£1 for first farm plus one-third of £15 for 30 acres of land)	6	0	0
16. Harvesting, fermenting, drying and carrying in 7th and 8th year at 17 man-days per annum	5	2	0
17. Contingencies including interest on borrowed money, transport, provision of fermenting-boxes and drying-trays, etc.	150	0	0

POSSIBLE COST IN THE FOLLOWING TWELVE YEARS

	£	s.	d.
18. Share of labourer-caretaker's pay (at £48 per annum)	576	0	0
19. Share of upkeep and rebuilding of mud and wattle house for labourer-caretaker	25	0	0
20. Share of building and upkeep of store with mud and wattle walls and pan roof	20	0	0
21. Provision of drying-trays, baskets, etc., over the period	15	0	0
22. Replacement of tools	2	10	0
23. Control of pests and diseases. It is assumed that the cost per annum would be progressively less as capsids were brought under control. Allow 10s. per acre per annum	60	0	0
24. Weeding, shade control, harvesting, fermenting, drying, transport at 30 man-days per acre per annum	540	0	0
25. Interest on borrowed money outstanding and incidental expenses	70	0	0
	£2,018	1	6

POSSIBLE RETURNS

	£	s.	d.
It is anticipated that with capsid control, and a reasonably good soil, the cocoa trees would give an economic yield from the 7th year onwards. 300 lb. per acre for 2 years (7th and 8th years) = 2·7 tons. A yield of 400 lb. per acre from the 9th year and for the following 12 years might be expected, making an aggregate of 24·1 tons. Assuming an average price of £150 per ton the return for 24·1 tons of cocoa for fourteen years would be	3,615	0	0

The price received for the plantain bunches may vary from 2s. to 3s. 6d. or more per bunch, depending on whether the farm is near to or some distance from a motorable road. A price of 2s. 6d. per bunch is assumed to allow for costs of harvesting and headloading to the roadside.

The farm is commonly cropped with plantains for five successive years. The second- and third-year crops are better

	£	s.	d.
Carried forward	£3,615	0	0

	£	s.	d.
Brought forward	3,615	0	0

than the first and by the fifth year there is a reduction in
yield. If an average yield of 1,200 bunches is assumed
(from the original 1,700 stands) for four successive years

	£	s.	d.
this gives a return of	600	0	0

Cocoyams should give a yield of 400 lb. per acre for two
successive years. This would be 8,000 lb. = 44 sacks (180
lb. per sack) at 20s. per sack

	£	s.	d.
	44	0	0
	£4,259	0	0

COMMENTARY

The above farm belongs to an educated African farmer with long
experience of planting cocoa. The farm is five years old and the
costs from the sixth year onwards inclusive are estimated. These
figures are reproduced as a helpful guide to the intending African
planter. They are not exhaustive and certain items are not taken
into account. For instance, no interest is charged on the capital
invested by the owner. It is assumed that cocoa farming is only a
part-time occupation, and there is no charge for management.

The cost of establishing and maintaining a 10-acre cocoa farm
over a period of twenty years under the conditions of the forest
region of Western Ashanti, in Ghana, is £2,018. At the yields estimated
above for the farm, giving a gross out-turn of about 24 tons during
the bearing period, the cost of production is £84 per ton.

It has been shown that an estimated yield of cocoa from 10 acres
over a period of twenty years from time of first planting, including a
yielding period of fourteen years, is 24·1 tons. Given a reasonably
good soil and capsid control, there should be an economic yield in
the seventh year from planting. There might be an economic yield
in the sixth year, or even earlier, but in the case of planting by the
small farmer in the past, where the trees are closely planted and
where there has been little or no capsid control, economic yields
were not expected until the ninth year or later. The yield of 300 lb.
per acre for the first two years of bearing and 400 lb. for the remaining period is based on the fact that a farm receiving so much attention should yield this amount as a minimum. If the yield were less,
then the assumption would be that the land was not suited for
cropping with cocoa.

The yield per acre may well be much more than the figure given
above, and will assuredly be more if the farmer has been guided to
good land as the result of advice or his own skill when an average
yield of 600 lb. to 800 lb. per acre, or more, could be expected.

The gross expenditure is £2,018 and the gross income is estimated as £4,259. Of this income, 15 per cent comes from the sale of plantains and cocoyams, and the balance, £3,615, from the sale of cocoa. The difference between the gross expenditure and the gross income is £2,242. It can thus be said that ten acres under cocoa would on the above basis provide a return equivalent to an income of £112 per annum over the twenty-year period, or equivalent to a return of £11 per acre per annum.

With an increase of 100 lb. or 200 lb. per acre, the profit on the venture would be greatly increased while the increase in expenditure would be small. For example, if the average yield were 600 lb. per acre per annum for fourteen years, the amount of cocoa harvested would be 37·5 tons, and at the same average price for cocoa the gross return on this venture would be £5,625.

These figures emphasize the necessity for choosing land which is reasonably fertile, so that the yields will be of an order which will give a profitable return. Furthermore, they emphasize the need for the control of capsids so that the yields will not be depressed and the productive capacity of the plantation permanently reduced by attacks of this pest. While the planting of cocoa in a food farm of yams, maize, etc., involves only a minimum outlay of capital, planting of cocoa in land which is in high forest where the returns depend mainly or wholly on cocoa inevitably requires a considerable outlay. Where cocoa is to be planted by method (c) in high forest, and economic crops, such as plantains and cocoyams are not to be planted, the importance of choosing good land and controlling pests becomes still more vital. A great deal of the cocoa that will be planted by smallholders in West Africa in the future will be planted as a sole crop, or with a cash crop which may make a small but nevertheless useful contribution to offset the total costs of the enterprise. Planting of cocoa through food farms will become less common.

A point which requires particular emphasis is the necessity for roads to serve the areas where cocoa planting is to be developed. Where the cocoa farms are remote from roads, the planter may incur heavy costs in transporting his cocoa to a point where it can be collected by lorry. These costs may be of the order of 5s. to 10s. or more per load of 60 lb. Where the cost of transport is 10s. per load, the price would be correspondingly reduced by £18 10s. per ton. If plantains or cocoyams were used as shade, the cost of transport on these would be so high that it would be unprofitable to harvest them.

Given good soil, reasonable success in control of pests and diseases, access to roads, and producer prices at a certain level,

R

cocoa planting on the lines followed by the West African farmer can be profitable. It is in fact the most profitable tree crop available to him and the one most suited to his particular conditions. But like all farming ventures there are risks to contend with, such as soil variations, pests, diseases and unfavourable distribution of rainfall. The increasing demand for labour in other directions makes it difficult for the cocoa farmer to secure his requirements. Much of the labour required is seasonal and he has to depend on getting his requirements at times when the demand is high.

Not the least of his difficulties is the finding of capital to finance his undertaking. The moneylender requires a high rate of interest, and borrowing from the professional moneylender has in the past brought to grief creditable efforts on the part of enterprising African cocoa farmers. If Government were prepared to provide capital to selected Africans, at a low rate of interest, progressive young men would be encouraged to take up the planting of cocoa.

ESTIMATED COSTS OF PRODUCTION AND RETURNS

A detailed analysis of production costs in Nigerian peasant cocoa farms has been made by Galletti, Baldwin and Dina in their book *Nigerian Cocoa Farmers*. The authors analyse the results of observations on seven pairs of plots in the 1951–2 season. They conclude that in recent years the cost of establishing an acre of cocoa has mounted from £15 (which was the cost previous to 1930) to "over £50 but not over £75 in 1951–2." In one case seven plots were under the management of the Department of Agriculture, the other seven were farmers' plots. The number of trees were 4,090 and 4,012 respectively, contained in each instance within 6·8 acres. The Departmental plots were harvested on the average 15·4 times and the farmers' plots 6·7 times. Surprisingly, the losses from black pod were almost identical for both—about 530 lb. It would be normal to expect that the more frequent harvesting would have reduced the losses from black pod. The Departmental plots gave a yield of 1·44 lb. per tree and 567 lb. per acre; the figures for the farmers' plots were 0·63 lb. and 367 lb.

Estimated costs of production were £54 12s. 3d. per ton for the Department and £24 4s. 11d. per ton for the farmers' plots. The former made a profit of £346 3s. 5d. and the latter £150 13s. 1d. The producer price was £170 per ton.

The Department of Agriculture employed permanent labour at 1s. 5d. per day, and the farmers mainly casual labour at 2s. 10d.

Remuneration of Labour. The above book discusses the remuneration of labour permanently employed by peasant farmers on cocoa farms. In 1951–2 the annual payment to labourers at Ibesse in Abeokuta Province was £22 10s. 0d., with share of farmers' crops; in Otta it was £18–£20 with free lodging and some land on which to raise food; in Owo it was £10–£15; wages were as high as £30 to £36 in Ibadan area.

The cost of casual labour was, of course, much higher. In 1950 daily wage rates were 2s. 6d. for lighter operations and 3s. to 3s. 6d. for heavy work.

PLANTING DISTANCES

1. *Planting on the triangle*

Spacing	Area occupied per Tree sq. ft.	Number of Trees per acre
7 ft.	42	1025
8 ft.	55	785
9 ft.	70	620
10 ft.	87	520
11 ft.	105	415
12 ft.	127	345
13 ft.	146	300
14 ft.	170	255
15 ft.	195	220

2. *Planting on the square (metres)*

Metres	Sq. Metres	Number of Trees per Hectare
2	4	2500
2·5	6·25	1600
3	9	1110
3·5	12·25	815
4	16	625
4·5	20·25	495
5	25	400

Appendix IV

PREPARATION OF ROOTED CUTTINGS

THE following additional information may be found useful by the planter who wishes to prepare his own rooted cuttings:

PREPARATION OF COMPOSTED SAWDUST

Medium grain sawdust of mixed hardwoods is composted by mixing it with farmyard manure in the proportion of 5 of sawdust to 1 of manure. In order to improve the aeration of this mass coarse grass or brushwood is inserted. The heap is soaked with water or a 1 per cent solution of sulphate of ammonia, which will accelerate decomposition, and it is covered with elephant grass or sugar cane trash to conserve moisture. If the heap is kept moist the sawdust is composted into a dark brown or blackish material in seven to eight months. It is then sifted and used as a rooting-medium.

PREPARATION OF THE POTTING-MIXTURE

Two parts of sifted soil are mixed with one part of sawdust. To each bushel of this mixture is added 4 oz. of sulphate of ammonia, 2 oz. of muriate of potash, and $\frac{1}{2}$ oz. of superphosphate.

The best results are obtained when the mixture is prepared ten days before it is used.

The weight of a basket containing soil and plant ready for the field is 6 to 7 lb. A 3-ton lorry will take 800 basketed plants. Care has to be taken to prevent undue drying of the plants while being transported in dry weather.

From the time the plants are first put in the baskets until they are planted in the field, the number of baskets used will work out on the average at about two-and-a-half baskets per plant. The number of times the baskets will have to be renewed will depend on the material used in making them.

NOTES ON COCOA PROPAGATION
BY THE COCOA BOARD OF TRINIDAD AND TOBAGO

TRINIDAD was the first country to go in for the production of rooted cuttings on a large scale. Since the first station for production was set up in 1942–4 the Cocoa Board has developed plant and equipment capable of turning out one million rooted cuttings per annum.

Mr. E. F. Moll has been in charge of the large organization which deals with this side of the Board's activities, and he has made a careful study of every aspect of rooted cutting production. The notes which appear below up to the heading "Watering Schedules" are a shortened version of a paper by Mr. Moll, the remainder are in the form written by him for the guidance of the planter.

THE PRODUCTION OF ROOTED CUTTINGS

Efficiency of Propagation. This depends on the variety, type and condition of cutting material, method used and environmental conditions during propagation. Easy rooting varieties will show a rooting percentage of over 60; an average variety 40 to 60, and difficult ones would be under 40. Cuttings from a vigorous plant are better than those from a mature cocoa tree, and fan growth is more suitable for the production of cuttings than chupon growth.

The Nursery which Supplies the Cuttings. The productive life of a nursery plant is about six years, during which time it supplies an average of 10 to 12 cuttings per annum after the first year of growth. At 6 ft. by 6 ft. spacing, 1,200 plants would occupy 1 acre. A 10,000 unit propagator would require 20,000 cuttings per annum, as the productive out-turn of a propagator is only 50 per cent of its intake. The nursery should be sited on a good soil conveniently near the propagator and sheltered from wind.

The nursery should be established 12 months before the building of the propagator, in order that this should not stand idle.

Land is cleared for the nursery, ground shade is provided by bananas planted 10 ft. by 10 ft., and supplemented with cassava and pigeon peas. This may be further strengthened by *Gliricidia* at 12 ft. by 10 ft.

Tephrosia as a secondary windbreak and source of mulch can be planted on the sides of the nursery exposed to the wind. Suitable trees are planted to provide overhead shade.

The holes (about 12 in. by 18 in.) in which the cocoa is to be planted are filled with earth mixed with one bushel of well-rotted pen-manure, and when the cocoa plant is in place the soil is pressed firmly round it.

246

A check should be made after two weeks to see that the plants are firmly in position,

During the first year, weeding will be necessary, and also control of the ground cover to prevent overshading. Mineral manure should be applied every 8 weeks in the form of alternate doses of NPK ($\frac{1}{2}$ lb. per plant) and sulphate of ammonia ($\frac{1}{4}$ lb. per plant). Collection of cuttings can usually begin six months after planting.

Nursery plants require constant care and have to be regularly weeded and manured, and also have the shade properly adjusted throughout the period of their use. The best results from the nursery plants will be obtained if the following precautions are observed: all the cutting material should not be taken at any one harvest, as complete harvesting at one time leads to a woody nursery plant with restricted production; cuttings should be taken from different parts of the plant each time of harvesting; the plant should be given a rest by omitting one harvesting after a flush, preferably in the dry season.

Terminal or lateral cuttings should be cut four to five inches longer than is required for rooting purposes. At least one-third of the available flush should be left to continue growth on the tree.

METHODS OF COCOA PROPAGATION

Closed Bin Propagators. The basic unit is a 9 ft. by 3 ft. bin, constructed in batteries consisting of:

Propagating battery 54 ft. by 7 ft., made up of two rows of six bins.

Hardening-off battery 36 ft. by 7 ft., made up of two rows of four bins. Light and humidity are controlled by:

Overhead shade of bamboo slats or camouflage net permitting the entry of 50 per cent light.

Frames consisting of clear glass covered with thin calico cloth which allows about 15 per cent light to enter the bin.

Temperature is partly controlled by reduced light and partly by internal and external irrigation which also keeps the humidity at nearly 100 per cent.

Open Spray-Bed Propagators. These are basically the same as the closed bin propagators except that there is no provision for sealing by means of frames. Light is controlled by overhead shade which allows about 40 per cent of light to enter.

Humidity is kept up by constant fine spray or mist which is turned on continuously during daylight.

Centrifugal Humidifier. This is housed in a building of special construction with shelves for holding the plants. The roof is of alternate panels of aluminium and glass; the sides are of either alternate panels of clear plastic sheeting and aluminium, or of opaque perspex. A Bahnson centrifugal humidifier provides a high humidity.

Important Variations to Closed-Bin Type of Propagator.

(a) The bin is enlarged to a surface area of 108 sq. ft. (18 ft. by 6 ft.) by removal of the centre walls, which are replaced by metal supports.

Drainage and propagating media are replaced by a metal wire shelf eight inches above the bottom, and irrigation is effected by means of a single central water line. This type of bin is used for propagation in the basket.

(b) This variation is identical with (a) except that the area below the shelf is watertight, and contains a constant supply of water below the plants. The desirable environmental conditions during propagation are: 10 to 12 per cent of direct sunlight; temperature not above 32° C. (87·6° F.).

WATERING SCHEDULES

Closed Bins

(a) The overhead perforated irrigation pipe is regulated to allow a constant drip to fall; this drip keeps the calico covers moist, increasing evaporation and thus controlling temperature. On dry days it is also necessary to open this line fully to allow for soaking the cloth.

(b) The internal perforated water lines are utilised at regular intervals to saturate the air within the propagator. This method is not as efficient as is desired, hence the variations in design, which

  (i) utilise an irrigation pipe containing atomising nozzles; the water discharge, in a given time, is less than from a perforated pipe, which allows for a more frequent internal watering.

  (ii) the water bath method, which allows for a saturated atmosphere through evaporation from the free water surface. This method may be supplemented by means of irrigation lines.

Open Spray Beds

The constant spray is provided by atomising nozzles; in Trinidad T-jets are utilised, spaced every 3 ft. on two sides of the spray bed. A *Centrifugal Humidifier* has the advantage over the previous method in that whilst a 100 per cent humidity is maintained, the output of water is small.

Environmental conditions are further influenced by the choice of media utilised for rooting the cuttings. The original medium developed at ICTA was coarse washed sea sand; this was in common use up to 1952. However, it had two main disadvantages:

(a) Poor water retentivity properties, hence more frequent watering required.

(b) Type of roots produced tended to be short and coarse.

Coconut coir residue has now been substituted; it has been found that the resulting rooting percentage is higher.

THE ROUTINE OF VEGETATIVE PROPAGATION

(1) STEM CUTTINGS

(a) Material utilised is a semi-hard cutting (either apical or lateral), preferably from a "fan" growth. Cuttings are selected as early in the morning as possible, and are immediately immersed in a pan containing water.

(b) Cuttings are transported to the propagating sheds in water, making

108. Cocoa awaiting shipment on the beach at Winneba, Ghana

109. Surf boats loaded with cocoa leaving the beach at Accra, Ghana

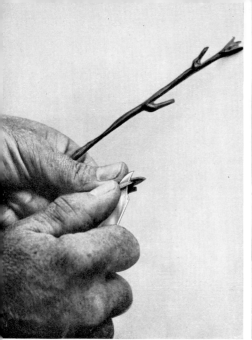

110. Removing the wood from underneath the bud, leaving the bark and
bud only

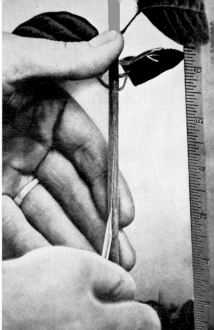

111. Preparing the bark of the sto
for reception of the bud. This is be
done at 4 inches above ground-lev
so that by earthing up later the scio
can be induced to root

THE TOPPER METHOD OF BUDDING

112. Inserting the bud in the stock

113. Wrapping the bud and stock
with Resinite budding tape

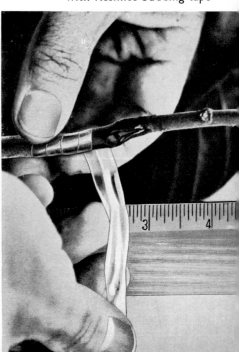

The bud and stock are completely
ped in tape. The complete
ping ensures the conservation
oisture around the bud. Three
ks after budding the tape is
oved, the stock is nicked and
en 4 inches above the bud

115. "Cleaning the bud union" which
consists of cutting off the stock
above the bud when scion has made
about two months' growth

Showing the growth of the scion. The
has been broken to check its growth

117. The scion has produced its own
roots

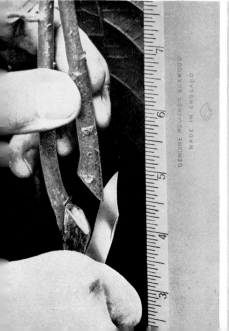

118. A lorry loaded with cocoa on its way from a buying station in Ghana to rail-h

119. Cocoa being loaded into lighters prior to shipment at Takoradi, Ghana

sure that the cut ends are immersed, the leaves being covered with wet calico cloth.

(c) Preparation of cuttings for propagation consists of:

    (1) Trimming of leaves—large leaves being cut in half, medium to small leaves having about a quarter cut, and small leaves the tip removed. Trimming of leaves is necessary to prevent overshading in the bins and to facilitate the setting of more cuttings per unit area.

    (2) Lower leaves are removed, so that the prepared cutting has five or six leaves remaining.

    (3) Any diseased or damaged tissue is removed.

    (4) A fresh cut is made in the semi-hard portion of the stem; this cut is made in an internode, preferably about a quarter of an inch from a node.

    (5) The prepared cuttings are dipped in the rooting hormone.

    (6) Where single leaf material is to be utilised, the above process is adopted, except that

        (i) more leaf area is retained;

        (ii) the cut is made between each node, about a quarter of an inch above the leaf axil (or node).

Hormone Treatment

The hormone utilised is as follows:

    3 gm. β-Indole-Butyric acid, plus

    3 gm. of α-Naphthylacetic acid dissolved in one litre of 50 per cent alcohol.

This solution should be kept in an amber-coloured bottle, and stored away from light; storage of the solution for more than a few days leads to deterioration. This prepared solution is placed in shallow (about 3 in. diameter by $1\frac{1}{2}$ in. deep) cups in which the cuttings are dipped.

Dipping consists of placing the freshly cut ends of the prepared cutting in the hormone solution for a few (5–6) seconds; after dipping, the cuttings are flicked to remove any surplus drops of hormone adhering to the ends and are then placed in the rooting bins.

Setting

The cuttings are set in the rooting bins by placing the cut ends some two to three inches deep in the rooting medium. The cuttings are placed nearly vertical (at an angle of about 70° to the surface of the medium). Then the surrounding surface is pressed down firmly to ensure that the cuttings cannot be displaced.

In setting, care should be taken to ensure that there is not too much competition for light. A typical box (3 ft. by 9 ft. in surface area) will contain some 70–90 cuttings, dependent upon the size of the material utilised. That is, cuttings are some three to four inches apart.

Rooting Schedule

In standard closed-bin type propagators, rooting is completed in 28 days. During this period treatment is as follows:

(1) Daily watering to maintain a humidity of nearly 100 per cent. Watering with perforated lines varies from three times in the wet season to five times in the dry season. Each watering should be of some two to three minutes' duration.

(2) Removal of any dead or diseased leaves or cuttings; this is especially important where an organic-type medium is employed.

Potting of Cuttings

On the completion of rooting (28 days) all cuttings are removed, those with roots being placed in shallow pans containing water so that the roots are immersed; the leaves are prevented from drying out by being covered with moist calico cloth. Potting is carried out in a glass-house.

The baskets are filled with prepared damp potting soil; this is pressed down firmly so that the soil level is about $1\frac{1}{2}$ in. below the top of the basket. The cutting is placed centrally in the basket with the roots spread out. More soil is added, to a level of about $1–1\frac{1}{2}$ in. above the top of the basket. This is firmed down so that the potted plant is erect and secure in the soil.

Immediately after potting, the plants are placed in hardening bins.

Hardening Schedule

Hardening-off is the term applied to the acclimatisation of the rooted plants to normal atmospheric conditions. In this process vegetative growth is minimised initially to ensure that the young roots have made contact with the soil; thus when leaf growth commences, food supply is via the root system and not from plant reserves.

Gradual acclimatisation is as follows:

(a) For the first 7–10 days the frames remain closed; watering is the same as during propagation. Internal watering, applied by means of hoses, should be less frequent.

(b) For the following five days the frames are opened in three stages, so that on the fourth day they are fully open. Internal watering is utilised only in the dry season.

(c) Visual signs that hardening is completed are:
  (i) The commencement of flush;
  (ii) appearance of roots through the basket sides (i.e. root growth is being made).

At completion of hardening (12–15 days), the plants are placed in glass-houses.

Glass-House Schedule

Glass-houses (providing 50 per cent shade) are utilised to protect the young plants whilst the first vegetative flush is being produced; this period generally lasts for some six to eight weeks. During this time the normal cultivation of the rooted plants commences. This is described below.

Storage-Area Schedule

In these 50-per-cent-shaded sheds, the plants remain until ready for distribution (some 5–6 months old for a stem cutting). Under Trinidad conditions distribution of plants takes place only in the wet season, June to October; thus it may be necessary to maintain some plants considerably past the stage where they are large enough for field planting.

Treatment in storage sheds is the same as in glass-houses and is as follows:

(a) *Watering* is not generally required in the wet season, except in dry periods. In the dry season, watering is carried out as required, which is generally every two to three days. This method has been, in the past, to water by means of hand-hose lines, but is being gradually changed to the use of overhead sprinklers.

(b) *Fertilizing*. Best results have been obtained by the application of a half-pint of a 1 per cent Urea solution every 10 days to each plant. In very wet periods this is replaced by the application of solid fertilizers at the rate of about 5 gm. per plant; when this is necessary the period is reduced to two to three weeks and sulphate of ammonia is alternated with a complete compound fertilizer (NPK).

(c) *Cultivation*. Weed removal and tilling the top soil is carried out roughly every two months. Tillage by means of a pointed stick is to a depth of about an inch.

(d) *Re-potting* is carried out when the basket has rotted or when the soil level has become low (i.e. the basket less than three-quarters full). Fresh soil is pressed firmly in the bottom of the new basket, and the plant, with its ball of earth, placed on it and more soil added until the basket is full and the plant is rigid.

(e) *Spraying* against pests and diseases is carried out as required. In the bamboo-covered sheds, spraying with a copper fungicide is carried out regularly every 14 days.

The above outline is the general practice for all methods of propagation. There are, however, certain variations as indicated below:

(2) SINGLE-LEAF CUTTINGS

The single-leaf method of producing plants was first developed by Stahel in Surinam and was used extensively in experimentation by Evans at the Imperial College of Tropical Agriculture.

The single-leaf method is suitable for small-scale propagators enjoying constant supervision and skilled operators, but attempts in Trinidad to propagate on a large scale resulted in a marked lowering of efficiency.

It takes an average of eight to nine months to produce a single leaf cutting suitable for planting in the field, compared with five to six months for a stem cutting. Since, however, stem cuttings taken during the period May to December have to be stored throughout the dry season, i.e. for up to 12 months, it may be advantageous to use single-leaf material during the period May to December and to change to stem cuttings during January to April. By this arrangement the danger of having to use overgrown, pot-bound plants is avoided.

A single-leaf cutting consists of the ordinary cutting material, i.e. semi-hard wood cuttings (but preferably three to four days younger), which are sub-divided by cutting the petiole about $\frac{1}{4}$ in. above each node. Each cutting consists of one leaf and a piece of petiole about 1–2 in. long. Thus each stem cutting is divided into four or five single-leaf cuttings. In preparation of single-leaf cuttings, it is better to use cutting material that has larger leaves and not to trim the leaves as heavily as with stem cuttings.

Propagating routine with single-leaf cuttings used in closed bins is as follows:

(a) Preparing as with stem cuttings but leaves are cut as described above.

(b) Hormone treatment—Quick dip, using hormone half the strength of that used for stem cuttings.

(c) The cuttings are set only $\frac{1}{2}$ in. to 1 in. deep in the rooting medium and therefore have to be supported between bars to prevent them from falling over and being uprooted.

(d) Treatment in propagation and hardening is the same, but greater care must be exercised in watering to prevent the spray of water from either washing the medium away from the cut end or covering the single axillary bud.

(e) In potting, the cuttings are supported by means of a "terite" or wooden stake. The stake can be inserted through the leaf, or the leaf can be nailed to the stake.

On the Board's central stations, the method of single-leaf propagation is used only as a means of bulking up scarce or new varieties. It has been found that even though extra supervision is given to this method, the actual efficiency of operation is about 25 per cent lower than with stem cuttings. However, the method has the advantage of producing three to four times as many plants as stem cuttings from a given quantity of material.

THE CONSTRUCTION OF COCOA PROPAGATING STATIONS

The following are actual average material requirements and costs (1954 basis) for a unit capacity of 25,000 plants per annum. Such a unit consists of a concrete slab 158 ft. by 144 ft., on which are constructed:

    4 propagating batteries   (54 ft. by 7 ft.)
    4 hardening batteries   (36 ft. by 7 ft.)
    1 50-per-cent glass-house   (100 ft. by 36 ft.)
Storage area covered with bamboo slats.

(a) *Material Costs in Approximate Order of Work* (Trinidad: $1 = 4s. 2d.)

			$	$
1. 3″ hardcore of 2″ broken stone				
210 cu. yd.	@	5.00		1,050.00
2. Boxing and formwork				
1,800 board feet second class lumber	@	0.12		216.00
2,400 board feet first class lumber	@	0.29		696.00
3. 4″ concrete slab of a mix—1 concrete to 3 sand to 6 stone				
940—96 lb. sacks cement	@	2.17		2,039.80

103—cu. yd. sand	@	3.50	360.50
206—cu. yd. broken stone	@	5.00	1,030.00

4. 4—propagating bins:

each, 5 cu. yd. concrete	@ 24.00	120.00	
736 hollow clay tile blocks			
$4'' \times 8'' \times 12''$	@ 0.125	92.00	
12 sacks cement	@ 2.17	26.04	
Steelwork		80.00	
4 at		318.04	1,272.16

5. 4 hardening bins @ ⅔ cost of propagators   848.10
6. 1 glass-house, Arcon prefabricated   6,000.00
7. Drainage work, propagators, hardeners and storage area   500.00
8. Storage sheds, consisting of teak post uprights at 12 ft. centres, with rafters of local lumber and shade provided by split bamboo slats

150 teak posts (9 ′. × 4 ″.)	@ 1.52	228.00
7 cu. yd. concrete for setting posts	@ 24.00	168.00
3024 board ft. 3″ ×2″ rafters	@ 0.20	604.80
10560 12′ pieces split bamboo	@ 0.04	422.40

9. Water lines—propagators each:

internal water line 108′—¾″ perforated pipe @ 0.38	41.04	
overhead water line 54′—½″ perforated pipe @ $0.30	16.20	
4—¾″ valves @ $3.06	12.24	
1—½″ valve @ $2.39	2.39	
4 propagators @	71.87	287.48

10. Water lines—hardeners each:

overhead water line 36′—½″ perforated pipe @ 30c.	10.80	
1—½″ valve @ $2.39	2.39	
4 hardeners	13.19	52.76

11. Water lines and sprinklers in storage area

14 Rain Bird ¾″ lath house sprinklers	@ 7.00	98.00
12 ½″ garden taps	@ 3.45	41.40
6 ¾″ valves	@ 3.06	18.36
850 ft. ¾″ pipe	@ 0.28	238.00
150 ft. ½″ pipe	@ 0.20	30.00
pipe fittings		50.00

Total material cost	$16,251.76
(b) *Labour Costs @ 60 per cent of Material*	10,061.07
(c) *Clearing of Site*	350.00
(d) *Preparation of Area, Levelling and Constructing Dwarf Retaining Walls*	2,400.00
Total	$29,062.83

(*e*) *Miscellaneous Charges at 15 per cent of above figure*
Includes Tools and Equipment, Supervision
and Loss of Time through Sickness, Leave
and Rainy Days   4,359.42

Total Cost of a Unit $33,422.25

From this it may be seen that the capital cost of a station such as La Reunion, which contains eighteen 25,000 plant capacity units, would be about $2.00 per plant.

(i)	Cost of units—$33,422.25 × 18, or	601,600.50
(ii)	Cost of main water supply	81,000.00
(iii)	Cost of roads	63,000.00
(iv)	Cost of administrative and other buildings	63,000.00
(v)	Cost of staff housing	27,000.00
(vi)	Cost of purchase of equipment	32,400.00
(vii)	Cost of transport in construction	36,000.00
	Total	$894,000.50

N.B.—Items (ii)–(vii) are actual costs, La Réunion.

Water Supply for Cocoa Propagation
(*a*) Chemical reaction:
   pH   5·5–7·0 (optimum 6·5)
   Electrical conductivity—not to exceed 1,000.
(*b*) Salt content:
   Where electrical conductivity is high, a complete analysis of water should be made and if it should be found to contain sodium chloride it is unsuitable for use.
(*c*) Quantity required:
   The Cocoa Board central stations consume (for all purposes) one quart of water per day per plant (annual capacity). Storage is provided for double this quantity of water, e.g. La Réunion has storage for 200,000 gallons.
(*d*) Pressure required:
   For closed bins with internal perforated pipes a pressure of 10–15 lb. per sq. in. is satisfactory. For sprinklers and nozzles a pressure of 40–50 lb. per sq. in. is generally required, e.g. T-jets used in open spray beds have an optimum discharge at a pressure of 50 lb. per sq. in.

Cost of Planting a Clonal Cocoa Nursery of One Acre
The following are on the assumption of a planting distance of 6 ft. by 6 ft. (1,200 plants per acre) and that the land utilised was in secondary forest.

In Trinidad some 200 pickets per acre (at 6 ft. by 6 ft.) are lost in allowing for paths and roads in the nursery.

Costs per acre:

Clearing land	20 man-days
Cutting pickets (for lining)	5 ,,
Lining (at 6′ × 6′)	10 ,,
Digging banana plants (300)	6 ,,
Planting bananas (12′ × 12′—or 300)	12 ,,
Planting cassava and/or tannia (2 per picket)	6 ,,
Planting immortelle (24′ × 24′)	3 ,,
Two cutlassings	9 ,,
Roundering (once)	5 ,,
Replacing casualties in shade	10 ,,
Digging cocoa holes (1,200)	10 ,,
Potting manure (1 bushel/hole)	12 ,,
Making cocoa mounds	6 ,,
Potting cocoa plants	6 ,,
Planting cocoa (75 per man-day)	14 ,,
Applying fertilizer 7 days after planting at $\frac{1}{4}$ lb. per plant	6 ,,
	140 ,,

12 loads of pen manure at $10.00	$120.00
3 cwt. of sulphate of ammonia at $6.00	18.00
	$138.00
140 man days at $2.70	378.00
Total	$516.00

i.e. cost per nursery plant is 52c. for preparation and planting.

Efficiency of Cocoa Propagation in Trinidad

The efficiency of cocoa propagation in Trinidad is expressed in terms of the production efficiency, which is the number of rooted plants suitable for field planting for every one hundred cuttings set in the propagating bins. The figures given below are averages.

(*a*) Propagation in closed-bin propagators:

From 100 cuttings taken

Loss during rooting	35	
Loss during hardening	7	
Loss during storage	8	
Production efficiency		50

(*b*) Propagation with open spray-bed propagators utilising **closed-bin** hardeners:

From 100 cuttings taken

Loss during rooting	30	
Loss during hardening	12	
Loss during storage	8	
Production efficiency		50

Preliminary results, utilising a continuous humidifier for hardening-off, show a reduction in losses during hardening-off from 12 per cent to some 4–5 per cent.

(*c*) Propagation in baskets:

This method has been in use for only 18 months, and on a relatively small scale. To date, some 12,000 plants have been produced.

From 100 cuttings taken

Loss during rooting and hardening 20
Loss during storage
    (i) in glass-houses 5 ⎫
    (ii) in storage sheds 8 ⎬   13
                    ⎭
      Production efficiency   67

It should be noted that in this method, rooting and hardening are completed in one month (normally: rooting one month, hardening 10 days). However, it has been found necessary for the plants to remain correspondingly longer in glass-houses.

REFERENCES

McKelvie, A. D., *Trop. Agric.* (1957), **34**, 260.

Murray, D. B., "A Report on Cacao Research," 53, Imp. Coll. Trop. Agric. (Trinidad, 1953).

Murray, D. B., and Bridge, C. J. R., "A Report on Cacao Research," 41, Imp. Coll. Trop. Agric. (Trinidad, 1957).

Appendix VI

COCOA FERMENTATION

THE importance to the manufacturer of the proper fermentation of cocoa has been stressed in Chapter VIII. The following paper advances a new theory of the process and embodies the result to date of research carried out by Mr. R. V. Wadsworth and Dr. G. R. Howat in the laboratories of Messrs. Cadbury Brothers Ltd. at Bournville. It is reproduced with their permission and that of the editors of *Nature* (1954, **174**, 392; Macmillan & Co. Ltd.), in which it first appeared.

PROPOSED METHOD FOR FERMENTING SMALL QUANTITIES

An attempt has been made to solve the problem of the fermentation of small quantities of cocoa beans. A solution to the problem is particularly urgent at the present time when botanists have made available a large number of new varieties of cocoa. What has been lacking is a satisfactory method of fermenting beans from only one or two pods from each variety, to enable an early and accurate assessment to be made of their quality and acceptability to chocolate manufacturers.

For our experiments, pods of West African Amelonado cocoa were flown from Ghana by commercial airline. Usually they arrived at Bournville about twenty-four to thirty hours after leaving Accra. On arrival the pods were swabbed with a solution of a quaternary ammonium compound to remove surface moulds and other organisms. Tests for viability were made on a few beans by staining technique, and by germination tests. It was found that no chocolate flavour could be developed from dead beans, and the time of death was an important factor.

Two methods of fermentation were developed. In the first method an apparatus similar to that described by De Witt was used. The pods were opened under aseptic conditions and the beans were sprayed with a mixed culture of a yeast, *Hansenula anomala*, and an acetic-acid-producing organism, *Bacillus orleanensis*.

Knapp (ref. 3, pp. 17, 30) states that both these organisms are found frequently in commercial fermentations. The inoculum was about 20 million organisms suspended in 10 ml. of Ringer's solution.

In accordance with the practice adopted in good commercial fermentations, the beans were well stirred every second day.

Fig. 10 shows the fermentation curve aimed at, using this method. It will be noted that during the first $3\frac{1}{2}$ days the temperature should not exceed 38° C. During the last three days the temperature should be about 50 to 51° C.

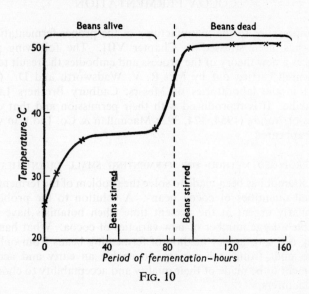

FIG. 10

At the end of the fermentation period, the beans were dried in a cabinet maintained at a high humidity to simulate West African conditions. Heat was supplied by a 100-watt electric light bulb. The temperature was not thermostatically controlled and it varied between 45° and 50° C. Under these conditions, drying to a moisture content of about 6 per cent took five or six days.

Beans prepared by this method and using the temperature limits shown in Fig. 10 were generally brown in colour and had cotyledons with an open texture. A few beans showing some purple colour in the cotyledons were found in most of the experiments. It was found that the beans from these fermentations, after roasting and shelling, could be made into chocolate with a good chocolate flavour.

The second method involved the use of "aseptic fermentations". In these, the beans were maintained at any desired temperature in a water-bath or incubator. The pulp was not removed; but the beans were sprayed with a very dilute solution of a quaternary ammonium compound to prevent the growth of organisms in the pulp during "fermentation". This method is capable of general application, and it is independent of the chance presence of desirable (or undesirable) micro-organisms in the atmosphere or the use of pure cultures. Suitably modified, we have been able to ferment successfully single beans by this method. In our later experiments the aseptic method was used exclusively, and we consider it less liable to variation than the traditional method.

Details of the aseptic method are as follows. The beans are removed from the pods under aseptic conditions and placed in sterile glass vessels. If the beans from two or three pods are being fermented, tall 600-ml. beakers are suitable. The beans are then sprayed with a solution containing 300 p.p.m. of a quaternary ammonium compound. The beakers are fitted with false bottoms prepared by placing inverted watch glasses on a framework of glass rod. Any liquid produced during "fermentation" consequently drains away from the beans. The top of each beaker is covered with several thicknesses of aluminium foil and this is kept in place with a tight rubber band.

The beakers are placed in a water-bath or incubator kept at a temperature of 35° C. and allowed to remain there for a period of 84 hours (3½ days). During this period a considerable volume of carbon dioxide gas is produced and it is essential that this should be removed. It can be done in one of two ways. A quantity of potassium hydroxide solution can be placed under the watch glass at the bottom of the beaker, or the beans can be thoroughly stirred after 24, 48, and 72 hours, and at 84 hours. The first method is probably the better; but it will be remembered that in no circumstances should the potassium hydroxide solution come into contact with the beans.

The beaker containing the beans is then transferred to a water-bath or incubator at 50° C. and kept at this temperature for a period of 72 hours (3 days). Although production of carbon dioxide at 50° C. is limited to the first few hours (until the death of the bean), it is desirable that even this small quantity of gas be removed. This can be done either by stirring after 24 hours at 50° C. or by the use of potassium hydroxide solution.

At the end of the period the "fermented" beans are plump, and when cut exude a small quantity of dark brown liquid. The cotyledons are open and can readily be separated from each other. They are a pale watery purple colour, possibly with a background of brown.

The beans are now transferred to a drying cabinet and dried under the same conditions as those fermented naturally. When dry, the beans will be found to have a loose shell and, on cutting, the cotyledons will be found to be dark brown in colour and to have an open texture. After roasting and shelling they can be made into chocolate which has a good chocolate flavour.

FACTORS INVOLVED IN FERMENTATION

Recent experiments on the fermentation of small quantities of West African Amelonado cocoa in these laboratories have directed attention to several aspects of the changes involved in fermentation which do not appear to have been noted previously. At least three factors play a part in the development of chocolate flavour.

The first is the germination processes in the bean during the first part of fermentation. This seems to have been accorded no importance in previous work. Indeed, Knapp (ref. 3, p. 134) states that "until the bean is killed no change takes place in the interior, so that it is desirable to raise the temperature rapidly to accomplish this". Our experiments have shown that this view is incorrect. Beans which have been killed by cold—24 hours in a refrigerator at 1° to 1·5° C.—and then fermented using pure cultures of organisms, or prepared by the aseptic method, do not produce anything resembling a chocolate flavour. Also, when beans are maintained at a temperature of 50° C. for several days without a prior period at a germinating temperature, no chocolate flavour is developed.

The second factor is that the beans must be maintained at a temperature of about 50° C. for several days after the initial germination period. If this is omitted and the beans maintained at around 35° C. for five days, they give either a mild flavour which is reminiscent of caramels, or have a slight liquorice character when made into chocolate. In addition, the colour of such beans after drying is not brown, it is purple. At higher temperatures the degree of purple remaining in the finished beans is less; but it is our experience that even when a temperature of 45° to 46° C. is maintained instead of 50° C., some purple background is present and there is bitterness in the chocolate produced. It should be noted that the temperatures used in our aseptic fermentations approximate roughly to those observed in good commercial fermentations. The nature of the changes produced during this period has not been studied by us in detail. They are, however, undoubtedly associated mainly with changes in the polyphenols, as has been noted by Forsyth.

The third factor is the removal of carbon dioxide from the air around the fermenting beans. It is well known, of course, that carbon dioxied is produced in fermenting cocoa. There appears, however, to be on published record that large quantities of carbon dioxide are produced by the bean itself—as distinct from fermentation of the pulp—during the early stages of fermentation.

Our experiments have shown that when fermented under aseptic conditions, the carbon dioxide content of the atmosphere around the cocoa beans may rise as high as 90 per cent during the first three days. In fermenting single-bean samples, we have found that a single cocoa bean (dry weight 1·2 gm.) produces up to 10 ml. carbon dioxide at N.T.P. during the early stages of fermentation. There is apparently no liberation of carbon dioxide after the bean dies.

In certain experiments an atmosphere of carbon dioxide was maintained around the beans during the period they were held at 50° C. or during drying. In each case it was found that the chocolate prepared from such beans was unpleasant and had no chocolate flavour.

It is interesting to note that in good commercial fermentations the practice is to turn the cocoa or to mix it every second day. This will have the desired result, if properly done, of removing the carbon dioxide.

Two other points have interested us. One is that during fermentation very little change takes place in the pH of the cotyledons. In our fermentations, using pure cultures of organisms, we found that the pH of the pulp fell from about 4 to 2·5. There was no similar fall in the pH of the cotyledons; here a slight reduction, from 5·5 to 5, was all that was noted.

This point is of particular interest in that it has been frequently suggested that the flavour of fermented beans is affected by the character of the fermentation which it has undergone, and that the esters formed during fermentation may permeate the testa and pass into the cotyledons. In the light of our findings, this seems unlikely.

The other point which interested us was the gap in temperature that exists between the thermal death-point of the organisms which occur in commercial fermentations and the maximum temperature recorded in a fermenting heap. The thermal death-point of most organisms occurring in commercial fermentations is 43° to 44° C. as observed by Rombouts. The maximum temperature recorded in good fermentation practice is, however, usually 50° to 51° C. It appears possible that the heat produced by the enzymic processes in germination is sufficient to raise the temperature of the whole fermenting mass sufficiently to bridge the gap between 44° and 51° C.

A fuller account of these experiments is in course of preparation and will be published elsewhere. We are indebted to the Directors of Cadbury Brothers, Ltd. for permission to publish this communication.

REFERENCES

Forsyth, W. G. C. *Biochem. J.* (1952), **51**, 516.
Knapp, A. W. *Cacao Fermentation* (Bale, Sons and Curnow, 1937).
Porter *et al.*, *Plant Physiol.* (1947), **22**, 149.
Rombouts, J. E. *Proc. Soc. App. Bact.* (1952), **15**, 103.
Witt, K. W. de. Cacao Research Report, Imperial College of Tropical
Agriculture, Trinidad (1952).

Appendix VII

PREPARATION OF BORDEAUX MIXTURE

BORDEAUX mixture is one of the oldest fungicidal mixtures but it is still one of the most effective for the control of black pod disease on cocoa. The quality of the mixture will depend on the materials used and the method of preparation. A 1 per cent mixture is normally used and is made up of 5 lb. of copper sulphate and 5 lb. of quicklime in 50 gallons of water. This is sometimes referred to as a "5-5-50" mixture.

A good quality quicklime or slaked lime should be used. It is difficult to store in the tropics and should not be kept longer than three months.

In Nigeria calcium carbide has been used successfully as a substitute for lime, $2\frac{1}{2}$ lb. being used in place of 5 lb. of lime.

The lime and copper sulphate are dissolved separately in water in a wooden tank which has two compartments of different sizes. In the smaller compartment 10 lb. of lime are dissolved in 20 gallons of water and agitated. In the larger compartment 10 lb. of copper sulphate are dissolved in 80 gallons of water. The crystals of copper sulphate should be placed in a small bag or on a perforated tray suspended just under the surface of the water.

The two solutions are mixed in the tank of the spraying machine, the lime being put into the tank first. During the mixing the individual liquids must be agitated continuously. Although copper sulphate solution is corrosive the mixture is not, so the mixing tank may be made of metal.

The mixture should be used within a few hours of preparation.

Appendix VIII

COCOA PRICE EQUIVALENTS

New York (c.i.f.)	United Kingdom (c.i.f.)	New York (c.i.f.)	United Kingdom (c.i.f.)
cents per lb.	s. d. per cwt.	cents per lb.	s. d. per cwt.
20	160 0	30	240 0
21	168 0	31	248 0
22	176 0	32	256 0
23	184 0	33	264 0
24	192 0	34	272 0
25	200 0	35	280 0
26	208 0	36	288 0
27	216 0	37	296 0
28	224 0	38	304 0
29	232 0	39	312 0
		40	320 0

REGULATIONS REFERRING TO COCOA IN GHANA

THE COCOA INDUSTRY (REGULATION) ORDINANCE, 1937
(No. 14 of 1937)
THE COCOA INDUSTRY REGULATIONS, 1958

In exercise of the powers conferred upon the Governor-General by section 16 of the Cocoa Industry (Regulation) Ordinance, 1937, the following Regulations are hereby made.

1. *Title.* These Regulations may be cited as the Cocoa Industry Regulations, 1958.

2. *Definitions.* In these Regulations unless the context otherwise requires:

"flat bean" means a cocoa bean from which the cotyledons are absent;

"foreign matter" means any material other than cocoa beans;

"germinated bean" means a cocoa bean the seed coat of which has been pierced, split or broken by the growth of the seed-germ;

"mouldy bean" means a cocoa bean in which mould or fungus is present and visible to the naked eye in the internal parts of the bean;

"slaty bean" means a cocoa bean which, on being cut lengthwise through the centre, shows a slaty colour on half or more of the cut surfaces;

"smoky bean" means a cocoa bean which has a smoky smell or taste or which shows signs of contamination by smoke or fire;

"weevily bean" means a cocoa bean the internal parts of which are found to contain insects or to show signs of damage by insects;

"certificate" means a certificate of registration issued under the provisions of regulation 5 of these Regulations;

"to adulterate" with its grammatical variations means:

(1) To mix or combine with cocoa which falls within a grade defined in regulation 13 of these Regulations, either—

(a) cocoa which does not fall within a grade defined in regulation 13 of these Regulations by virtue of the fact

265

that it is damp or that it contains foreign matter, or smoky beans, or

(*b*) any foreign matter.

(2) To mix or combine cocoa which falls either in Grade I or Grade II cocoa as defined in regulation 13 of these Regulations with cocoa inferior to Grade II.

"occupier" includes the owner or occupier of the building, his servants and any other person using the building at the instance of the owner or occupier.

3. *Care and Storage of Cocoa.* (1) After removal from a cocoa farm, cocoa shall be stored in a building and the occupier thereof shall ensure that:

(*a*) the building is rainproof;

(*b*) its floors are dry and properly constructed of cement, concrete, stone, brick or wood;

(*c*) it is provided with sufficient doors and windows to allow adequate ventilation;

(*d*) the inside walls are painted or whitewashed and re-painted or re-whitewashed annually or at such other period as the the Chief Inspector may specify.

(2) Notwithstanding the provisions of paragraph (1) of this regulation, the Chief Inspector, or an officer acting on his behalf, may, if in his opinion the circumstances so require, issue a permit authorising cocoa to be stored in the open or in lean-to sheds or on verandahs.

(3) Where cocoa is stored under the provisions of paragraph (2) of this regulation, the cocoa shall be:

(*a*) stored on gratings or deckings which allow at least six inches air space above the ground or the floor;

(*b*) protected from rain and moisture by being covered with waterproof coverings; and

(*c*) stored under such additional conditions as the Inspector may in writing specify so as to maintain quality.

(4) The occupier of buildings in which cocoa is stored after removal from a cocoa farm shall ensure that:

(*a*) the cocoa is stored on gratings or deckings which allow at least three inches air space above the floor;

(*b*) the cocoa is stored so that alleyways are left opposite doors and windows and between stacks and walls to allow adequate ventilation and access to all sides of each stack;

(*c*) the cocoa is not stacked above the height of the side walls of the building, except with the written permission of an Inspector;

(d) the building is kept clear of dust, cocoa debris, loose cocoa beans and refuse and the air space beneath the gratings or deckings is free therefrom;

(e) insects in the building are destroyed and the premises are kept free from insects and rodents;

(f) the seams of bags containing cocoa are kept free from insects, insect eggs and dust;

(g) substances which may be injurious or deleterious to cocoa, in particular cement, kerosene or tar, are not kept in a building in which cocoa is stored;

(h) wet cocoa, unsealed insect-infested cocoa, or cocoa containing smoky beans is kept in a building other than that in which sealed cocoa is stored;

(i) agricultural produce are kept in a building other than that in which cocoa is stored;

(j) empty bags are kept away from any building in which cocoa is stored;

(k) sufficient doors and windows are kept open during the day to provide adequate ventilation.

(5) After removal from a cocoa farm, cocoa shall not:

(a) be transported, or loaded on to, or unloaded from, vehicles under conditions which may cause the cocoa to deteriorate or become contaminated by any substance which might injuriously or deleteriously affect the cocoa; and

(b) be stored in bags infested with insects.

(6) Cocoa shall be bagged in clean dry bags of strong and unimpaired texture.

(7) Cocoa which has been graded and sealed shall be stored only in premises in respect of which a certificate has been issued.

(8) The provisions of sub-regulations (1) and (4) of this regulation shall not apply to the dwelling-house of a farmer.

(9) Any person who contravenes any of the provisions of this regulation shall be guilty of an offence.

4. *Places of inspection for grade-marking and sealing to be appointed.* The Chief Inspector may by notice published in the *Gazette* appoint places at which inspection for grade-marking and sealing of cocoa shall be carried out and may specify the period of the year during which such inspection for grade-marking and sealing shall be carried out.

5. *Certificate of Registration of premises for storage of cocoa.*
(1) The Chief Inspector may issue to any person a certificate of registration of premises in the form set out in the First Schedule to these Regulations for the storage of cocoa and such certificate shall be:

(a) issued only in respect of premises situated in places appointed by notice published in the *Gazette* under the provisions of regulation 4 of these Regulations;

(b) issued only in respect of premises which comply in all other respects with the provisions of these Regulations;

(c) applicable only to the premises in respect of which it has been issued;

(d) prominently displayed at all times in the premises to which it refers when cocoa is stored in such premises;

(e) liable to revocation by the Chief Inspector by notice in writing if he is satisfied that the premises are no longer suitable for the storage of cocoa or for any other reason;

(f) returned by registered post to the Chief Inspector by a holder on whom has been served a notice of revocation.

(2) The use, or attempted use, of a certificate in premises other than those to which it refers or the use or attempted use of a revoked certificate in any premises or the non-compliance with the provisions of paragraph (d) of sub-regulation (1) hereof shall be an offence.

6. *Notice to be given for inspection.* Any owner or exporter requiring his cocoa to be inspected, graded and sealed shall give to the Inspector at one of the places appointed under the provisions of regulation 4 of these Regulations not less than ninety-six hours' notice in writing. The Inspector may, if he thinks fit, accept a shorter period of notice.

7. *Method of obtaining samples.* Samples for inspection shall be obtained either:

(a) by taking at random samples from the beans entering the hopper or from beans in unclosed bags or on tarpaulins; or

(b) from closed bags containing cocoa by taking samples through the meshes of the bags by means of a stab-sampler provided by the Chief Inspector.

8. *Amount of samples to be taken.* Samples taken under regulation 7 of these Regulations shall be at the rate of not less than three hundred beans for every ton of cocoa or part thereof, provided that in respect of a consignment of one bag or part thereof, a sample of not less than one hundred beans shall be taken.

9. *Separate inspection of samples.* Notwithstanding the provisions of regulation 7 of these Regulations, an Inspector may draw a sample from any bag or from any part of a consignment and inspect such samples separately.

10. *Number of beans for inspection.* Where the beans taken for inspection in respect of any consignment, under regulations 8 and 9 of these Regulations, exceed three hundred they shall be mixed together and from such mixture there shall be drawn a final sample of three hundred beans for inspection; provided that in respect of a consignment of one bag or part thereof, there shall be drawn a final sample of one hundred beans for inspection.

11. *Sampling not to be continued in certain cases.* Where an Inspector finds in the course of sampling any cocoa that such cocoa, in whole or in part, does not comply with the provisions of regulation 13 of these Regulations, he shall not proceed with the sampling until the defects have been remedied.

12. *Method of inspection and determination of grade.* (1) For the purposes of inspection, every bean shall be cut lengthwise through the middle, and a count shall be made of the number of beans which are defective in that they are mouldy, weevily, germinated, slaty, flat or decayed. Where a bean is defective in more than one respect, only one defect shall be counted, and the defect to be counted shall be the defect which occurs first in the defects aforementioned.

(2) From the count of defective beans so made the Inspector shall determine the grade of the cocoa in accordance with regulation 13 of these Regulations.

13. *Cocoa grades.* Cocoa shall be inspected and graded as follows:

(*a*) Grade 1.—Cocoa which is thoroughly dry, free from foreign matter, smoky beans and any evidence of adulteration, and contains not more than five per centum by count of mouldy, weevily, germinated, flat or decayed beans, and not more than five per centum by count of slaty beans;

(*b*) Grade II.—Cocoa which is thoroughly dry, free from foreign matter, smoky beans and any evidence of adulteration, and contains not more than ten per centum by count of mouldy, weevily, germinated, flat or decayed beans, and not more than fifteen per centum by count of slaty beans, and in which neither mouldy nor weevily beans exceed five per centum by count;

(*c*) Grade III.—Cocoa which is thoroughly dry, free from foreign matter, smoky beans and any evidence of adulteration, and contains not more than fifteen per centum by count of mouldy, weevily, germinated, flat or decayed beans; and

(*d*) Sub-grade.—Cocoa which is thoroughly dry, free from foreign matter and smoky beans and contains more than fifteen per centum by count of mouldy, weevily, germinated, flat or decayed beans.

14. *Cocoa to be bagged after inspection.* The owner of cocoa or his agent shall immediately after sampling in accordance with paragraph (*a*) of regulation 7 of these Regulations bag or cause to be bagged and sewn up any cocoa so inspected.

15. *Method of sewing up bags.* (1) Bags containing cocoa for export shall be closed and stitched by the owner or his agent with a continuous length of tape or twine without knots (except as provided in paragraphs 3 and 4 of this regulation) which shall be of a type and colour approved by the Chief Inspector.

(2) Bags may be sewn by machine or by hand and the manner of sewing shall be such that no person can open the mouth of any bag without breaking the seal or cutting the tape or twine, or extract cocoa between the stiches.

(3) Each end of the tape or twine of machine-sewn bags shall be secured in a knot.

(4) The tape or twine of hand-sewn bags shall, at commencement of sewing, be securely fastened by a slip-knot on the inside of the bag and sewing shall extend down each side seam to a depth of two inches.

(5) Non-compliance with the provisions of this regulation shall be an offence.

16. *Method of grade-marking and grade-marks.* (1) All inspected cocoa shall be grade-marked by the Inspector and such grade-mark shall be appropriate to the grade determined by the inspection provided that where more than one final sample is inspected in respect of any consignment or part thereof, each bag shall be grade-marked according to the most inferior sample taken therefrom.

(2) Grade-marks shall be in the form set out in, and shall be affixed according to, Part I of the Second Schedule to these Regulations and shall be placed on bags by means of a stencil or stamp.

17. *Seals and method of sealing.* (1) Seals shall be of the design set out in Part II of the Second Schedule to these Regulations and:

    (*a*) shall have on one face below the broad arrow such number as the Chief Inspector shall specify for the month in which the bag is sealed;

    (*b*) shall be blank on the other face save for a number which shall be assigned to each Inspector by the Chief Inspector; which number shall be impressed on the seal by the Inspector in a manner specified by the Chief Inspector.

(2) Seals shall be affixed only by an Inspector and in a manner specified by the Chief Inspector.

18. *Notice of Export.* (1) No person shall export cocoa without giving the Inspector concerned not less than 48 hours' notice in writing of his intention to export. The Inspector may, if he thinks fit, accept a shorter period of notice than that required under the provisions of this regulation, and such notice shall state:

    (*a*) the name of the exporter;

    (*b*) the anticipated date of exportation;

    (*c*) the name of the vessel by which the cocoa will be shipped;

    (*d*) the number of bags to be exported, grade(s) and the identification on the bags; and

    (*e*) the place and premises wherein the cocoa is stored.

(2) The export of a consignment of cocoa shall not be permitted unless the notice of intention to export has been received and countersigned by the Inspector concerned.

(3) Any person who contravenes any of the provisions of this regulation shall be guilty of an offence.

19. *Detention of cocoa awaiting shipment* (1) An Inspector who finds in a boat or barge, or in a consignment awaiting shipment, any bag of cocoa or any cocoa, which appears to him to be wet, or which in any other way contravenes the provisions of the Ordinance or of these Regulations, may detain such bag of cocoa or such cocoa, any may order such bag of cocoa or such cocoa to be removed by the owner or his agent to the premises of such owner or agent or to and other place as the Inspector may specify, for desealing, inspection, reconditioning, re-bagging, grading and sealing as the Inspector may consider necessary.

(2) Any person who fails to comply with an order given by an Inspector under the provisions of this regulation shall be guilty of an offence.

20. *Treatment of sealed cocoa found not to comply with Regula-*

tions. Any cocoa which has been graded and sealed and which on subsequent inspection by an Inspector does not comply with the provisions of the Ordinance or of these Regulations shall be dealt with in a manner, including desealing, as the Inspector may deem fit, and failure to comply with any directions given by the Inspector regarding such cocoa shall be deemed to be an offence.

21. *Transfer of cocoa to other bags.* Where for any reason cocoa which has been graded and sealed is to be transferred to other bags, the Chief Inspector may permit such transfer and authorise the removal of the seals.

22. *Period of validity of grade-marks.* The period of validity of any grade-mark shall be four months from the end of the month during which the cocoa was graded and sealed.

23. *Re-grading of cocoa by request.* Any owner or his agent who considers that the grade-mark on any bag of cocoa belonging to him does not denote correctly the grade of the cocoa contained therein may apply to the Inspector and shall be entitled to have the cocoa re-inspected and re-graded as appropriate. Such an applicant shall pay a fee of one penny per bag to be re-inspected, and the fee shall be returned to the applicant if his contention is justified.

24. *Certificate of inspection.* An Inspector may, in his discretion, furnish an owner or his agent with a certified true copy of the results of the inspection of any bags of sealed cocoa on payment by the owner or his agent of a fee of three pence per one hundred bags or part hereof; provided that an owner or his agent who requires a bag-by-bag examination, shall pay a fee of one penny per bag.

25. *Adulteration of cocoa.* Any person who—
    (*a*) adulterates or permits or causes to be adulterated any cocoa intended for sale; or
    (*b*) sells, or has in his possession, or tenders in satisfaction of any claim or demand, any adulterated cocoa,
shall be guilty of an offence.

Provided that it shall be a defence for any such person if he proves to the satisfaction of the court either that—
    (*a*) (i) he was not aware and could not with reasonable diligence have become aware that the produce was adulterated;
        (ii) he had taken all reasonable precautions against the commission of the offence; and
        (iii) on demand made by the prosecutor, he gave all the

information in his power with respect to the person or persons from whom he obtained the produce; or

(b) the cocoa concerned consisted of sweepings from a place of storage and that there was no intention to sell or otherwise deal in the same.

Provided further that any previous grading or certification by an Inspector of such cocoa shall not be a defence.

26. *Unauthorised possession of seals or placing of grade-marks prohibited.* Any person, other than an Inspector, who knowingly possesses any instrument or article which is capable of reproducing an impression or imprint of a grade-mark or seal or any colourable imitation thereof, or who knowingly possesses any seal or colourable imitation thereof, other than a seal attached to a bag containing cocoa and sealed by an In spector, or who places on any bag containing cocoa any colourable imitation of a grade-mark or seal shall be guilty of an offence.

27. *Inspector shall comply with Regulations.* An Inspector shall not inspect or grade cocoa or affix grade-marks or seals or issue any certificate except in accordance with the provisions of these Regulations and shall in respect of any contravention of such provisions, unless he acted to the best of his knowledge and belief and bona fide, be guilty of an offence.

28. *Remuneration for extra service.* It shall be lawful for the Chief Inspector to pay from his departmental votes to officers who render services outside normal office hours, extra remuneration as set out in the Third Schedule to these Regulations.

29. *Penalties.* (1) Any person who is guilty of an offence under the provisions of regulations 15, 19 and paragraph (d) of sub-regulation (1) of regulation 5 of these Regulations shall be liable on summary conviction to a fine not exceeding ten pounds or in default of payment to imprisonment not exceeding two months.

(2) Any person who is guilty of an offence under the provisions of regulations 3, 18, 20, 25, 26, 27 and sub-regulation (2) of regulation 5 shall be liable on summary conviction to a fine not exceeding one hundred pounds or in default of payment to imprisonment not exceeding six months.

30. *Legal proceedings.* (1) No prosecution for any offence under these Regulations shall be instituted without the consent in writing of the Chief Inspector or an officer authorised by him in that behalf.

T

(2) A prosecution for any offence under these Regulations may be instituted and conducted in the same way as any prosecution for a criminal offence, or may be instituted in the name of the Chief Inspector, and shall be deemed to have been commenced with his consent.

31. *Revocation of Regulations. L.N.* 269/53. The Cocoa Industry Regulations are hereby revoked.

Appendix X

REGULATIONS REFERRING TO COCOA IN NIGERIA
MADE UNDER THE PRODUCE INSPECTION ORDINANCE, 1950 (No. 24 of 1950)

IN exercise of the powers conferred upon the Produce Inspection Board by section 8 of the Produce Inspection Ordinance, 1950, the following regulations are hereby made:

1. *Short title.* These Regulations may be cited as the Cocoa (Inspection for Export) Regulations, 1951.

2. *Definitions.* In these Regulations

"adulteration" of cocoa means the admixture or combination together of a quantity of cocoa which is of such quality that it can be graded and passed for export as provided in regulation 3 of these Regulations with any of the following:

(*a*) a quantity of cocoa which is of such quality that it cannot be graded as provided in regulation 3 of these Regulations by reason of the fact that it is wet or damp, or that it contains fifteen per centum or more, of mouldy, weevily, decayed or flat beans, or twenty per centum or more of defective beans;

(*b*) a quantity of cocoa consisting of or containing either velvety beans, black beans, smoky beans or obviously rotten beans;

(*c*) any substance, matter or thing, whether deleterious or not, solid or liquid, or partly solid and partly liquid, which is foreign or superfluous;

"defective" applied to cocoa beans, means and includes all mouldy, weevily, decayed, germinated and flat beans;

"the Ordinance" means the Produce Inspection Ordinance, 1950.

INSPECTION AND GRADING OF COCOA

3. *Grading.* Cap. 151. Cocoa shall be graded in accordance with the grades prescribed from time to time by the Nigeria Cocoa Marketing Board in accordance with the provisions of the Nigeria Cocoa Marketing Board Ordinance.

4. *Tolerances.* For purposes of these regulations cocoa shall be deemed to be free from black or velvety beans if after examination the black or velvety beans are found to be not more than three per nine hundred beans in any representative sample; and to be free

275

from stones if after examination such stones do not in the aggregate exceed half an ounce in weight in any one bag.

5. *Inspection.* (1) For the purposes of inspection a parcel of cocoa shall be spread out on a clean tarpaulin or on some clean firm cemented surface, but not on the ground, so that all the beans can be inspected and representative samples taken without difficulty and in any case shall not exceed the contents of one hundred bags.

(2) From any such parcel an examiner shall take indiscriminately a representative average sample from which he shall draw a further sample of twenty ounces and from this a final sample of three hundred beans. All germinated beans in this final sample shall then be counted, after which all the beans shall be cut in half and examined. If the results of the examination show that the parcel can be graded as provided in regulation 3 of these Regulations, the parcel shall forthwith be graded.

(3) The examiner shall complete the testing, passing, sewing and sealing of each separate parcel before commencing to examine another parcel.

6. *Sifting.* Before the cocoa is placed in bags the storekeeper shall ensure that

(a) cocoa, other than Light Cocoa, which has been graded is at once thoroughly riddled with a sieve having a mesh of seven-sixteenths of an inch, and

(b) Light Cocoa which has been graded is at once riddled with a sieve having a mesh not less than five-sixteenths of an inch.

7. *Packing.* Cocoa which has been inspected, graded and riddled, as provided in regulation 6 of these Regulations, shall at once be bagged in sound dry bags having no holes. The bags shall be sewn up at once without lugs by means of lock-stitches, placed not more than one inch apart. The twine used shall be strong and continuous with the ends so disposed that no knots are accessible and that the ends can be securely sealed.

8. *Parcel number.* Commencing on Friday in each week each parcel of cocoa passed and graded in each registered produce store shall be numbered serially and consecutively, commencing with number one upwards. Such number shall be known as the parcel number and shall be clearly stencilled on each bag comprising that parcel. The parcel number shall be not less than three inches and not more than four inches high, and the lettering of each digit shall not be less than three-quarters of an inch wide. Such parcel number shall be stencilled on the bag immediately beneath the grade marks.

9. *Sealing.* The examiner who graded cocoa as above shall verify that each bag has been securely sewn, shall seal each bag with a seal

or seals each bearing the design as prescribed in the Schedule hereto and also the steel seal press number officially allotted to such examiner, legibly impressed, and shall ensure that each bag is correctly marked with the parcel number and stamped correctly according to the grade of the cocoa therein contained and to the week of grading as prescribed in the said Schedule.

10. *Storage.* The storekeeper shall ensure that bags of cocoa which have been sealed and stamped as above are forthwith stored on a wooden platform or on such dunnage as may be considered suitable and adequate by a produce officer, assistant produce officer or examiner, in such a manner that no part of any bag shall come into contact with the floor of the store, that a space of at least three feet is left between the stacked bags of cocoa and the walls of the store, and that the bags of cocoa are stacked in such a manner that they can be counted without difficulty.

11. *Destruction of siftings, etc.* As soon as cocoa has been inspected, and whether such cocoa has been graded or not, the storekeeper shall ensure that all cut, smoky, defective and/or velvety cocoa beans and all other extraneous matter removed in the course of inspection, sampling, cutting and sifting are removed from the registered produce store and as far as possible destroyed.

Appendix XI

THE COCOA ASSOCIATION OF LONDON LTD.

Official Contract for West African Cocoa
Cost, Freight and Insurance (Shipping Weights)

LONDON,   19

C.A.L.
Messrs.   Form A.11

We have this day
upon the terms of this contract and in accordance with the
Rules, Regulations and Bye-laws of the Cocoa Association of
London Limited

Quantity | 1.   tons of
2,240 lb. (1,015 kilos) (3 per cent more or less) shipping
weights in bags.

Description | 2.

Price | 3. At   per
shipping weights

Terms and
Destination | 4. Cost, freight and insurance, to

Insurance | 5. Marine Insurance shall be covered by sellers at the price
of this contract with Lloyd's and/or first class Underwriters and/or first class Insurance Companies, for whose
solvency sellers are not to be responsible, on the terms of
and according to the Institute of London Underwriters'
Cargo Clauses (Extended cover), with Particular Average
(warehouse to warehouse) including theft, pilferage, short
and non-delivery, shipowners' liability, and loss or damage by freshwater, oil, other cargo, sweat, hookhole and
other loss or damage however arising, whether by perils
of the sea or otherwise, all irrespective of percentage:
including war, riots, strikes and civil commotions as per
Institute War Clauses and Strike Clauses (Extended

278

cover), current and available at time of shipment. Should the War Risk insurance premium exceed ten shillings per cent the excess shall be for account of the Buyer.

Shipment 6. To be shipped per steamer or steamers (in all cases the word "steamer" is understood to include any fully powered primarily engine driven vessel) during
from West Africa direct and/or indirect, with or without transhipment at sellers' option.
Each Bill of Lading from origin shall be treated as a separate contract.
Received on board Bills of Lading shall be considered proof of shipment.

Advice of 7. After shipment has been effected Sellers shall declare to
Shipment Buyers with due despatch the name of the steamer, marks and the quantity shipped. Should Sellers fail to declare with due despatch Buyers shall not for that reason be entitled to reject but any extra expenses incurred thereby shall be borne by Sellers responsible for the delay. Sellers shall be entitled to declare a shipment against Contract ship lost or not lost. Declarations of shipment made on cable or radio advices shall be subject to errors of cable or radio transmission companies only.

Quality 8. Quality on arrival to be   if
inferior thereto a fair allowance to be made, in case of need to be settled by arbitration in London.
Samples from not less than 30 per cent of the sound bags only weighing approximately not less than 2 kilos or 4 lb., shall be drawn and sealed promptly at the time of discharge in accordance with Clause 10.
Buyers shall notify Sellers of any claim for inferiority of quality within 28 days of the final day of landing and arbitrations must be held within eight weeks. At time of making the claim Buyers shall send one sealed sample with full particulars to The Cocoa Association of London Ltd., 84 Leadenhall Street, London, E.C.3., and a duplicate of the sealed sample to Sellers.

Weights 9. Invoice to be established on shipping weights, 142½ lb. gross and 140 lb. net per bag. All charges incurred in landing, weighing and sampling shall be paid by Buyers. Official weights and tares shall be taken at port of destination promptly in accordance with the custom of the port.
Any loss in weight exceeding 1½ per cent calculated on the nett weight of the sound and full bags delivered, but applied to the whole parcel, shall be borne by Sellers. Claims for excess loss in weight shall be submitted to

Sellers within 28 days of the final day of landing and shall be accompanied by certified official weights and tares.

Super-
vision

10. Sellers may appoint a representative to supervise weighing and sampling and must inform Buyers the name of such representative before arrival of steamer at port of discharge, but should they not name their representative or should their representative fail to be present after having received due notice of time and place of weighing and sampling, weights certified and samples sealed by sworn weighers and samplers and provided by Buyers shall be accepted by Sellers. Should Buyers fail to notify Sellers' representative in accordance with this clause, shipping weights shall be accepted and no quality claim shall be admitted.

Force
Majeure

11. Should shipments be prevented or delayed owing to prohibition of exports, loading port or ports being officially declared in quarantine, fire, strikes, lockouts, hold-ups, riots, war, revolution, or any other cause beyond Sellers' control, the period of shipment shall be extended by three months, but should the delay exceed three months, the contract shall be cancelled for any quantity not shipped.

Payment

12. Payment to be made by cash in   for 100 per cent of the invoice amount against presentation and in exchange for shipping documents which shall comprise complete set on board Bills of Lading and/or Ship's Delivery Order and Certificate of Insurance. Buyers shall accept approved letter of guarantee for any documents which may be missing at time of presentation. In the event of the steamer becoming a casualty, payment shall be made by Buyers for full invoice value against shipping documents on presentation.

Arbitration

13. Any dispute arising out of this contract shall be settled by Arbitration in London as provided for by the rules, regulations, and bye-laws of the Cocoa Association of London Limited, whether endorsed hereon or not, of which both parties hereto shall be deemed to be cognisant.

Confirmation of Contract for West African Cocoa on Cost, Freight and Insurance Terms—Payment on Presentation of Documents -Shipping Weights

The Cocoa Association of London Ltd.

C.A.L.
Form A.11

To Messrs.

I
—— hereby acknowledge and confirm your Contract No.
We

dated   for

at   per

for shipment   to

INDEX

Personal and documentary authorities quoted in the text have been omitted from this Index when they are mentioned in the References at the end of chapters.

A

Accommodation for plantation staff, 62
Achras sapota: as windbreak, 117
Acidity. *See* Soils
Acioa spp.: poor shade tree, 115
Acrocercops cramerella (cocoa moth), 160
Adaptability of cocoa tree, 18
Adoretus beetles, 159
Adoxophytes fasciculana, 160
Aeration: of cuttings, 95; of beans, 129
Africa, Central: capsids in, 156. *See also* Congo
Africa, West. *See* West Africa, *also under individual countries*
After-care of new plantings, 99 ff., 118
Afzelia africana, 37
Agaric, Honey, 175
Age distribution of trees, 203
Agral spray, 179
Agriculture, Departments of: services by, 61, 150 ff., 200, 223. *See also under* Ceylon; Ghana; Malaya; Nigeria; Papua and New Guinea
Agriculture, Tropical, Imp. Coll. of (Trinidad). *See* Imperial
Akokoaso (Ghana), 236
Albizzia spp.: as shade trees, 106–9; *A. ealensis*: effect on yield, 114
"Albolineum" spray, 179
"Aldrin" insecticide, 154
Algal disease, 174
Alkalinity: detrimental in raising cuttings, 70, 93. *See also* Soils
Allanblackia floribunda: poor shade tree, 115
Alluvial soils, 35
Alstonia congensis: as shade tree, 115
Altitude: effect on growth, 20; suitable for cocoa-growing, 22
Amazonian Basin, Upper: origin of cocoa in, 7
Amazonian types: 15, 16; self-pollinated, yield from, 85, 127; shaping and pruning, 121; introduction to West Africa, 80, 81; to West Indies, 186

Amelonado: importance of, to manufacturers, 2, 185, 186; flavour, 2, 187; in Bahia, 2; in West Africa, 2, 80, 184, 185, 187, 257, 260; shade experiments, 56, 58; yield from, 58, 85, 127; Amazonian hybrids, 81; shaping and pruning, 120; harvesting, 124; fermentation, 127, 129 ff.
America, Central and South (*see also under individual countries*): origin and early development of cocoa in, 1, 2, 7; types of tree in, 9; consumption statistics, 4, 211, 214, 220; nomenclature, 14; *Criollo* in, 15, 16; establishing young cocoa, 65; pests and diseases, 157, 160, 167, 169, 172, 173
Americas, the (*see also under* America Central and South; Canada; U.S.A. and other individual countries): history of cocoa-growing in, 2, 193, 197; shell percentage, 193; age distribution of trees in, 203; production statistics, 209; consumption statistics, 211, 214, 220; demand for "flavour" cocoa, 2, 186, 187
Ammonia: phosphate of, 56 ff.; sulphate of, 49, 50, 51, 55, 93, 103, 245, 247
Anacardium occidentale: as windbreak, 117
Animal pests, 12, 162 ff.
Annonidium manii: host for *Sahlbergella*, 114; poor shade tree, 115
Anthracnose (fungus), 172
Ants, 158 ff., 164
Aphides: pollination by, 12; as pest, 158 ff.; as disease vector, 159. *Aphis gossypii*: in Fiji, 159
Araecerus fasciculatus: as pest of stored cocoa, 191
Arboricides, 66
Argentine: consumption in, 211
Armillaria mellea, 175
Arsinette spray for beetle control, 179
Artificial shade, 55, 113; drying, 133
Ashanti: planting in, 202, 240. *See also* Ghana

283